The Story of Living Things

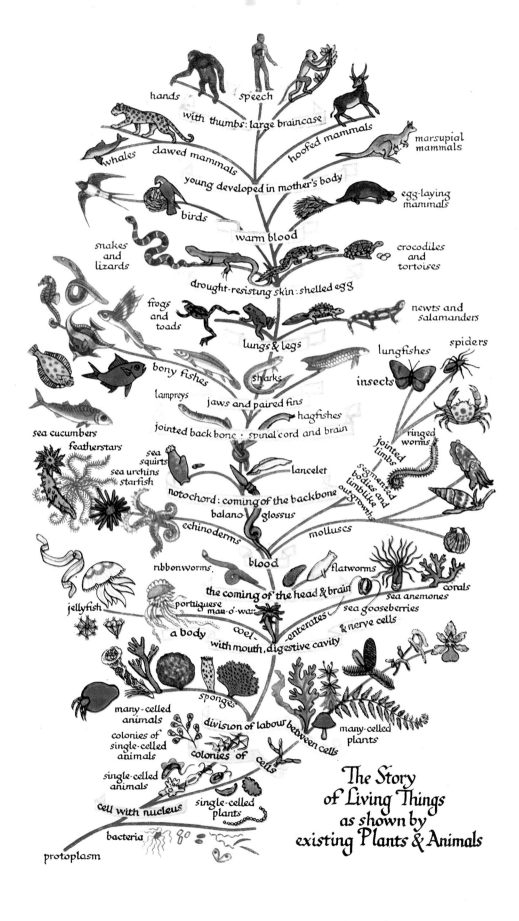

The Story
of Living Things
as shown by
existing Plants & Animals

THE STORY OF
LIVING THINGS
AND THEIR EVOLUTION

by EILEEN MAYO

With a Foreword by
Professor JULIAN HUXLEY, F.R.S., D.Sc.

Nearly 1,000 Original Illustrations in Full Colour

THE WAVERLEY BOOK CO., LTD.
Farringdon Street, London, E.C.4.

Produced by Percy R. Gawthorn.

Foreword

by

Professor *JULIAN HUXLEY*, F.R.S., D.Sc.

THE discoveries of the nineteenth century concerning life rank with those of the seventeenth concerning lifeless matter as the two achievements of science which have had the greatest influence on general thought. Galileo and Newton, following on Copernicus and Kepler, finally robbed our earth of its claim to a central position in the universe. At the same time they introduced us to the idea of universal scientific law, by demonstrating that the behaviour of the moon, the earth and the other planets was due to the same force of gravity that makes a raindrop or a stone fall to the ground.

So two centuries later Darwin, following on Lamarck and the other great naturalists, comparative anatomists and physiologists who preceded him, finally dethroned man from his claim to a unique position as Lord of Creation. At the same time he introduced us to the idea of universal law in biology, by demonstrating that all plants and animals, including man himself, share many basic similarities, and that the origin of the human species is due to the same general type of agency which is involved in producing a local variety of snail or a new breed of poultry: evolution operates as automatically as gravity.

NO one can call themselves educated today without some knowledge of the meaning and the results of Evolution. It is essential as a background to our general thought. Human history is itself a part of Evolution, and acquires new significance by being related to the long-term trends of the evolutionary process. For, as a result of studying evolution, we now know not merely that man has evolved from lower animals, but that he is now the sole trustee of life for further evolutionary progress in the future. We also receive some very real comfort from the realization that man is, biologically speaking, a very young type, and that his recorded history, since the time when he first achieved civilization, is negligibly short compared both with the time needed to achieve major evolutionary results in animal evolution in the past, and with the ages still to come in which our species may learn to control its own destiny and happiness.

LIFE has been in existence over a thousand million years; man less than one million; modern man, perhaps a hundred thousand; and civilized man less than ten thousand. The astronomers give us at least a couple of thousand million years before conditions on this planet render existence impossible. Thus we can regard human history, with its wars, its famines, its miseries and cruelties, as the merest fumbling beginnings of man's career. Only within the last hundred years has it been possible even to envisage our truest, most comprehensive task— that of introducing life to new experiences and new achievements, of continuing the rare upward progress of Evolution's past in a richer, speedier and more conscious advance.

Here, modern biology is indispensable as providing the necessary evolutionary basis for our thought. However, it is of value in a quite different way as well—in reminding us of the range and variety of life, and thus preventing us from falling into a self-centred intellectual parochialism.

We are surrounded by myriads of existences which are *different* from our own. That is the primary biological fact which the products of urban civilization are so apt to forget. Bee and spider, swallow and owl, hare and weasel—they exist alongside of men and women, with their own distinctive lives to lead. Once we grasp this, we realize that their existence as well as our own contains something of intrinsic value.

But if it has intrinsic value, and value to its possessors, it also has value for us, in enlarging our experience, our understanding, and our sympathy. Every child for the first time discovering the queer creatures of the sea-shore, every student freshly introduced to the world of microscopic life, every boy or girl suddenly touched by the passion of natural history, is made aware of something new and exciting in the world. The life that thrusts itself upon him is different from himself; but by his interest he makes it in a sense part of himself. Water-skater and crested newt, Volvox and Daphnia, sea-holly and flowering rush— these are all alive, they have their own nature, they possess their own beauty or strangeness far beyond anything we could sit down and imagine for ourselves. Those who concern themselves solely with man and his works are cut off from great territories of experience.

$\mathcal{I}$N each of these various fields, Miss Eileen Mayo's *Story of Living Things* is performing a valuable function. Her charming and unusual illustrations at once attract our attention and capture our fancy. But they have the further merit of being based on careful study of the facts of nature and of biological authorities, and, with her equally careful text, combine to give an excellent popular presentation of evolutionary biology.

In a book of this scope, it is probably impossible for an author to avoid occasional minor errors, or occasional general statements to which exceptions can be pointed out. However, in the present work such errors seem to be few and trivial, and the book can be commended as providing the layman with a picture of life's unfolding and of the rich variety it has produced, more vivid than most professional biologists could achieve.

Contents

Section 1 — Under the Sea

Section 2 — Plants

xi

the parent plant—by beasts, birds, man and ants. FRUITS · THE WORK
OF THE PLANT · THE PARTS OF THE PLANT-BODY · THE WORK
OF THE LEAF—breathing and food-making. FOOD and WATER
STORAGE · WINTER and WINTER-SLEEP—evergreens. ROOTS ·
STEMS · FOOD STORES—in stems, leaves and roots. THE SEED—
embryo and food store. GERMINATION · THE NEW PLANT.

Section 3 — Arthropods

THE "JOINTED-LIMBED" ANIMALS · SEGMENTS and LIMBS ·
WORM and ARTHROPOD—Peripatus. PAST HISTORIES · MYRIA-
PODA—the "numberless-limbed" animals : centipedes and millipedes.
CRUSTACEANS · SPIDERS · HOW ARTHROPODS GROW—moulting.
INSECTS—the most numerous land animals. HOW INSECTS ARE BUILT
—three parts, head, thorax and abdomen. INSECTS' LEGS · INSECT
TRAVEL—wings and wing-beats. HOW INSECTS BREATHE—air-tubes.
EYES—simple and compound. EARS : grasshoppers. HOW INSECTS
TALK—bee-dances : nectar-dance and pollen-dance. ANTENNÆ . HOW
INSECTS FEED—mandibles—proboscis : flies : mosquitoes, bees and
butterflies. LIFE HISTORY—larva—pupa—imago. Nymphs. SOCIAL
INSECTS : Bees : Wasps : Termites : Ants—honey-pots—harvesters—
leaf-cutters—slave-makers—spinners—farmers. INSECTS and CULTIVA-
TION : Beetles : ladybirds : greenfly : earwigs. USEFUL INSECTS :
bees : silkmoths : cochineal and cactus. ARTHROPODS and the VERTE-
BRATES

Section 4—Amphibians and Reptiles

EARTH'S HISTORY · THE FIRST LIFE · FISHES—learning to breathe.
AMPHIBIANS—learning to walk and to grow hard skin. REPTILES—the
first true land animals. THE AGE of REPTILES—dinosaurs—pterodactyls
—mammals. AMPHIBIANS and REPTILES of TODAY · Amphibians'
larvæ. CÆCILIANS—the legless amphibians. NEWTS and SALA-
MANDERS—the tailed amphibians—reproduction. FROGS and TOADS—
the tail-less amphibians—eyes—ears—mouths—breathing—voice—eggs and

Section 5 — Birds

Section 6 — Mammals

—small and large ears. THE ORDERS of the MAMMALS · EGG-LAYERS · POUCH-BEARERS : kangaroos, opossums. PLACENTALS. The "Toothless" Animals : sloths : armadillos : ant-eaters. Sea-cows. Whales. The Hoofed Animals—walkers and runners. The Rodents—the "gnawing" animals. Carnivores—the beasts of prey : the cats and dogs : bears : seals and walruses. Insect-eaters. The "Finger-winged" bats. The Primates : monkeys, apes and man. BRAINS · HANDS · MAN .

Section 7
How Animals Behave — Form and Colour

EVOLUTION OF MIND · SENSES · THE NERVOUS SYSTEM—like the telephone. PLANTS and ANIMALS · NETLIKE NERVOUS SYSTEMS—hydra : jellyfishes : starfishes. THE COMING of the HEAD and THE CENTRAL EXCHANGE · NERVOUS SYSTEMS of BACK-BONED ANIMALS · SMALL BODIES and LARGE BODIES—depend on breathing systems. INSTINCT v. INTELLIGENCE · INSTINCT plus INTELLIGENCE—living things and machines. ANIMALS LIVE IN DIFFERENT WORLDS · SENSES OF ONE-CELLED CREATURES · SENSES OF INVERTEBRATES · INSECTS—bees and colour—some intelligent ants. FISHES—lateral line. AMPHIBIANS · LAND VERTE-BRATES—difficulties of life on land. BIRDS—quick eyes and good colour sense. MAMMALS—keen ears—fur and whiskers—eyes and the hand. LEARNING—method of trial and error. APES—reasoning powers—solving problems. MAN—the power of thinking, hoping, remembering, speaking. HANDS · PROTECTIVE COLOURING — counter-shading — dazzle patterns. SPECIAL COLOURINGS—panda. COLOUR CHANGES—seasonal colours—quick changes : flat-fish : coral fish : cuttle-fish : flower-spiders. Colour change and emotion : fighting-fish. FORM and COLOUR—protective shapes : leaf-butterflies : twig-caterpillars : stick-insects. CAMOU-FLAGE IN ATTACK : tigers : crocodiles : flower-mantises : angler-fish. LIGHT-ORGANS · "WARNING" COLOURS : wasps : salamanders : coral-snakes. ALARM COLOURS : rabbits. TERRIFYING ATTI-TUDES—bluff : frilled-lizard : caterpillars. MIMICRY—of warning colours —of ants—of harmless animals—cuckoos' eggs. Mimicry among Plants. DIFFERENT GROUPS with COMMON TRADEMARKS · DISGUISES :

crabs and seaweed: caddis-fly grubs. MATING DRESS: butterflies: lions and monkeys: birds: newts: fishes. FORM AND COLOUR plus BEHAVIOUR: bitterns: butterflies: caterpillars: stick-insects. All animals behave in accordance with their form and colour

Section 8 — Homes and Families

FEEDING and GROWING · REPRODUCTION—dividing—budding—two cells become one and form SEEDS or EGGS. POLLINATION OF FLOWERS · EGGS—of mammals—of fishes. NUMBERS OF EGGS AND YOUNG—fishes—insects—reptiles—birds—mammals. YOUNG ANIMALS —growing outside the egg—inside the egg—well developed and less developed birds and mammals. PARENTAL CARE OF PLANTS—food stores—seed dispersal. PARENTAL CARE OF ANIMALS—of insects—of spiders—of fishes—of frogs and toads—of reptiles—of birds—of mammals. THE HOMES OF MAMMALS—burrows—beavers' homes—nests of dormice—harvest-mice — squirrels—foxes' earths — monkeys and apes. WATER HOMES—corals—sea-worms. SPIDERS' HOMES—trapdoor and water-spiders. COURTSHIP—of worms—of crabs—of insects—of fishes—of newts—of birds: bower-birds: the dance of the grebes. PLAYING AND LEARNING. WATER EGGS and LAND EGGS—the shelled egg has led to courtship, homes, parental care and family life. CHILDHOOD.

Section 9 — Societies and Partnerships

CELL DIVISION and CELL COLONIES · SPECIALIZATION: Volvox. MANY-CELLED BODIES: sponges: corals: sea-anemones. CENTRAL GOVERNMENT OF THE BODY—head and brain. REGENERATION—growing new parts. THE FORMING OF SOCIETIES · TEMPORARY ASSOCIATIONS — overcrowding— food — breeding — migration — hunger marches. PERMANENT SOCIETIES—shoals of fishes—colonies of sea-birds—rooks. Hunting—packs. Herds. Sign language. Families—tribes—villages—towns—cities—nations—the world-state. SOCIAL INSECTS: honey-bees: wasps: ants: termites. INSECT-SOCIETIES and HUMAN-SOCIETIES. PARTNERSHIPS—parasites—"guests," welcome and unwel-

Section 10 — The Head of the Family

The Story of Living Things as shown by the rocks

Each layer of rock was once on the surface of the earth. In these layers are found the remains of plants and animals which lived while the rocks were being formed.

UNDER THE SEA

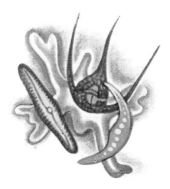

Life began in the sea.
The simplest living
things still live
in water.

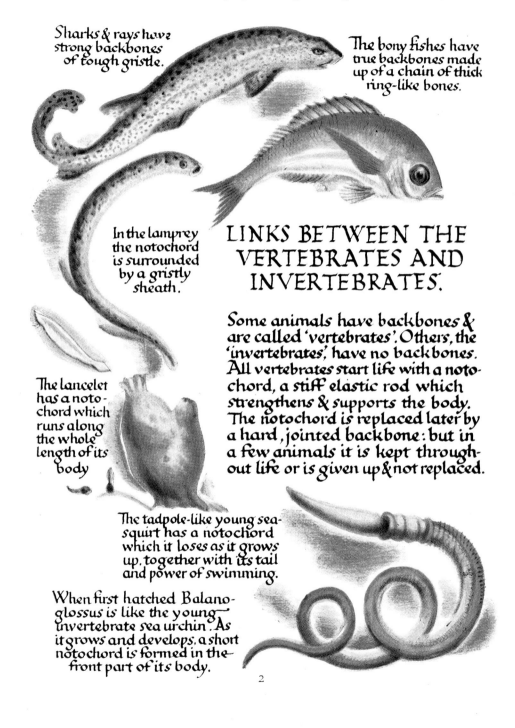

Sharks & rays have strong backbones of tough gristle.

The bony fishes have true backbones made up of a chain of thick ring-like bones.

In the lamprey the notochord is surrounded by a gristly sheath.

LINKS BETWEEN THE VERTEBRATES AND INVERTEBRATES.

The lancelet has a noto-chord which runs along the whole length of its body

Some animals have backbones & are called 'vertebrates'. Others, the 'invertebrates', have no backbones. All vertebrates start life with a noto-chord, a stiff elastic rod which strengthens & supports the body. The notochord is replaced later by a hard, jointed backbone: but in a few animals it is kept through-out life or is given up & not replaced.

The tadpole-like young sea-squirt has a notochord which it loses as it grows up, together with its tail and power of swimming.

When first hatched Balano-glossus is like the young invertebrate sea urchin. As it grows and develops, a short notochord is formed in the front part of its body.

2

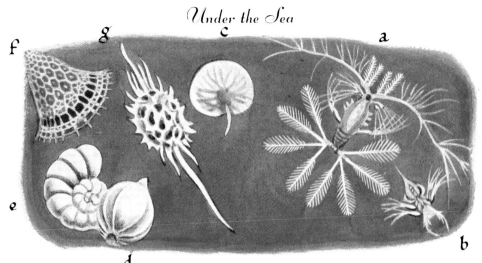

The living things which drift on and near the sea's surface are called plankton. Most of them are microscopic. Among them are single-celled plants & animals, and the eggs and larvae of many-celled animals. Much of the plankton consists of young crustaceans [a & b]. The phosphorescence of the sea is often due to myriads of one-celled animals called Noctiluca [c] Chalk cliffs are formed of the shells of Foraminifera [d & e]. Radiolaria have flinty shells of various intricate shapes [f & g].

Section 1 — Under the Sea

THE MAKING OF EARTH About two thousand million years ago, the earth was a knot of fiery matter, spinning in endless space round its parent, the sun.

Through millions of years this molten mass cooled, and a rocky shell was formed on the surface. The inside stayed hot and turbulent, and the seething core forced out streams of heavy molten rock on to the cooler, lighter crust. Some of the lighter rocks remained on the surface of the globe and became land-masses; but in places the earth's crust was dragged downwards by the heavy streams of lava. These sunken parts became the beds of the first seas. The inside of the earth went on cooling and shrinking, and pulled the outer crust into the thousands of wrinkles which we know as mountains and valleys.

During the earth's cooling, water vapour and other gases were **WATER** pouring out from it, surrounding it with a hot and steamy atmosphere.

The water vapour condensed into an unbroken blanket of cloud, through which the sun's rays never reached the gloomy surface beneath. Rain fell unceasingly from the cool upper part of the world-cloud, but the water was turned again to steam before it could touch the hot earth. At last the crust cooled enough for the rain to fall upon it, and the first seas and rivers were

3

SUNSHINE formed. The blanket of cloud became thinner and thinner: it tore apart, and for the first time the rays of the sun lit up the earth. So LIFE became possible, for without the sun there could be no living thing.

The dry land of those very early days must have been bare and lifeless rock. Soil is largely a product of plant and animal life, and these were not to appear on land for long ages to come. While stifling volcanic gases still hung over the earth, the sea became the first home of life.

LIFE It is not known how life first came on this planet. The first living things may have been minute specks of protoplasm which were neither plant nor animal. Protoplasm is a clear, jelly-like stuff which looks like the uncooked white of an egg. It goes to make up the bodies of all living things, from those which can only be seen with a microscope, to great animals CELLS such as elephants and whales.

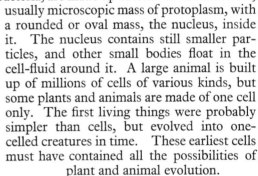

Living things, except bacteria, are made up of *cells*. A cell is a small, usually microscopic mass of protoplasm, with a rounded or oval mass, the nucleus, inside it. The nucleus contains still smaller particles, and other small bodies float in the cell-fluid around it. A large animal is built up of millions of cells of various kinds, but some plants and animals are made of one cell only. The first living things were probably simpler than cells, but evolved into one-celled creatures in time. These earliest cells must have contained all the possibilities of plant and animal evolution.

FIRST It is not known what formed
PLANTS the food of the first living things or how they absorbed it. Eventually some of them developed a tough covering of cellulose, and produced chlorophyll in their bodies. Chlorophyll is a green colouring matter, which gives to the cells which contain it the power of using the energy of

Sponges are water-living creatures. They are sometimes brightly coloured, and have fine skeletons of horny, chalky or flinty material. The Venus' Flowerbasket sponge lives in very deep water, & its skeleton is made of glassy fibres which are woven into a lacy network.

4

Sea animals often grow on other living things. ← A Sea-fig sponge begins to grow on a small whelk shell in which lives a young hermit-crab. Crab and sponge grow together, until the sponge surrounds the crab's body and takes the place of a shell.

sunlight to change the carbon-dioxide in air and water into food matter. These tiny green cells by slow degrees evolved into PLANTS. Other single-celled creatures did not develop a cellulose wall, but changed the shape of their bodies frequently and became very active. Without chlorophyll, they could not make their food from the gases and salts in their surroundings, and so they fed on their neighbours the green cells. They became ANIMALS.

FIRST ANIMALS   A third group stayed much as they were, and did not develop into plants or animals. Their descendants are living to-day, and the very simplest of them may be like the first living creatures.

The sea covers nearly three-quarters of the whole surface of the earth, and there are probably more living things in it than in the rest of the world, though they do not vary so much as the plants and animals on dry land. Under its

THE SEA   apparently flat surface (which, however, has its hills and valleys and streams like the land) there lies another world of mountains and plains and great depressions. There are forests of seaweed and floating "meadows" : and groves made by coral-animals and gardens of sea-anemones. Fishes flit like birds in the green light, which becomes dimmer and darker, until there is utter blackness half a mile below the surface. Here the only light comes from the luminous animals which swim in those inky

The sponge protects the crab by being distasteful to animals which would otherwise eat it, & the crab carries the sponge to fresh feeding-grounds.

5

The Coelenterates or hollow-bodied animals include jelly-fishes, sea-anemones & corals. Their bodies are soft and bag-like with a single opening which is surrounded by tentacles. Some of them build hard skeletons, in or round which they live.

End of a branch of Red Coral. The red skeleton is clothed with a soft flesh out of which grow the white coral polyps. [Actual size: about 1/5 th. of an inch]

depths, or which crawl or grow on the sea floor. Sometimes the floor is covered with a deep layer of fine mud. This is made of the skeletons of millions of minute plants and animals, whose dead bodies have sunk down to form the various "oozes." These layers are often a hundred feet deep.

DIATOMS AND FLAGELLATES
The microscopic plants whose shells help to make this mud are one-celled and comparatively simple. The least complex of them, which are without shells, may be like some of the early plants from which all vegetable life has evolved. These tiny plants are of great importance in the life of the sea, for it is upon them that the other creatures depend. In the same way, plants make life on land possible, by providing earth-living animals with food and much of their oxygen. Even the sea and land animals which eat other animals, depend indirectly on plants for food, for the last link in the chain of animal food is always an animal which feeds on plants. The one-celled sea plants are mostly of two types : diatoms, with beautiful flinty shells, and flagellates, which are on the borderline between plants and animals. The flagellates have no hard shells, so they do not help to make up the sea oozes, but, with the diatoms and the various animals which float near the surface of the sea, they form what is known as the "plankton"—"that which is drifted about." It is on the plankton that almost all sea animals depend, from the smallest fish to the largest whale.

PROTOZOA
The microscopic animals which help to form this floating food supply are called "protozoa" or "first-animals," because it is thought that the simplest of them may be similar to some of the early forms of animal life. The protozoan consists of one cell only, while all other animals are built up of a great number of cells of different kinds, each cell doing its own special work in the body of which it forms a part. These single-celled proto-zoa are often far from simple. Many of them have chalky or flinty shells of intri-cate design which, with the shells of the diatoms, sink to the bottom of the sea when empty, and form the soft mud there. Others are phosphorescent, and when millions of them are floating together on the sea at night, they light it up with a

6

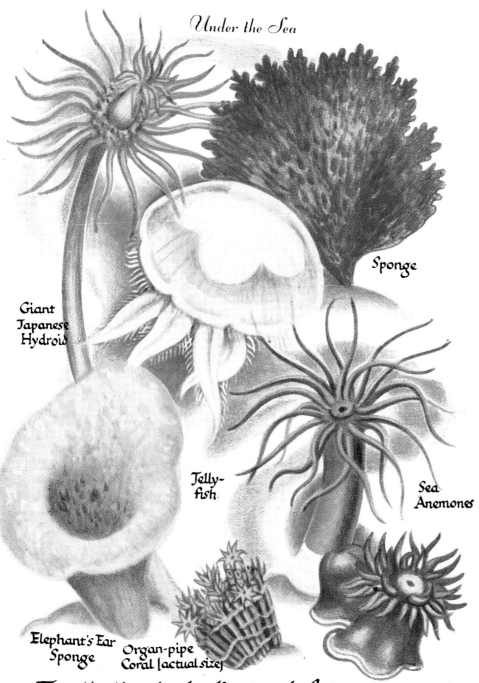

Sponge

Giant
Japanese
Hydroid

Jelly-
fish

Sea
Anemones

Elephant's Ear
Sponge

Organ-pipe
Coral (actual size)

Five 'hollow-bodied' animals & two sponges

7

greenish-white glow. Some of the protozoa do not live in the sea, though they must always be surrounded by liquid of some kind. They live in fresh water or damp soil, or even in the bodies of larger animals. One of the

AMŒBA simplest, the amœba, looks like an irregular speck of almost colourless jelly. It is about one hundredth of an inch across, and lives on the mud or weeds in ponds.

The sponge is the lowest type of many-celled animal. It is scarcely more than a loosely organized colony of protozoa, living in a finely woven skeleton which may be either quite rigid, or soft and pliable like the bath-sponge. The

SPONGES jelly-like cells which make up a sponge are divided into several kinds according to the work which they do. Some of them have long, whip-like tails which they lash continually, and this movement draws a constant stream of water through the sponge body. Sponges cannot move about except during the first few hours of their lives. They stay rooted to one spot, more like plants than animals. They are often brilliantly coloured, red, orange, purple, green or yellow.

CŒLENTERATES The cœlenterates, the hollow-bodied animals, are more successful as many-celled bodies than the sponges. Their cells are more highly specialized, and some of them can move from one place to another. Each animal of this group has a simple nervous system, and a mouth

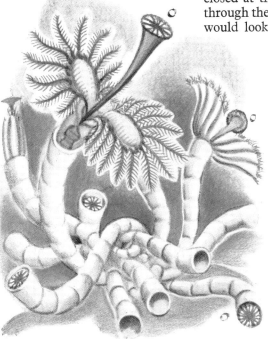

which opens into a digestive cavity, which is closed at the other end. If it were cut down through the middle, the body of such an animal would look rather like an unspillable inkpot.

The tentacles round their mouths are sensitive, and are often provided with stinging cells. The animal catches its prey, feeds and defends itself by means of them. Some of the

The Worms are more active animals than the Coelenterates. Some of the sea worms build tubes to protect their soft bodies and feathery gills: The Serpulas form chalky tubes, into which they disappear when alarmed, closing the entrance with a horny stopper [o]

most beautiful of sea creatures belong to this group : the sea-anemones and corals are called "anthozoa" or "flower-animals," and strew the floor of shallow waters with their brightly coloured, daisy-like forms. The anemones are single animals, but most of the corals form colonies. They build hard skeletons of lime, around which or inside which they live. The tiny coral-animals are of various colours, often contrasting with the colours of their skeletons, which grow into many different shapes. The red-purple organ-pipe corals grow together in parallel tubes : other corals are branching and tree-like. Some, such as the brain-coral, grow rounded and ridged; others look like mushrooms turned upside down. There are fan-like and finger-like corals, and the corals which through countless years have built up reefs and islands. Sea-fans and sea-pens are feathery, plant-like animals, which belong to the cœlenterate group. So also do the jelly-fishes, who are milky white or delicately coloured. The Portuguese man-of-war and its relations are small, but poisonous animals, coloured blue, pink and crimson, which drift through the water supported by gas-filled bladders and swimming bells. The cœlenterates which live in fresh water are much smaller and less brilliantly coloured than their sea relatives, but are no less interesting in their ways of living.

Some sea worms build leathery tubes and others make their shelters of sand and shells. The Lug-worm tunnels through the sand but does not make a tube. The Sea-mouse worm is thickly covered with iridescent bristles.

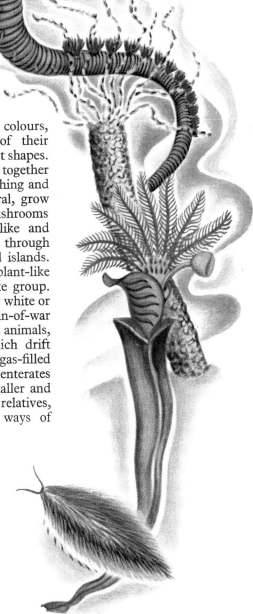

All Echinoderms live in the sea and most of them are built on a five-rayed plan. They have hard spiny skins. Starfishes crawl by means of their tube-feet: brittle-stars move about by lashing their snake-like rays.

The worms are less plant-like and jelly-like than the cœlenterates, though among the sea-worms there are some which look like flowers.

WORMS — Worms vary greatly in shape. There are ringed worms such as the earth-worm and leeches, the last having suckers at each end of the body; there are ribbon-worms and tape-worms, and leaf-shaped flat worms. Some of the sea-worms are beautiful creatures, brightly coloured and crowned with white and crimson feathery gills which wave gracefully from the tops of their chalky, sandy or leathery tubes. The worms build these tubes in order to pro-tect their soft bodies, and at the first hint of danger they dart back into the safety of their shelters. The chalk-tubed worms often build their tubes together, so that they look like a mass of twisted pinky-white snakes. Some of the "leathery-tubes" lie buried in the sand, others cover their tubes with mud, sand or shells; while the sand-tubed worms make their homes of small shells, fine sand and gravel.

Among the sea-worms there are some which are phosphorescent, while others have sequin-like scales. There is the flattened, oval sea-mouse, with its felting of iridescent bristles which, as the body moves, change their colour from gold to peacock blue. The common Rag-worm or Nereis, whose bronze-coloured skin flashes with changing colours, is one of the "ringed worms." Along its sides are a great many oar-shaped swimming bristles.

In the ringed worms, the body is divided up or ringed off into segments, each segment, except in the earth-worms and leeches, bearing an out-growth of bristles, or a sort of limb. It is thought that from creatures such as these, the insects and other creep-ing many-legged animals may have evolved. They have much in common with the ringed worms, for their bodies also are divided into segments each bearing some kind of limb, and their nervous systems are arranged on the same plan.

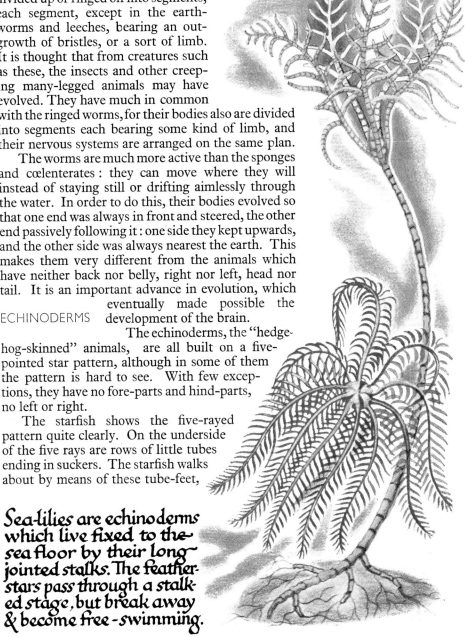

The worms are much more active than the sponges and cœlenterates : they can move where they will instead of staying still or drifting aimlessly through the water. In order to do this, their bodies evolved so that one end was always in front and steered, the other end passively following it : one side they kept upwards, and the other side was always nearest the earth. This makes them very different from the animals which have neither back nor belly, right nor left, head nor tail. It is an important advance in evolution, which eventually made possible the development of the brain.

ECHINODERMS

The echinoderms, the "hedge-hog-skinned" animals, are all built on a five-pointed star pattern, although in some of them the pattern is hard to see. With few excep-tions, they have no fore-parts and hind-parts, no left or right.

The starfish shows the five-rayed pattern quite clearly. On the underside of the five rays are rows of little tubes ending in suckers. The starfish walks about by means of these tube-feet,

Sea-lilies are echinoderms which live fixed to the sea floor by their long jointed stalks. The feather-stars pass through a stalk-ed stage, but break away & become free-swimming.

In sea-urchins the five rays
are fused together to form a
hollow skeleton, ball-like
or flattened, out of which
grow spines and tube-feet.

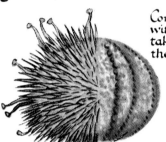

Common sea-urchin
with some of the spines
taken away to show
the skeleton.

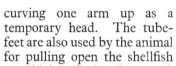

curving one arm up as a temporary head. The tube-feet are also used by the animal for pulling open the shellfish on which it feeds. Its mouth is in the centre of the underside of its body, and the starfish can turn its stomach inside out through the mouth on to its prey, digesting it outside the body. The starfish has no internal skeleton, but it has a hard covering stiffened with a network of bony plates and spines. It also has tiny pincerlike teeth mounted on short stalks and scattered all over the top of its body. It uses these to clean and to defend itself.

Brittle-stars, and their rather distant relatives the sea-lilies and feather-stars, look much like starfishes with long, slender, fringed rays. The rays are clearly marked off from the body, instead of merging gradually into it. The brittle-stars swim actively about with lashing movements of their snakelike rays. The sea-lilies can creep or swim, but most of them live attached to a large shell or stone. Some of them have stalks and look very plant-like.

In the sea-urchin, the five rays have turned upwards, put their tips together, and joined along the sides to form a thin, brittle shell. The tube-feet are still there, but are protected by spines of various lengths, working on ball-and-socket joints. The mouth is usually on the underside, surrounded by soft skin, and has five large teeth. Sea-urchins are shaped either like oranges, eggs, or thick biscuits.

The sea-cucumbers are like sea-urchins which have grown long and sausage-shaped instead of round or flat. They have head-ends, tail-ends, and top- and under-sides. Their skin is thick and leathery, and the skeleton is made up of microscopic rods and plates which are embedded in it. They walk, like their cousins the starfishes, and sea-urchins, by means of their tube-feet. The mouth is at one end of the body, and is surrounded by tube-feet which have become tentacles. The animals feed themselves with these tentacles, which are sometimes spadelike, and which they use for shovelling mud into themselves. Others have feelers with long thin branches covered with slime, on which they catch the small animals that form their food.

MOLLUSCS   The molluscs, or "soft-bodied" animals, include some of the most beautiful and some of the least attractive creatures. Under this heading are grouped the painted, many-shaped "sea-shells," the slimy slugs and snails which do so much damage in the garden, and the writhing, sucker-armed squids and octopuses.

The molluscs are more complex than the animals in the starfish group. They have better digestive and nervous systems ; they have bloodvessels, heart and gills, and some of them have well-developed eyes. The "shellfish" wear their skeletons outside their bodies, and it is these empty skeletons which are picked up on the shore and known as "sea-shells." Some of the shelled molluscs have double (bivalve) shells, hinged along one side, like those of the

BIVALVES   oyster, mussel and cockle : others have single, hollow shells, like those of snails and limpets.

The bivalves are sluggish animals on the whole. Their heads are less developed than those of the other molluscs, and they have no means of capturing or chewing their prey. Most of them anchor themselves to a rock, or bury themselves in sand or mud, or burrow into sunken wood. They feed and breathe by passing a continual current of water through their shells. From this water they take oxygen and the minute creatures on which they feed. Oysters and mussels live in this way, but the scallop spends its early days swimming about quite actively, by opening and

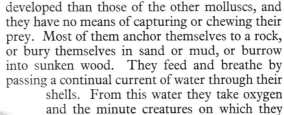

Sea-cucumbers are sausage-shaped echinoderms with leathery skins. Their mouths are at one end of the body and are surrounded by feelers.

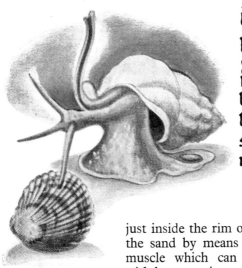

The Molluscs have very soft bodies, but most of them are protected by hard shells. The gastropods have single, hollow shells, often coiled and brightly coloured. These molluscs move about actively in search of food which they rasp with their file-like tongues.

closing the two parts of its double shell. It has a row of shining eyes just inside the rim of each shell. The cockle leaps along the sand by means of its long "foot," a lobe of strong muscle which can be pushed through the shell and withdrawn again.

Most of the single-shelled molluscs are gastropods, or "stomach-footed" animals. They move about by means of a flat, muscular sole on the underside of the body, so that they seem to walk upon their stomachs. Sometimes there is a hard plate on the back of the "foot" which acts as a lid to the opening of the shell when the animal goes inside. The gastropods have long

GASTROPODS ribbon-like "tongues" set with minute teeth, with which they tear up their food and draw it into the mouth. The whelk bores through the shells of other molluscs, and sucks out their soft bodies; slugs and snails use their "tongues" to rasp away the leaves of plants. The gastropods have well-formed heads, and eyes which are set at the base or tips of their tentacles. Their shells are usually coiled clockwise into a spiral cone, and are of many beautiful shapes and colours. Sometimes they are smooth or highly polished; sometimes they are moulded into elaborate shapes. They may be of rich dark colours, or delicately washed with pink, yellow or lilac. Some of them are speckled, some striped, others are decorated with intricate designs.

The cephalopods, the "head-footed" animals, walk with

CEPHALOPODS their mouths underneath them. In these molluscs the head and the "foot" have become fused together, and the mouth is in the middle of the head-foot mass. It is provided with a pair of horny jaws shaped like a parrot's beak, and ringed about by eight or ten long arms set with suckers, with which the animals catch and hold their prey.

The octopus has eight arms, and spends much of its time on or near the sea bottom, lurking in holes and caves. It often builds a shelter of stones from which it pounces out upon other sea creatures as they pass by.

The squids and cuttlefishes have ten arms, two of which are very long and

14

end in powerfully gripping "hands." They are active animals and hunt their prey, swimming either backwards or forwards by means of fins which run along each side of the body. Like all the cephalopods, they breathe by taking in water which passes over their plumelike gills and is breathed out again. By shooting the water out with great force, these animals can drive themselves rapidly backwards. This is their way of escaping danger. The cuttlefishes can also baffle their enemies by changing their colours, and by squirting out a dark inky fluid called sepia, which clouds the water and covers their retreat.

Long ages ago all cephalopods had external shells, but to-day there is only one, the *Pearly*-nautilus, which still wears its hard, coiled shell outside. The female *Paper*-nautilus, or argonaut, has a delicately built spiral shell, which is used partly to protect her own body, but chiefly as a cradle for her developing eggs. The shells of the octopuses, squids and cuttlefishes have dwindled into flat plates and rods of varying sizes, which are embedded in their bodies.

The big cephalopods are the largest invertebrate animals. Some of the giant octopuses are from thirty to fifty feet long. They are also in some ways the most highly organized and the most intelligent of the invertebrates. They have large, well-developed eyes which look very much like the eyes of a backboned animal.

ARTHROPODS It is thought that the molluscs sprang from the same stock as the worms, for in the early stages of their lives the animals of both these groups are very much alike. It is almost certain that the arthropods have evolved from creatures like the ringed worms.

The arthropods, or "jointed-limbed" animals, include all those creatures who wear their jointed

The shells of the bivalves are in two parts, hinged along one side. Most bivalves are sluggish animals: they live buried in sand & mud or fixed to rocks. These molluscs get their food & oxygen from the current of water which they draw through their shells.

15

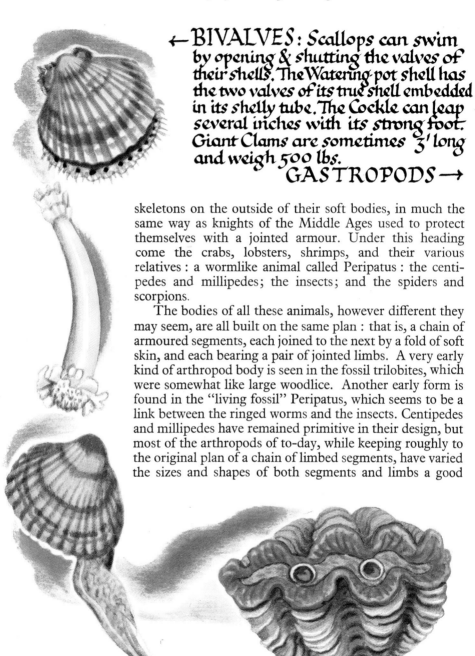

←BIVALVES: Scallops can swim by opening & shutting the valves of their shells. The Watering-pot shell has the two valves of its true shell embedded in its shelly tube. The Cockle can leap several inches with its strong foot. Giant Clams are sometimes 3' long and weigh 500 lbs.
GASTROPODS →

skeletons on the outside of their soft bodies, in much the same way as knights of the Middle Ages used to protect themselves with a jointed armour. Under this heading come the crabs, lobsters, shrimps, and their various relatives : a wormlike animal called Peripatus : the centipedes and millipedes; the insects; and the spiders and scorpions.

The bodies of all these animals, however different they may seem, are all built on the same plan : that is, a chain of armoured segments, each joined to the next by a fold of soft skin, and each bearing a pair of jointed limbs. A very early kind of arthropod body is seen in the fossil trilobites, which were somewhat like large woodlice. Another early form is found in the "living fossil" Peripatus, which seems to be a link between the ringed worms and the insects. Centipedes and millipedes have remained primitive in their design, but most of the arthropods of to-day, while keeping roughly to the original plan of a chain of limbed segments, have varied the sizes and shapes of both segments and limbs a good

Ianthina makes a float of bubbles of mucus: the eggs are fixed to the underside. Sea-butterflies have wing-like lobes on the foot, which they use to swim in the open sea.

deal. In most of them a number of the segments have fused together, and there is not always a pair of limbs to each segment. From something which may have been like the small, bristled outgrowths of the sea-worms, the limbs of the arthropods have become jointed, often long, and specialized into walking-legs, swimming-paddles, feelers and even jaws. The jointed armour and long legs make it possible for the arthropods to lead a more varied and active life than any of the other invertebrates. This has enabled them to adapt themselves to living on land and breathing air, until to-day the insects are the most numerous of all land creatures. All these animals have a well-developed nervous system, running along the lower side of the body and if, as is usual, they have a heart, it is in the back. Their eyes, especially in the higher insects, are much more efficient than those of most other invertebrates. Insects, centipedes, millipedes and spiders and scorpions, are air-breathing animals,

Glaucus is a sea-slug and has no shell. It floats near the surface of the sea

Some of the Cone-shells have a poisonous bite
↓   A purple dye used to be made from the bodies of the Rock-Whelks →

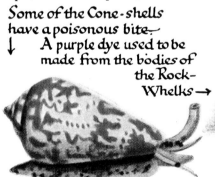

In past ages cephalopods, like other molluscs, had shells which covered them. The Pearly Nautilus is the only one which has kept its coiled shell: the others have shells, or horny rods & plates inside their soft bodies.

The Pearly Nautilus

A cephalopod which lived about 300 million years ago

Cephalopods, the 'head-footed' animals, are the most active and also the largest molluscs. They move swiftly, unhampered by a heavy shell, and are protected by their power to change colour & to give out a cloud of inky fluid.

18

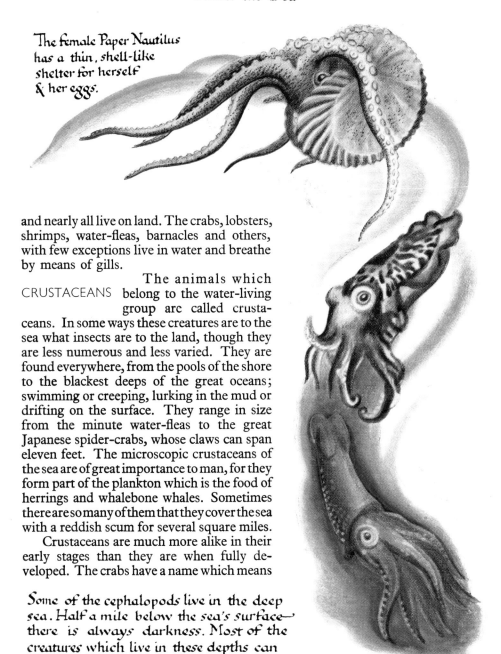

The female Paper Nautilus has a thin, shell-like shelter for herself & her eggs.

and nearly all live on land. The crabs, lobsters, shrimps, water-fleas, barnacles and others, with few exceptions live in water and breathe by means of gills.

The animals which CRUSTACEANS belong to the water-living group are called crusta-ceans. In some ways these creatures are to the sea what insects are to the land, though they are less numerous and less varied. They are found everywhere, from the pools of the shore to the blackest deeps of the great oceans; swimming or creeping, lurking in the mud or drifting on the surface. They range in size from the minute water-fleas to the great Japanese spider-crabs, whose claws can span eleven feet. The microscopic crustaceans of the sea are of great importance to man, for they form part of the plankton which is the food of herrings and whalebone whales. Sometimes there are so many of them that they cover the sea with a reddish scum for several square miles.

Crustaceans are much more alike in their early stages than they are when fully de-veloped. The crabs have a name which means

Some of the cephalopods live in the deep sea. Half a mile below the sea's surface there is always darkness. Most of the creatures which live in these depths can give out light from their own bodies.

19

The King-crab belongs to the same class as the spiders, but it lives in the sea and breathes with gills.

In the Arthropods, or 'jointed-limbed' animals, the body is covered with a stiff armour. This skeleton is not rigid like the shell of the mollusc: it is jointed so that the animal can move freely & quickly. Insects & spiders are air-breathing arthropods & live on land. Most of the crustaceans live in water and breathe by means of gills.

Barnacles are free-swimming when they are young: then they change their shape & become fixed.

"short-tailed," because their "tails" are small and are tucked under the large, shielded body: but in their early life they have a long hind-part somewhat like that of a shrimp or a lobster. The barnacle used to be classed with the molluscs, until it was found that in its larval stage it was free-swimming, and much like the young of other crustaceans. After changing its skin and its appearance several times, the barnacle fixes itself by the head to something hard, such as a rock or a ship, and gradually takes on its final form. Its fringed legs are no longer of use for rowing it about, and they are used as a net for catching food.

Nearly all the crustaceans are sea animals, though some of them live in fresh water. A few have learnt to live on land and to breathe air. The woodlice and pillbugs are completely adapted to life on the earth, and the Land hermit-crabs travel far from the shore, only returning to the sea to breed. The Robber or Coconut-crab climbs tall coconut palms and eats the nuts, which it breaks open by hammering on one of the "eyes" with its great claw. Like the Land hermit-crabs, it starts life in the sea and has to go back to the sea to spawn. Most of the hermit-crabs live in the water. They are somewhat like lobsters, but have a soft instead of a hard-shelled hind-part. In order to protect this part of its body, the crab tucks it into the empty shell of a whelk. It uses its last two pairs of legs to grip the inside of the shell firmly, and to hold it in place. The Coconut-crab is a hermit-crab, but its hind-part is tucked under the rest of the body and is protected by shelly plates, so it has given up borrowing the shells of other creatures.

Some crabs use living animals or plants with which to defend themselves. One crab whose claws are small and feeble, carries in each one a stinging sea-anemone. It uses these for protection, and it eats the food which they catch. The sponge-crabs disguise themselves with a piece of sponge, which they hold on to their backs with their hind legs. The spider-crab plants pieces of seaweed or living sponge on its shell. It does this so carefully that the weeds or sponges go on living

The Giant Japanese crab is the largest arthropod. The lobster is one of the long-tailed crustaceans. Its two great claws are unequal in size. The larger is armed with blunt knobs, and the smaller has sawlike teeth.

21

and growing, and mask the crab completely. If a spider-crab finds itself in different surroundings, it tears off its old disguise and plants a new one on its body. The Aesop-prawn has the power of changing its colour according to the colour of the weed to which it clings. It takes two or three days to do this, and if it is

LIGHT-BEARING ANIMALS

among feathery, branching weeds, it can make its body barred or lined with colour. At night it always becomes a delicate, transparent blue.

The prawns, shrimps, lobsters and crayfishes belong to the "long-tailed" crustaceans. These animals swim with rapid jerks of their long hind-parts, though the large, heavily-armoured lobsters usually crawl about on the sea-floor like the crabs. Some of the crustaceans, and many other sea creatures, are luminous. The light-bearing animals often live in the depths of the sea which no gleam of daylight can reach. Some creatures glow all over with a pale radiance, others are red or brown or black, and are lit up with small lights. The lights are of

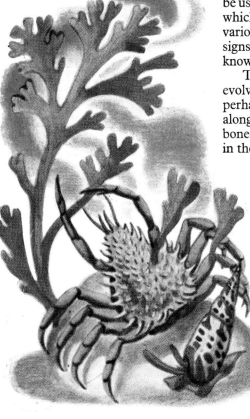

various colours and are differently arranged in each kind of animal. They may either be used as lures to the smaller creatures on which the light-bearer feeds; or the various colours and patterns may serve as signs by which each deep-sea animal can know its friends and enemies.

The arthropods are the most highly evolved of the invertebrates. They have, perhaps, developed as far as they can along their own special lines. The back-boned animals took a different direction in the early days of animal evolution, and their road has taken them much further.

The mammal is the highest form of backboned animal or verte-brate, and the fish is the lowest. Between the fishes and the back-boneless animals there are several

Spider-crabs disguise themselves with pieces of sponge or seaweed, which they plant on their backs & legs. The weeds or sponges live and grow, until the crab is completely covered.

The Robber-crab spends most of its life on land. It climbs tall coconut palms and eats the nuts.

creatures, which seem to bridge the gap which separates these two great divisions of the animal kingdom. Instead of the strong but flexible column of small bones which is the sign of the true vertebrate, these semi-vertebrates have a stiff elastic rod running through their bodies. This is known as the notochord, and is still to be found in the vertebrate in its embryo stages when the body is being formed, though it is later SEMI-VERTEBRATES replaced by the firm, supporting backbone.

One of the semi-vertebrates, the wormlike Balanoglossus, has only a trace of the notochord, at the front of its body. Others, the sea-squirts, are rounded, jelly-like animals, who spend most of their lives firmly anchored to a rock. When they are young, the sea-squirts are active little creatures, somewhat like tadpoles. Each has a nervous system, well developed sense organs, a heart, a powerful tail, and a notochord. At the time when they might be expected to change into something like a fish or a frog, they fix themselves head downwards on to seaweed, a stone, or a shell. The tail is lost, the notochord disappears, the nervous system dwindles into a small knot of nerve cells. The animal becomes little more than a double-mouthed water bottle, drawing in water by one mouth, straining off the food from it, and squirting the water out again through the other mouth. These creatures begin life as semi-vertebrates and end as invertebrates. (*See illustrations on page* 2.)

The lancelets are more like backboned animals than Balanoglossus or the sea-squirt. They are about two inches long, white, translucent, and pointed at both ends. During their early days they swim actively, but when they are full grown they lie buried in the sand with only their heads above the surface. They have tails, and their internal organs are in many ways like those of the true vertebrates. The strong elastic notochord runs the whole length of the body, but there is no skull to surround it at the head end. In the lampreys and hag-fishes there is a gristly box which foreshadows the brain-case of the higher animals. The notochord of these fish-like creatures is encased in a stout envelope,

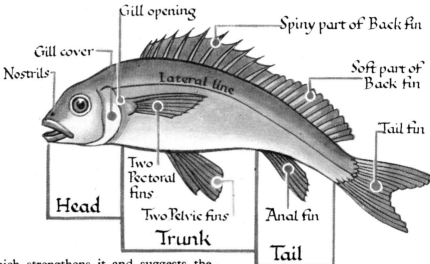

Gill opening

Gill cover

Nostrils

Spiny part of Back fin

Soft part of Back fin

Lateral line

Tail fin

Two Pectoral fins

Two Pelvic fins

Anal fin

Head

Trunk

Tail

which strengthens it and suggests the
beginning of a bony spinal column. The lampreys and hagfishes are not true
fishes, for they have no paired fins, and no jaws or teeth. Their mouths are
funnel-like suckers, with a rough, boring tongue coming up through the
centre. But from their gristly skeleton it is only a step up to a bony skeleton
with a skull and a backbone.

FISHES The sharks, dogfish, rays and chimeras of to-day, all have skeletons
of gristle strengthened in places by the addition of limy matter. They
have jaws and teeth, and most of them have, embedded in their skin, little hard
lumps which are just like teeth. The teeth of the vertebrates may have developed
originally from such small, bony lumps lying in the skin near the edges of the
mouth. All the gristly fishes have the paired fins of the true fish, which when
life left the water and took to the land, were replaced by four strong, supporting
limbs. As fishes evolved, their skeletons became hard and bony, and they
developed skulls. It is to this class of bony fish that most of the present-day
fishes belong.

Most fishes have a streamlined body, well-suited for cutting through the
water. They swim with a kind of sculling movement of the tail, which swings
from side to side and drives the fish forwards. The fins are used for balancing
and steering. The fish's body is, as a rule, covered with thin, transparent scales,
which overlap each other like tiles on a roof. They are marked with rings, and
each group of rings on a scale represents a year in the fish's life; so that the
age of a fish can be read from its scales, just as the age of a tree may be
read from the growth-rings in its trunk. Most fast-swimming, open-sea fish
have a gas-filled bladder inside them. This helps to keep them at their right
level in the water. These bladders may also tell the fish when it is moving up

Two Gristly Fish:
a Thresher Shark
& an Electric Ray.

into a region of less pressure, or down to one of greater pressure. The median or lateral line which runs along the sides of the fish's body perhaps records the pressure of water against its flanks. As fishes swim by pushing against the water from side to side, it is important that they should do this evenly if they want to go in a straight line.

Fishes are cold-blooded animals, that is, the temperature of their blood varies with the temperature of their surroundings. The shape of the mouth generally shows on what the fish feeds. Those which kill other sea creatures, have large and powerful jaws, while those which live on plankton or on seaweeds, have as a rule small mouths. All GILLS fishes have gills, fine, blood-filled fringes of skin, which are covered by a gill-cover in the bony fish, but are usually uncovered in the gristly fishes. The gills, which are at the sides of the head, are used in breathing. The fish

The fish is a VERTEBRATE or backboned animal. It has a firm skeleton inside its body, instead of a hard covering on the outside. The sharks & rays have gristly skeletons and their gill-clefts are un-covered. The other fishes have bony skeletons & covered gills.

25

Sun-fishes are about
8 feet across & have
very short bodies.
Coral-reef fishes can
change from one
brilliant colour
to another.

Flying-fishes
glide on their
large pectoral fins.

The Deep-sea Angler
fish has a luminous
lure which attracts
its prey.

takes a gulp of water and sends it out through the gill-openings. As the water passes over the gill-filaments, the oxygen in it is absorbed by the blood inside them. At the same time the blood gives up its waste products, which are carried away in the water. The gills must be kept wet, or the fish soon suffocates. The animal may be surrounded by air, but it cannot make use of the oxygen in it when its gill-filaments get dry and stick together. The herring has very delicate gills, and dies almost as soon as it is taken out of the sea. The carp, whose gill-covers hold a certain amount of water, can survive for some time on dry land. The fresh-water climbing-perch has an additional breathing organ, and can actually travel from one pool to another, pushing itself along by means of the spines on its gill-covers and anal fin. The mud-hoppers or jumping-fish spend as much time out of the water as in it. They live on the mud-flats at the mouths of tropical rivers, and walk on their pectoral fins which are very muscular and are bent under the body like a land limb. The lung-fishes have turned their swim-bladder into a lung which can take oxygen from the air, so that they are no

Some Scorpion-fishes have poison-glands at the bases of their back-fin spines.

The Globe-fish can puff itself out with air or water to frighten its enemies.

longer dependent on water and gills for their breathing. They can live for a long time out of water in a hole in the mud. From animals such as these who, though water-living, have adapted themselves to periods of drought, it can be seen how lungs and limbs were developed and the land-vertebrates evolved.

BACK TO THE SEA Sometimes evolution goes back on its tracks, and creatures whose ancestors lived on land have returned to life in the water. Since nature never restores what has once been given up as useless, these animals have not developed gills again, but still breathe by the lungs which their ancestors struggled to acquire. They have to come to the surface of the water for air, and they drown if they cannot do so. Many of them come back to the shore to breed, just as some shore-living creatures spend their early days in their original home, the open sea.

The first land-living vertebrates were amphibians, whose small descendants are the frogs, toads and newts of to-day. Although they spend most of their time in water, none of them has taken to the sea, for salt water kills them. Reptiles are far less dependent on water than the amphibians

When first hatched, Flat-fishes are like other young fish. Then one of the eyes moves round to the other side of the head, and the fish sinks to the sea-floor. It becomes flattened & the skin on the under — side grows white.

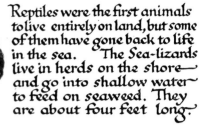

Reptiles were the first animals to live entirely on land, but some of them have gone back to life in the sea. The Sea-lizards live in herds on the shore— and go into shallow water to feed on seaweed. They are about four feet long.

from whom they evolved. They developed hard, scaly skins which could withstand lack of moisture, and they encased their eggs in shells, so that they could be laid away from water. In the days when reptiles were the largest and most numerous of land animals, many of them went back to the sea, and their land limbs became flippers. To-day there are comparatively few reptiles on land, and fewer still in the sea.

SEA-REPTILES   The salt-water crocodile is the largest living reptile, sometimes growing to the length of twenty or thirty feet. All the other crocodiles make their home in fresh water, spending their time in rivers or on the mud of the banks. Their short, weak limbs are of little use for walking on land, and their nostrils and eyes are specially adapted for water life. Their strong flattened tails are as effective as swimming organs as the tails of fishes.

Turtles are descended from animals like tortoises who took to a water-life, though they still go back to the land to lay their eggs. Their fingers and toes have become webbed to form flippers, with which they row themselves gracefully through the water.

The sea-lizards or iguanas do not live in the sea, but bask on the sand or rocks, and go into the water to feed on the seaweeds which grow near the shore. They reach a length of four feet, and with their scales and sharp spines they look like small dragons.

The sea-snakes are probably descendants of land snakes, but they venture right into the open sea, and are found in shoals or "schools" hundreds of miles from land. They are not very large, being from three to five feet long, and they are often brightly coloured. They have a broadly flattened tail which acts as a paddle. None of them can breathe under water, and

Sea-snakes live entirely in the water and cannot move on land. They swim with their flattened paddle-like tails, and come to the surface of the water to breathe air. The nostrils are at the top of the snout and are closed when the snake swims under water.

many of them come to shore to produce their young.

SEA BIRDS Birds probably evolved from reptiles, and are far in advance of them in many ways. Few of them have become adapted for sea life except on the surface of the water. The sea birds feed on fish for which they have to dive, and many of them have beaks which are well fitted for catching and carrying their food. The penguin is the most thoroughly aquatic bird, for it has sacrificed its most birdlike feature, the feathered wing, to form a powerful swimming flipper. It can dive and swim under water as easily as a fish, although it can still walk on dry land.

SEA MAMMALS The whale lives entirely in the sea and does not even come to shore to bear its young. It is smooth and fishlike in shape, yet it does not belong to the fish group, but to the highest order in the animal kingdom, the mammals. The whale, like the birds, is warm-blooded; it breathes air with its lungs and feeds its single young one on milk. Long ago it left the land and went back to life in the sea which now supports the great weight of a body which no limbs could carry upon the earth. In the whale's skeleton there are still traces of the hind legs of its ancestors. The fore-limbs have become balancing flippers, though the bones show that they were once like the five fingered front limbs of land animals. In their evolution as water animals, whales became hairless and developed a layer of fat or blubber, which helps to make them buoyant as well as keeping them warm. The remains of the hairy coat can still be seen in a few bristles which sometimes grow round the

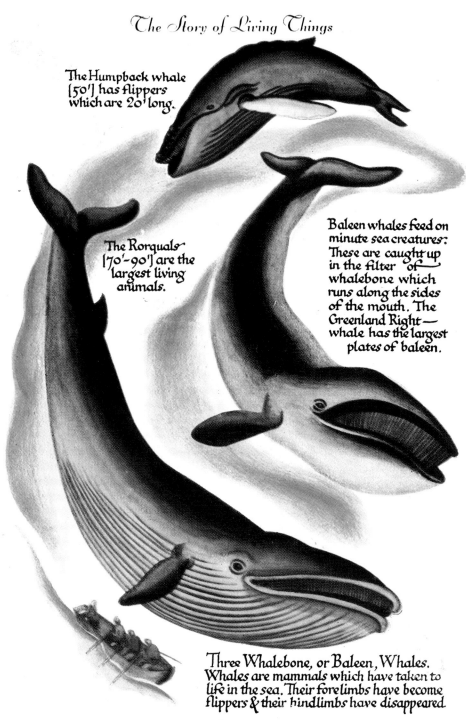

The Humpback whale
[50'] has flippers
which are 20' long.

The Rorquals
[70'–90'] are the
largest living
animals.

Baleen whales feed on
minute sea creatures:
These are caught up
in the filter of
whalebone which
runs along the sides
of the mouth. The
Greenland Right —
whale has the largest
plates of baleen.

Three Whalebone, or Baleen, Whales.
Whales are mammals which have taken to
life in the sea. Their forelimbs have become
flippers & their hindlimbs have disappeared.

30

The Sperm-whale or Cachalot
[60'] has teeth in its lower
jaw and feeds on squids.
It is hunted for the clear
oil called spermaceti
which is found
in its head.

mouth and jaws. The tail has spread out into two
large and powerful lobes which are used with an up and down movement, not like
the tail of the fish, which moves from side to side. The nostrils have shifted to the
top of the head, so that the animal may breathe without lifting too much of its body
out of the sea. They are closed when diving. Whales have large lungs which they
fill before going under water, blowing the air out again with great force when they
reach the surface. They never spout water, though a little may be carried up with
the air which they breathe out.

There are two groups of whales, those with teeth and those with flexible
fringed plates at the sides of their mouths. There are from five to six hundred of
these plates which are called whalebone or baleen, and together they act as a sieve.
The whalebone whale takes a mouthful of sea-water, which is full of the minute
animals on which it feeds. Then it closes its mouth and forces the water out
through the baleen, leaving the food inside. This highly specialized way of
feeding has been evolved by animals whose far-distant ancestors must have had
teeth; for the unborn young of the whalebone whales have
two sets of teeth, though they never cut the gum. The toothed-
whales—sperm-whales, dolphins, killers and porpoises, have
sharp teeth with which they catch fishes and cuttlefish.

The seals, who belong to the same order as the cats,
dogs and bears, have only partly gone back to
sea life. They come on to dry land, not only
during the breeding season, but also
when they want to rest. They
are, however, well adapted for
life in the water. Their bodies

The Narwhal [15']
has only two teeth. One of
them grows into a tusk about 12' long.

31

are cone-shaped, the hind legs are thrown backwards beside the short tail to form a propeller. The nostrils can be closed under water and the sensitive whisker-hairs are of use when the beast dives into dark hollows. A lining of blubber adds to the warmth of the close, short fur. The teeth, with their tips tilted backwards, are useful for gripping the slippery fishes on which the animal feeds.

It is a long step in evolution from the single-celled protozoa to the warm-blooded, milk-giving whales and seals, and there are a great many stages in between. Yet there is less variety among the sea creatures than among the animals on land. Conditions under the sea vary far less than on the earth. In the seas the temperatures are less extreme, and there are no sandy or snowy deserts to which some living things on land have had to learn to adapt themselves. There is seldom any overcrowding in the sea, and there is usually an abundance of food. The water acts as a support, and often as a means of transport, doing away with the necessity for strong limbs. In the dim, cloudy, underwater light, good eyes would not be able to see far and so good eyes have not

SEA-EGGS AND LAND-EGGS

been developed. Sound waves travel only a short way through water, so keen ears would be useless. The water cradles the eggs of sea creatures and prevents them from drying up, so that they do not need to have shells; but they are not so well protected as the larger, *shelled* egg of the land animal which is fertilized in, and kept in the body of the female for a longer period. From the fish downwards, most sea animals lay a great many eggs which are fertilized in the water, and then left to look after themselves. Thus parental care and family life have scarcely been developed in the sea.

Sea creatures have evolved in a limited way because their surroundings lack the variety, and do not present the difficulties, of dry land. It was not until life left the sea and began to adapt itself to the innumerable conditions of life on land, that it produced a greater variety of bodily forms, and with them, a greater capacity for feeling and thinking.

PLANTS

All Life depends on the Sun and the Green Leaf

Brightly coloured,
scented flowers, to
attract insects &
ensure pollination.

Flowering trees & grasses:
true flowers & enclosed
seeds: generally wind-
pollinated.

Conebearers: primitive flowers:
the first seeds.

Ferns, horsetails & clubmosses: no flowers nor seeds,
but true roots, stems & leaves. Some of them
bear spores in cones.

Liverworts: no flowers nor
seeds: no true roots nor stems.
Mosses: simple roots and
water-conducting stems.

Algae, fungi, lichens: no flowers nor
seeds: no roots, stems nor leaves.

34

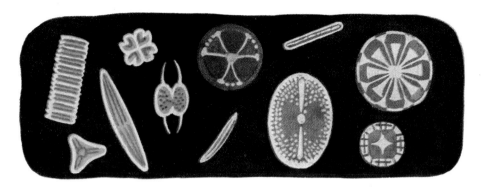

Most plants and animals are built up of many cells, but some consist of one cell only. Desmids are single-celled plants which live in fresh water and together form a green scum. Diatoms live both in fresh & salt water. They have finely patterned flinty shells, which sink to the sea floor when the plants die and form thick layers of fine— mud, or ooze. Desmids and diatoms are from 1/100" to 1/500" in size.

Section 2 — Plants

PLANTS AND ANIMALS Long ages ago, the simple cells which were the earliest living things in the world, branched off along two different courses of evolution. One division became ANIMALS, the other division became PLANTS. These two branches sprang from a common source which was neither animal nor plant, and though they have evolved along different lines, they are still closely linked together. Plants depend on animals to some extent for food, and for help in fertilizing and spreading their seeds. Animals depend entirely on plants for all their food, and for some of the oxygen which they breathe.

The most important difference between the two divisions of living things, plants and animals, is the way in which they build up the elements in their food to form the stuff of life, or protoplasm, of which their bodies are made. Animals must find their food already partly built up, and do so when they feed on the bodies of other animals or plants. The green plant can build up its food in its own body, out of water, carbon-dioxide from the air, and a few simple salts from the soil. To do this, the plant must have light, since its green colouring-matter, chlorophyll, uses the energy of the light-rays to convert the carbon-dioxide and water into the essential food of the plant. All life depends on the sun and the green leaf: for plants make their own food by means of sunlight and their chlorophyll-containing leaves, and animals feed on the plants or on other animals which have fed on plants.

There is no sharp dividing line between the two great kingdoms of living things. They may be said to differ in that animals can move about, while plants

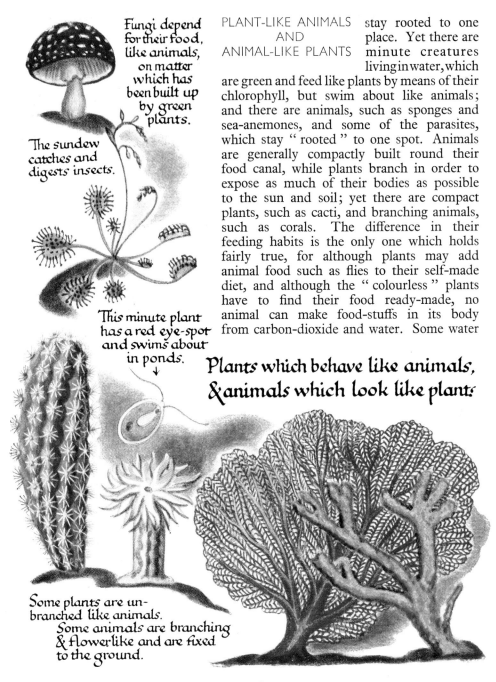

Fungi depend for their food, like animals, on matter which has been built up by green plants.

The sundew catches and digests insects.

This minute plant has a red eye-spot and swims about in ponds.

PLANT-LIKE ANIMALS
AND
ANIMAL-LIKE PLANTS

stay rooted to one place. Yet there are minute creatures living in water, which are green and feed like plants by means of their chlorophyll, but swim about like animals; and there are animals, such as sponges and sea-anemones, and some of the parasites, which stay " rooted " to one spot. Animals are generally compactly built round their food canal, while plants branch in order to expose as much of their bodies as possible to the sun and soil; yet there are compact plants, such as cacti, and branching animals, such as corals. The difference in their feeding habits is the only one which holds fairly true, for although plants may add animal food such as flies to their self-made diet, and although the " colourless " plants have to find their food ready-made, no animal can make food-stuffs in its body from carbon-dioxide and water. Some water

Plants which behave like animals, & animals which look like plants

Some plants are un-branched like animals.
Some animals are branching & flowerlike and are fixed to the ground.

36

animals which are coloured green are able to do this, but it is only because they have single-celled sea-plants living in their transparent bodies.

Although plants and animals are so different on the whole, there are several ways in which they are alike. They need the same chemical elements in their food, with which to grow, to work, and to repair their bodies.

BOTH plants and animals make and give off heat, though the amount given off by plants is very small. The effect of it can be seen in the garden when the snow melts round the plants before melting anywhere else. Plants and animals take in oxygen when they breathe and give off carbon-dioxide. Plants and many animals stop working at night, and many of them have a winter sleep.

Almost all plants, like nearly all animals, can reproduce themselves by the union of male and female cells. In most plants and in many of the lower animals, both kinds of cell are found in the same body. Though they have no sense organs such as an animal's, plants respond to stimuli such as light and

The movements of plants are fewer and slower than those of animals. Since most plants are fixed in the ground they do not move from one place to another: but their growing parts move in definite directions and mature plants have special movements which they make in response to light and dark, warmth, cold, and touch.
The dandelion opens its flowers each day and closes them at night. It lowers them before seeding, then raises them above the rest of the plant so that the seeds may be caught by the wind.

moisture, and some of them are affected by touch. Both plants and animals give off water from their bodies through minute holes on the surface. Excepting some of the one-celled plants which are active swimmers, plants do not move from one place to another; but they have movements of growth, and can turn slowly towards light or water. They can fold their leaves and petals at night, and some of them shrink from the touch of an outside object. Others can close, and even snap, their leaves on insects which settle on them.

Living things tend, as they evolve, to increase in size; and the original

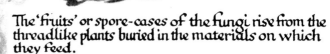

The 'fruits' or spore-cases of the fungi rise from the threadlike plants buried in the materials on which they feed.

one-celled plants in time became many-celled. At first there was merely a multiplication of simple cells, then the cells became different, or *specialized*, according to the work which they had to do. The first specialized cells were the germ or reproductive cells. Then came roots and stems and leaves, and finally flowers. The cells became of many different shapes and sizes; oblong, oval, six-sided, star-shaped, or threadlike.

Animals' bodies are also built up of microscopic cells of different shapes, but in plants the cells are nearly always surrounded by a tough wall of cellulose, so that each cell is shut up in a little box. The varying shapes of plant cells, and the different kinds of wall which they build round themselves, are responsible for the various organs in each plant and for the thousands of different species.

THE SIMPLEST PLANTS: ALGÆ

Some of the earliest plants were probably minute cells which swam about in the sea by means of fine, lashing hairs. Similar plants are found to-day among the algæ, or water-weeds. The simplest of the algæ are one-celled, and form the green scum on fresh water, and help to make up the plankton of the sea. Some of them, the diatoms, are enclosed in elaborately modelled shells of flint, which fit together like

The algae or seaweeds are simple plants with no true roots, stems or leaves. Although some of them are red or brown, they all contain chlorophyll. The fungi – toadstools mushrooms, moulds, — are like algae in some ways but they have no chlorophyll.

38

flat pill boxes with lids. The desmids are also one-celled; they live in ponds and have no shells but are of many beautiful shapes (*See illustration, p.* 35).

In most of the algæ, the cells unite to form larger plants. They may link up like a string of beads, or form a thread, or spread out into flat, leaf-like shapes, or be packed together in layers to form stem-like columns. Such plants are little more than colonies of simple cells, and the plant-body which they make is not divided into true stems, roots and leaves, though its reproductive cells may be highly specialized. The algæ range in size from the microscopic one-celled plants, to huge seaweeds six hundred feet long. Although seaweeds are brown, red, pink and purple, as well as green, they all contain chlorophyll.

THE "COLOURLESS" PLANTS: FUNGI

Closely related to these water-plants are the land-living fungi, whose bodies and methods of reproduction are in many, though not all, ways similar to those of the algæ. Like the water-plants, the fungi have neither stems, leaves nor roots, but they differ from them in having no chlorophyll. They depend for their food, like animals, on matter which has been directly or indirectly built up by the green, chlorophyll-bearing plants. Some of them live on dead and decaying matter; they are called saprophytes. Others grow and feed on living plants and animals, and are called

bacteria which turn wine into vinegar

bacteria used in the making of butter & cheese

bacteria which live in swellings on the roots of red clover

Bacteria are single-celled, plant-like creatures. Various kinds are used in the manufacture of tea, vinegar etc. Some bacteria which live in the soil take nitrogen from the air & with it form nitrates which can be absorbed and used by plants. Some of the nitrogen-fixing bacteria live in swellings on the ← roots of pod-bearing plants. Yeasts are single-celled fungi. When added to bread-dough they feed on the starch & give off carbon dioxide. The bubbles of this gas make the bread light & spongy.

GREEN PLANTS:
LIVERWORTS
AND MOSSES

damp. In these plants are found roots, stems, and leaves, though in an undeveloped form. The mosses are a step higher than the liverworts, for some of them have stems up which water is drawn from the soil, and also leaves which make use of or evaporate this water. This regular water current from soil to leaves is found in all the land-living plants in a simple form in the mosses, and highly developed in the more complex plants.

Fern

FERNS,
HORSETAILS
AND
CLUBMOSSES

There is an important advance in the plants which are next to the mosses in evolution, and which include the ferns, horsetails and clubmosses. These plants have true roots, leaves and stems. The *roots* are parts of the plant-body which grow down into the soil, fix the plant in it, and draw up water and mineral salts. The *leaves* are organs for breathing and food-making : they are covered with a waterproof layer and pitted with minute lipped openings, called stomata. The *stems* are supports, often strong and upright, which carry the leaves and, in the higher plants, the flowers. They also serve as channels for the plant's water and dissolved food. The soil water is drawn in through the root-hairs of the roots, and is carried up to the leaves by means of microscopic tubes in the stems. These "pipes" are made up of cells which have built

Horsetail

Ferns and horsetails have true roots, leaves, and stems which carry soil-water & dissolved food to all parts of the plant-body. They can grow tall and strong, but as they need water for their reproduction they can only grow where the soil is very damp.

42

seeds

thick walls round themselves and have then died, leaving their walled cavities empty. A *downward* current of dissolved food-stuff is carried, from the leaves to all parts of the plant, by the living, active sieve-tube cells. Plants with stems of this kind are seen in their simplest form in the Fern group, and in their most developed state in the Seed-plants. The possession of true roots, stems and leaves is the mark of the land plant, for with these it can live in the earth and air, and grow to a great size; while the water plant must depend on water for its food and support, as well as for its reproduction.

Plants had reached this stage

seed·box

Cone-bearing plants such as pines & larches have SEEDS & do not depend on water for their fertilization. They are true land-plants. In the flowering plants the seeds are better protected than in the cone-bearers, for they are enclosed in ovaries.

of evolution when the great coal measures were being laid down, about two hundred million years ago. While giant amphibians which were quite unlike the newts and frogs of to-day, crawled about the swampy ground, huge ferns and clubmosses and horsetails towered above them in the green light of the coal forest. Like the amphibians, whom they resemble in that they need much warmth for

COAL

43

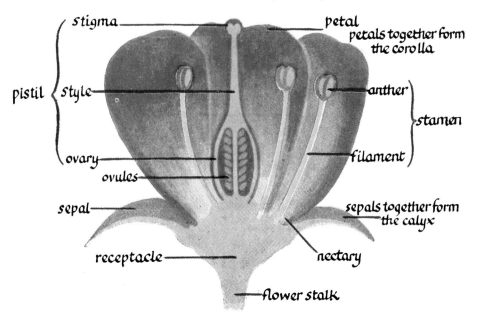

their activity and water for their reproduction, these plants have dwindled in size and numbers since those days. Tropical ferns and horsetails still reach tree-like heights, but those in cooler countries are small and lowly plants.

SPORES v. SEEDS — Most of the plants so far mentioned, notably the mosses, ferns and horsetails, reproduce themselves by an alternation of sexless spores, and egg-cells fertilized by sperms. The sperms need at least a film of water in which to swim to fertilize the eggs, so the plants must live in water or moist places. The *Seed* plants enclose their egg-cells and embryos in a protective case with a reserve store of food, and for that reason, and because they are not dependent on water for fertilizing the eggs, they include the greater number of plants.

CONE-BEARERS — Between the seedless plants and the flowering plants, which reach the highest point in plant evolution, a link is formed by the pines and firs. These are called gymnosperms, or naked-seeded plants. They produce seeds instead of spores, but bear them uncovered at the bases of their cone-scales; instead of shut safely in little containers like the seeds of the angiosperms, or plants with "boxed" seeds. They are classed with the flowering plants, but their flowers are not like true flowers. The cone-bearers or conifers sometimes grow to a gigantic size. The Big Trees of California (Sequoia gigantea) are the largest living things in the world. The tallest is over three hundred and twenty feet high, and the trunk is thirty-five feet across. It is certainly not less than two thousand years old. The conifers have been flourishing for about a hundred million years, and used to grow all over the earth. They were in their heyday at the same time as the

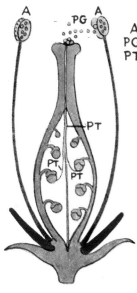

Fertilization of a flower [by self-pollination]
A Anther shedding pollen-grains
PG Pollen grains
PT Tubes from pollen grains growing down through
the style, entering the ovary, and reaching ovules.

giant reptiles. The reptiles were the first true land animals, for they had evolved the shelled egg among other things. The eggs of the amphibians were without shells and had to be laid in water. Reptiles laid their eggs on dry land, and were independent of water for breeding purposes. In a similar way the conifers, which had evolved a hard-coated seed, depended on air and wind rather than water for their reproduction.

FLOWERING PLANTS The flowering plants are the most highly evolved of all plants. They hold in the vegetable kingdom a position corresponding to that held by the mammals in the animal world. They evolved along with birds and mammals, and became dominant at much the same time as these animals. They include the most useful besides the most beautiful plants. They produce their seeds in variously shaped containers, and have developed more certain and less wasteful ways of reproduction than any other plants; just as mammals have evolved a safer and more economical way of producing offspring than the other animals.

THE FLOWER The unopened flower is enclosed in a calyx, which is a little cup, often made up of small leaves called sepals. When the flower opens, the sepals fall back and disclose leaves which are generally larger and more brilliantly coloured. These are the petals, which together form the corolla, the "little crown" or "garland." Immediately inside the petals there are delicate, often hair-like stalks, with heads full of tiny pollen-grains which generally look like fine golden dust. These are the stamens. Their stalks are called filaments; the pollen-sacs at their tops are named anthers. In the centre of the flower is the pistil, or a group of pistils. The pistil is made up of two or three parts: a sticky top, the stigma; a supporting stem, the style, which may be missing; and a swollen base, the ovary, which contains one or more ovules, or "little eggs." Before a new plant can be formed, the egg-cell must be united with a growth from a pollen-grain, just as in animals a male sperm must as a rule enter the female egg before a new life can begin.

stamens dusting bee's back with pollen

bee going into flower of deadnettle

hairs to protect nectar from other insects

nectary

Spring flowers are often yellow or white. and not Highly scented. They attract the small early insects

When the anthers are ripe they burst open, and the pollen-grains in one way or another are carried on to a stigma, where they stick to its moist surface. Each pollen-grain then begins to grow a tube, which pushes its way down the style until it enters the ovary, where it unites with an egg-cell. The egg is now said to be fertilized, and develops into a seed. As a child inherits qualities from both its parents, so the plant which grows from such a seed is in some ways like the two plants which produced the male pollen and the female ovule. Sometimes a plant fertilizes its egg-cells with pollen from its own anthers, in which case it is said to be self-pollinated. More often the pollen is taken from one plant to another in various ways, often by insects, and in that case it is described as cross-pollinated.

INSECT
POLLINATION

To ensure cross-pollination by insects and other animals, many flowering plants have evolved brightly coloured and sweetly scented petals. At the bases of the flower petals there is often stored a sweet fluid called nectar, which forms the food of many insects. When an insect sees a splash of light or bright colour standing out from the green of the leaves, it knows where its sugary food can be found. As it pushes itself down the flower to get to the nectar, its legs and body become dusted with pollen. When it flies off to the next flower, it again pushes down to the base of the petals, and this time it is likely that some of the pollen-grains on its body will be rubbed off on to the stigma of the flower. The egg-cells of this flower will then be fertilized by

Bees & butterflies come later, and seem to prefer pink and blue, sweet-scented flowers. Bees generally visit only flowers of the same kind during each journey.

pollen from another flower. This is generally better than self-pollination, for the seed made by cross-fertilization is more likely to be slightly different from either of its parents, and in this way new species are evolved.

BEES Bees are the most important of the flower visitors, for they not only have to find food for themselves, but are busy all through the warm days collecting food for the present and future use of the hive. They suck up and make honey of the nectar, and gather quantities of pollen which they take back to the hive in the "baskets" on their hind legs. They do not see colours in the same way as human beings, for red seems the same as dark grey to them, but they can see colours which are invisible to man. They prefer blue flowers to those of any other colour.

The insect-pollinated plants have a pollen which is slightly sticky, so that it clings to the hairs of the insect as it flies from one flower to the next. Since insects probably do not see very far, the sweet scents which are given out by many flowers may also serve as guides as well as the coloured petals. Most insects have a good sense of smell, though that of the bees is only at the same level as the smell-sense of man, and is surpassed in keenness by that of many other insects. In the evening, when even the most brilliantly coloured petals are hard to see, a strong scent must be an advantage to those flowers which are pollinated by insects. Flowers such as those of the Evening Primrose and the Tobacco plant, which do not open until dusk, usually have white or very pale petals and a heavy scent.

Some plants are cross-pollinated by the wind. They do not need to attract insects to them, so their flowers are generally small and inconspicuous, and without nectar or scent. The wind is less effective than the insect as a carrier of pollen, scattering it broadcast instead of taking it directly from flower to flower. The flowers which rely on this method of pollination, have to produce large quantities of pollen to make up for the great amount which is wasted. The pollen is dry instead of sticky. The stamens are long and the anthers

WIND POLLINATION

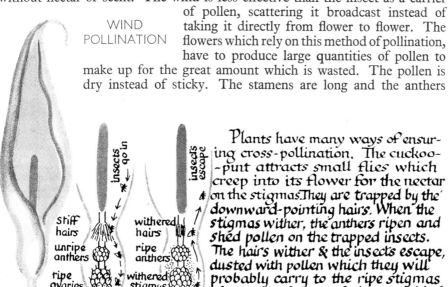

stiff hairs
unripe anthers
ripe ovaries

insects go in

withered hairs
ripe anthers
withered stigmas

insects escape

Plants have many ways of ensuring cross-pollination. The cuckoo-pint attracts small flies which creep into its flower for the nectar on the stigmas. They are trapped by the downward-pointing hairs. When the stigmas wither, the anthers ripen and shed pollen on the trapped insects. The hairs wither & the insects escape, dusted with pollen which they will probably carry to the ripe stigmas of another flower of the same kind.

hang out of the flower, so that the pollen may be easily caught up in the wind. Wind-pollinated plants often flower early, and thus the pollen is not stopped on its journey by the leaves of other plants. The catkin-bearing trees, such as hazel, oak, willow and poplar, and the grasses and sedges, have flowers which are pollinated in this way.

SEED DISPERSAL When it has made its ripe seeds the parent plant must find some way to get them into the ground so that they may grow into new plants. It is better that the seeds should be sent some distance away, otherwise the young plants, crowded together round the parent, would die from lack of food and air.

Plants have several ways of broadcasting their seeds. They may drop them in or near water, and let it carry the seeds away. Some seeds can float across the sea for weeks or even months, and germinate when they reach another land. Many plants rely on the wind to carry their seeds away from them. Some seeds are so small and light that they may be blown for many miles. The seeds of some orchids weigh only one-fifteen-thousandth part of a grain, and float in the air for hundreds of miles. Heavier wind-borne seeds are provided with little parachutes, or delicate hair-like growths, or a pair of wings, which keep them up in the air, until they are some distance from the parent plant.

The pod-bearers, which include the peas and beans, the brooms and the lupins, scatter their seeds by themselves. The pods dry up, split open, and the seeds are thrown out on to the ground. Violets and pansies have capsules instead of pods. The capsule splits into three valves; then the edge of each closes over and presses on the smooth, pear-shaped seeds, which are thrown out with some force. Other plants, by a sudden bursting of the dried-up capsule, can shoot their seeds some distance away. In the Touch-me-not or Balsam, the five divisions of the capsule split apart when

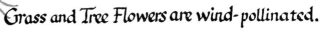

Grass and Tree Flowers are wind-pollinated.

Some tropical
flowers are pollinated
by birds. The bills of
these humming birds are long
enough to reach the nectar
in trumpet-shaped flowers.

E   49

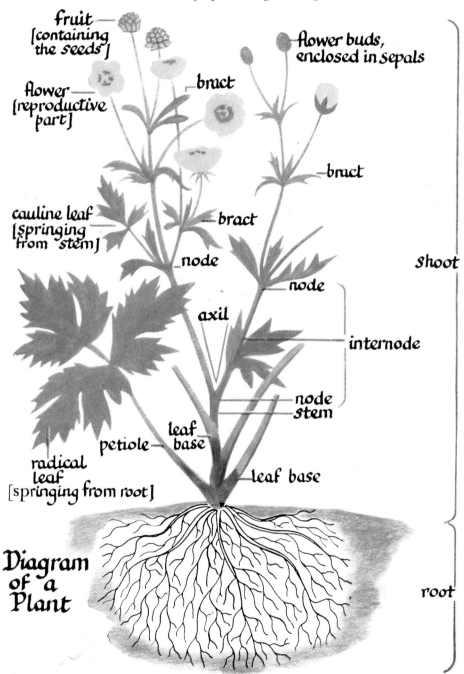

fruit
[containing
the seeds]

flower buds,
enclosed in sepals

bract

flower
[reproductive
part]

bract

cauline leaf
[springing
from stem]

bract

node

node

shoot

axil

internode

node
stem

leaf
base

petiole

radical
leaf
[springing from root]

leaf base

Diagram
of a
Plant

root

Diagram of a Plant

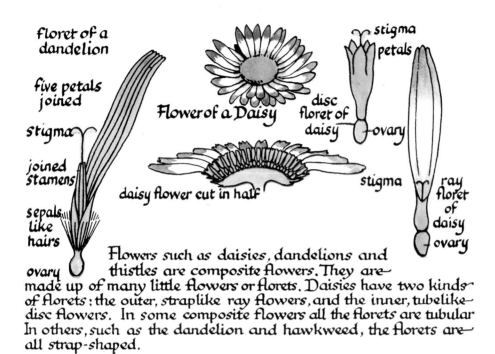

floret of a
dandelion

five petals
joined

stigma

joined
stamens

sepals
like
hairs

ovary

Flower of a Daisy

daisy flower cut in half

stigma
petals

disc
floret of
daisy

ovary

stigma

ray
floret
of
daisy

ovary

Flowers such as daisies, dandelions and thistles are composite flowers. They are made up of many little flowers or florets. Daisies have two kinds of florets: the outer, straplike ray flowers, and the inner, tubelike disc flowers. In some composite flowers all the florets are tubular In others, such as the dandelion and hawkweed, the florets are all strap-shaped.

the seeds are ripe, and by twisting up suddenly throw the seeds away from the plant. The tropical Sandbox nut has a hard fruit about the size of an orange, which bursts open with a loud report. Poppies and campanulas sprinkle their seeds, like pepper from a pepper-pot, as their ripe seed-boxes wave in the wind.

ANIMALS may help plants to scatter their seeds, either by carrying them outside or inside their bodies. In the first case the seeds stick in mud on the animals' feet, or cling to their fur. Such seeds are provided with hooks or barbs, which catch on the animals' coats as they pass, and may be carried long distances before they are rubbed off. The seeds which travel inside the bodies of birds or beasts, generally have an attractive and brightly coloured outer covering which is also sweet and juicy. The covering of the fruit or berry is eaten, but the hard seed is either thrown away, or passes unharmed through the animal's food canal, and falls on the ground with other undigested parts of the food. Sometimes the seeds of small juicy fruits stick to the beaks of birds which have eaten them, and the bird wipes the seed off some way from the parent plant. Mistletoe seeds are spread in this way. Man may play a similar part when he throws away the stone of a cherry or plum, or the core of an apple. Ants are fond of seeds which have "oil-bodies," such as those of violets, bluebells, mignonette, gorse and broom. They carry them underground, or drop them on the way home, and sow many seeds in this way.

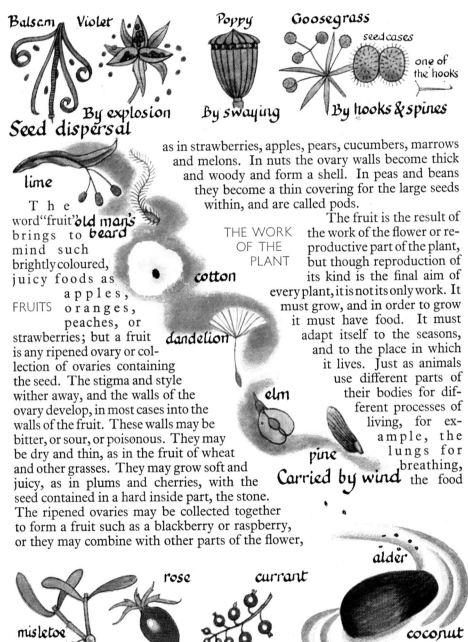

Balsam Violet

Poppy

Goosegrass

seedcases

one of
the hooks

By explosion

By swaying

By hooks & spines

Seed dispersal

lime

old man's
beard

cotton

dandelion

elm

pine

Carried by wind

mistletoe rose currant

Eaten and carried by birds

alder

coconut

Carried by water

as in strawberries, apples, pears, cucumbers, marrows and melons. In nuts the ovary walls become thick and woody and form a shell. In peas and beans they become a thin covering for the large seeds within, and are called pods.

The word "fruit" brings to mind such brightly coloured, juicy foods as apples, oranges, peaches, or strawberries; but a fruit is any ripened ovary or collection of ovaries containing the seed. The stigma and style wither away, and the walls of the ovary develop, in most cases into the walls of the fruit. These walls may be bitter, or sour, or poisonous. They may be dry and thin, as in the fruit of wheat and other grasses. They may grow soft and juicy, as in plums and cherries, with the seed contained in a hard inside part, the stone. The ripened ovaries may be collected together to form a fruit such as a blackberry or raspberry, or they may combine with other parts of the flower,

FRUITS

THE WORK
OF THE
PLANT

The fruit is the result of the work of the flower or reproductive part of the plant, but though reproduction of its kind is the final aim of every plant, it is not its only work. It must grow, and in order to grow it must have food. It must adapt itself to the seasons, and to the place in which it lives. Just as animals use different parts of their bodies for different processes of living, for example, the lungs for breathing, the food

FRUITS

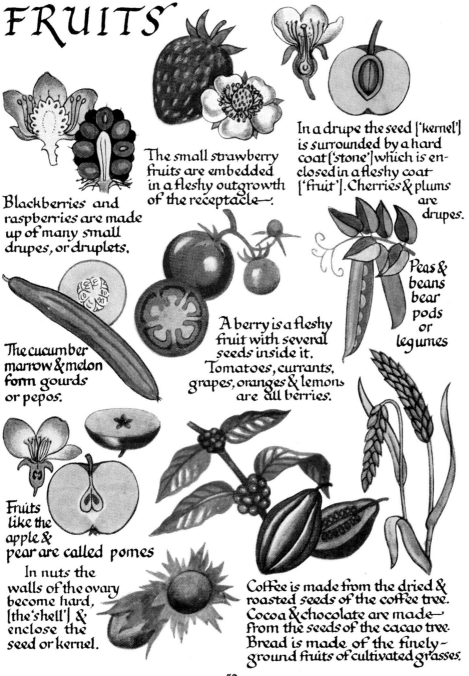

The small strawberry fruits are embedded in a fleshy outgrowth of the receptacle—.

In a drupe the seed ['kernel'] is surrounded by a hard coat ['stone'] which is enclosed in a fleshy coat ['fruit']. Cherries & plums are drupes.

Blackberries and raspberries are made up of many small drupes, or druplets.

Peas & beans bear pods or legumes

The cucumber marrow & melon form gourds or pepos.

A berry is a fleshy fruit with several seeds inside it. Tomatoes, currants, grapes, oranges & lemons are all berries.

Fruits like the apple & pear are called pomes

In nuts the walls of the ovary become hard, [the 'shell'] & enclose the seed or kernel.

Coffee is made from the dried & roasted seeds of the coffee tree. Cocoa & chocolate are made from the seeds of the cacao tree. Bread is made of the finely-ground fruits of cultivated grasses.

53

Some plants add animal food to the food which they make with their green leaves. Such plants usually grow in swampy soil which is poor in nitrogen & mineral salts. They trap insects in various ways, then pour out digestive juices on them and absorb the liquid nourishment.

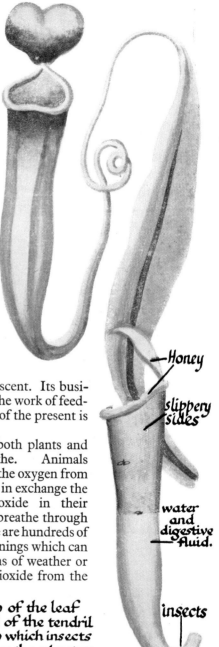

Honey

slippery sides

water and digestive fluid.

insects

canal for digestion: so plants also have bodies in which each part is adapted for its particular work. The variations of this body-pattern are almost endless, but the pattern itself can nearly always be found, in one form or another, in all plants.

THE PARTS OF THE PLANT-BODY
A typical plant has four distinct parts: roots, stem, leaf, and flower. The flower is only concerned with reproduction; it carries the male and female organs, and may proclaim the presence of nectar by showy petals and by scent. Its business is only with the plants of the future. The work of feeding, developing and keeping alive the plant of the present is carried out by the root, stem and leaves.

THE WORK OF THE LEAF: BREATHING AND FOOD-MAKING
In order to live, both plants and animals must breathe. Animals breathe by absorbing the oxygen from the air, and giving out in exchange the excess of carbon-dioxide in their bodies. Land plants breathe through their stomata. These stomata, of which there are hundreds of thousands in the green leaf, have lipped openings which can be opened or closed according to conditions of weather or light. Plants take in oxygen and carbon-dioxide from the

In the tropical pitcher-plant the midrib of the leaf grows into a long tendril. At the end of the tendril there is a brightly coloured pitcher into which insects slip, to be drowned and digested by the plant.

54

air through their stomata, but during the daylight carbon-dioxide, instead of being given off, is absorbed by the plant; for this gas is used in the complex process of building up its food.

The first step in this process is the making of a kind of sugar, of which the elements are carbon, hydrogen, and oxygen. The leaves of the plant are green, on account of the large number of cells in them which contain a green substance called chlorophyll. In a way which is unknown, chlorophyll can trap the energy of light which it gets from the sun, and can use this energy to make the carbon-dioxide from the air and the water from the soil combine into a sugar. Some of the oxygen is split off and is given off through the stomata. The process of making sugar, which is the chief food and body-building material of the plant, goes on in the green leaves through all the hours of daylight. The part which is not used at once is stored in various places in the plant in the form of an insoluble sugar. This solid form of food is only used by the plant in its food-*stores*, and is known as starch. When the plant needs food from its store, the starch has to be changed back into a sugar which can be dissolved in the sap, and which can then be carried to all parts of the plant which need energy or building material. Plants are the only living things which can make up sugar and starch from carbon-dioxide and water with the help of chorophyll and sunlight. Man and beast cannot build up sugars but have to turn to plants for this part of their food.

THE plant can onlymake sugar in the presence of light, and has to rely on its stored food in the darkness. The green parts of the plant, usually the leaves, are the food factories, and the chlorophyll which colours them can itself only be made in the light. For this reason most plants are branching in growth, and the leaves are arranged so that as much of their surface as possible may be exposed to light and air. In the winter, when there are fewer useful light-rays, the leaves are of little use in food-making. Many plants shed them altogether and live on the food which is stored in their bodies.

Plants need nitrogen besides their sugar food, and they get this from the nitrates in the soil. These are drawn up, together with other mineral salts, dissolved in the water which is taken from the soil by the root hairs. The nitrates usually come from the waste products of animals, or from the decaying bodies of plants and animals. In this way, animals, all of whom depend on

An Ivy leaf-mosaic, showing how leaves fit together so that all can catch sunlight.

plants for their food, help in their turn to provide food for the plants.

The most important work of the leaf is to breathe and to make food. Leaves may be used as a storehouse for starch, as well as the stems or roots. They also give off water in much the same way as animals give off sweat. As sweat cools the animal, so the evaporation of water cools the plant, besides causing more water to flow up the plant's body from the soil. The steady current of water from roots to leaves brings with it the dissolved food-making substances which the plant needs from the soil.

THERE are times, however, when it is better for a plant not to lose moisture through its leaves. In very dry places, where it may not rain for years, plants must save as much water as they can. They do this in various ways. Some of them have fleshy leaves, which hold plenty of water inside them, and which in comparison with their bulk expose a small surface to the hot, dry atmosphere about them : or they develop a thick coat of hairs, which covers up the stomata and prevents the water from evaporating. They may have leaves covered with glossy scales: or the leaves may become rolled up, as the leaves of many plants do on hot days in cooler countries. This allows only a small part of the leaf to be exposed to the sun, and checks evaporation. Some plants bear their leaves upright instead of flat, so that only the edges face the strong heat. In the cacti, which live in hot, dry countries, the leaves have become scales, hairs or sharp spines. The stems and branches are green, fleshy and sometimes flattened, and they do the work of the leaves. In dry regions where, through lack of water, plants run an extra danger of being eaten by animals, they protect themselves by having leaves of strong scent or unpleasant taste, or by thorns, spines and prickles. Even in milder climates many plants protect themselves from animals in similar ways. Nettles have poisonous hairs; the lettuce has a sticky juice which protects it from ants and other insects; and the holly has prickles on its lower leaves. The holly leaves which are too high for browsing animals to reach do not have any prickles.

In winter there is little useful daylight, and plants are too cold to WINTER   carry on their full work of making food, drawing water from the soil, growing, and forming seeds. The cold makes them sluggish, in the same way as it affects insects and reptiles and other "cold-blooded" creatures. Protoplasm becomes less active as it grows colder, and only birds and mammals have the power of keeping their bodies at an even temperature, and so remaining lively all the year round. In the cold, sunless weather, leaves are of little use to the plant for food making, and would give off the small amount of water which its roots could draw from the frozen soil. They might also become heavy with snow and cause the branches to break. For these reasons, many plants shed their leaves when the cold days come, and some plants disappear altogether from above the ground. Their pace of living is slowed down almost to a standstill, and like the winter-sleeping animals, they live on food which they have stored in their bodies during the warm, sunny weather.

In the autumn, trees generally have next year's leaves ready in the form of buds. In order to protect the delicate shoots, and lest water should be lost

ANNUALS· BIENNIALS· PERENNIALS

An annual is a plant which lives for only one season. It begins as a seed, grows up, produces its flowers and seeds, then dies.

A biennial lives for two years. In the first year it produces only roots and leaves, and stores food to use the following year for developing flowers and seeds.

A perennial lives for several or many years. All shrubs & trees are perennials. Trees may live for many hundreds of years.

Scarlet Pimpernel
an annual

Goat's Beard
a biennial

Germander Speedwell
a perennial

57

Movement in Plants

The Wood Sorrel is one of the many plants which closes its leaves at night.

leaf folded at night to protect it from cold.

leaf opened in daytime

young leaf

Sunflower turning its head towards the morning sun.
The same flower at sunset. Only the young heads turn in this way, not the fully-opened flowers.

A certain Mimosa responds very quickly to touch, light & shock. If one of the end leaflets is touched, the leaflets close together, one after the other, until the whole leaf is folded. The stalk then turns downward.

leaflets closing

58

Plants

White Water Lily

Evening Primrose

Mouse-ear Hawkweed

Plants open their petals to attract the insects which pollinate them. The flowers which are pollinated by day-flying insects are open by day, & are closed at night to protect the honey and pollen from cold & damp. Flowers such as the Evening Primrose which are visited by night-flying moths open at dusk & are closed during the day. Many flowers close some hours before dark & at a definite time each day. The White Water-lily and Mouse-ear Hawkweed shut their petals in the middle of the afternoon. Most flowers close during cold, dull or wet weather.

through them, they are wrapped throughout the winter in some sort of covering. This is generally made up of waterproof brown scales. Sometimes, as in the Willow, they are coated with soft hair or down, or they may be, as in the Horse-chestnut, sticky with gum.

EVERGREENS Evergreens shed only some of their leaves each year, and every spring these leaves are replaced. On the Scots-pine they remain on the tree for three years; on the Spruce, Fir, Yew and other cone-bearers, they may live for eight or ten years before falling. The leaves of trees such as hollies and laurels have to withstand several winters of ice and snow, but they are provided with tough, glossy skins. These hard, shiny leaves tend to let the snow glide off them, and they lose less water through their stomata than the soft leaves of trees such as oak and beech. Firs, pines and cedars, and similar trees, have needle-shaped leaves which preserve their water supply, in the same way as the small-surfaced, fleshy leaves of those plants which grow in dry places. The needle-shaped leaves are hard and glossy like the leaves of holly and laurel.

The roots of a plant have as a rule two kinds of work. They hold the plant

59

STEMS

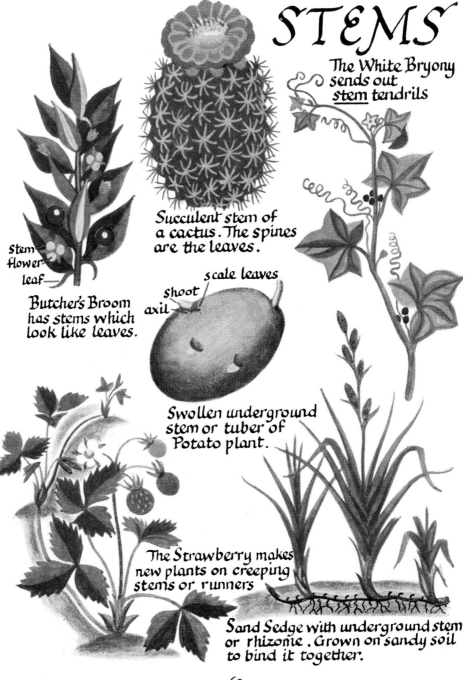

The White Bryony
sends out
stem tendrils

Succulent stem of
a cactus. The spines
are the leaves.

Stem—
flower—
leaf—

Butcher's Broom
has stems which
look like leaves.

shoot
axil

scale leaves

Swollen underground
stem or tuber of
Potato plant.

The Strawberry makes
new plants on creeping
stems or runners

Sand Sedge with underground stem
or rhizome. Grown on sandy soil
to bind it together.

60

animal's body combined, by supporting the plant-body and carrying nourishment to all parts of it. The stems in each plant vary according to their work. The floral stems bear the flowers, the foliage stems carry the leaves. Buds are special types of shoots or branches containing the delicate growing part of the stem. Thorns or spines are formed by branches which have grown short, hard and pointed. Under cultivation the thorns may disappear, and fruitful branches grow in their place.

Stems differ widely in different plants. There are the great woody stems, or trunks, of trees. There are climbing stems which are too weak to support themselves, and twine round stronger plants or cling to something firm by means of suckers, tendrils or hooks. There are stems, as in the strawberry, which creep along the ground for some way then send out roots and develop a new plant. There are burrowing stems or "rootstocks" which run underground, as in bracken and Solomon's-seal, and which send up

firmly in the ground and by means of their ROOTS root hairs they take in water, with the soil food-stuffs dissolved in it. Roots may also be used as food-stores, in which case they become thick and fleshy, as in carrots, turnips and dahlias. They need oxygen to breathe just as the rest of the plant, and they always grow better if the soil round them is kept loose and full of air, as it is by hoeing.

STEMS The stem is that part of a plant which bears the leaves, flowers and fruits. It supports the leaves so that they can get plenty of light and air. It also carries water and food-stuffs from the roots to the leaves, and food from the leaves to the rest of the plant. Stems act in some ways much as the bones and arteries of an

61

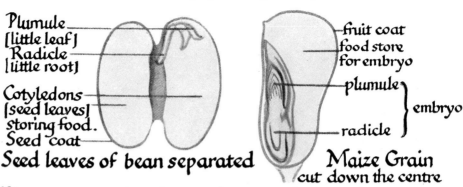

Plumule [little leaf]
Radicle [little root]
Cotyledons [seed leaves] storing food.
Seed coat

fruit coat
food store for embryo
plumule
radicle
} embryo

Seed leaves of bean separated

Maize Grain cut down the centre

Plants store food in their seeds on which the embryo plants can draw until they are developed enough to make food for themselves.

leaf- and flower-bearing shoots. Such plants form large colonies in time. A "bulb" is really an underground stem covered with thick, overlapping leaves, in which the plant stores its winter and spring food. A corm, such as that of the crocus or cyclamen, is also a thick underground stem, but it is not surrounded by fleshy leaves like the bulb. All the food is stored in the stem, which grows fat and often flattened. The potato is the end of a rootstock which has become swollen with stored food, its "eyes" being buds. Some plants are almost made up of stems alone: these are the cacti, whose soft, juicy, leafless stems armed with bristles and prickles grow as tall and thick as the trunks of trees.

FOOD STORES   Plants store their food in various parts of their bodies. Those which live for more than one year store food for use during the winter months and in the early stages of their spring growth. Trees use their trunks and branches as storehouses. Some plants, such as cabbages, store food in their leaves; when they have done this well, the cabbages have hard, tightly-packed hearts. The plants which die down in the cold weather keep their sugar and starch underground, in swollen roots or rootstocks. Plants use their food very slowly all the winter, and when spring comes they draw upon their stores while they are growing, for in the early days of the year there is little sunshine to help them make new food. Annuals live only for one year; they do not build up winter food supplies, for when they have made their seeds they die.

THE SEED   A plant stores food for its seeds so that the new plants of the following year may have nourishment on which they can draw until they are old enough to make food for themselves. The food for the seed is stored while the fruit is being formed. In some seeds it is stored in the seed-leaves or cotyledons. These are easily seen in the bean, which is actually made of two fleshy leaves enclosing the tiny root and shoot of the new bean plant. In other cases the food is stored round or at one side of the embryo or future plant. The embryo needs the same elements in its food as the grown plant.

Food Stores in Plants

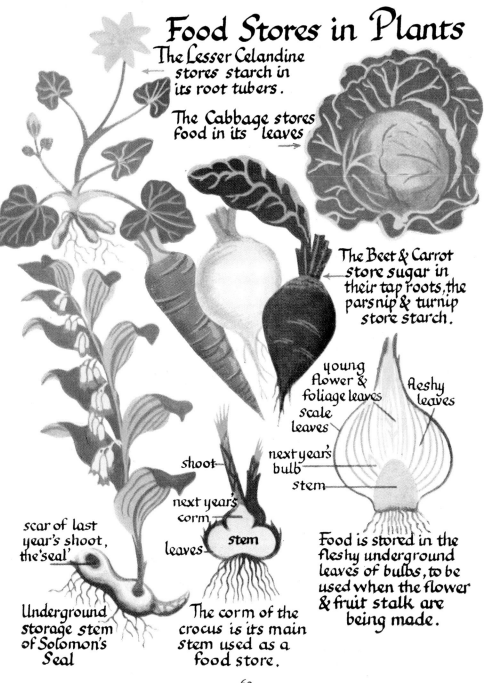

The Lesser Celandine stores starch in its root tubers.

The Cabbage stores food in its leaves

The Beet & Carrot store sugar in their tap roots, the parsnip & turnip store starch.

young flower & foliage leaves

scale leaves

fleshy leaves

next year's bulb

stem

shoot

next year's corm

stem

leaves

scar of last year's shoot, the 'seal'

Underground storage stem of Solomon's Seal

The corm of the crocus is its main stem used as a food store.

Food is stored in the fleshy underground leaves of bulbs, to be used when the flower & fruit stalk are being made.

63

The starch which makes up most of its food-store is used in the form of sugar. Nitrogen is stored as protein. Oil is sometimes found in the seed's food-store, especially in the nuts, and in cotton and flax seeds.

GERMINATION   The future plant needs air, moisture and warmth, as well as food, to make it grow. If it lacks these it will lie dormant but alive for some time. Occasionally seeds have germinated after many years of resting in this way, but on the whole the plant is stronger if it begins to grow soon after leaving the parent plant. Extreme cold prevents or delays germination, and extreme heat kills the embryo. Seeds may begin to grow without oxygen, but they cannot continue long, and no seed can grow when it is dry.

THE NEW   Under the right conditions, the seed *germinates* or sprouts. Its
PLANT   little root pierces the seed coat and pushes down into the soil. Root-hairs appear on it through which the young plant takes food from the ground. The plumule or upward growing shoot, bearing tiny leaves at the tip, grows larger. It bursts open the seed coat, and in various ways pushes itself out of the ground up into the air. Soon the leaves unfold to the quickening rays of the sun, and the plant continues its life-circle of growth, flower, seed, and again growth.

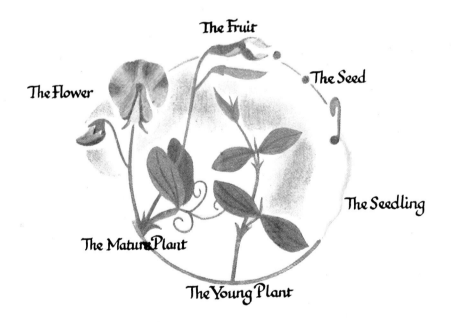

The Fruit

The Flower

The Seed

The Seedling

The Mature Plant

The Young Plant

ARTHROPODS

Armoured bodies and jointed limbs.
The first land animals·

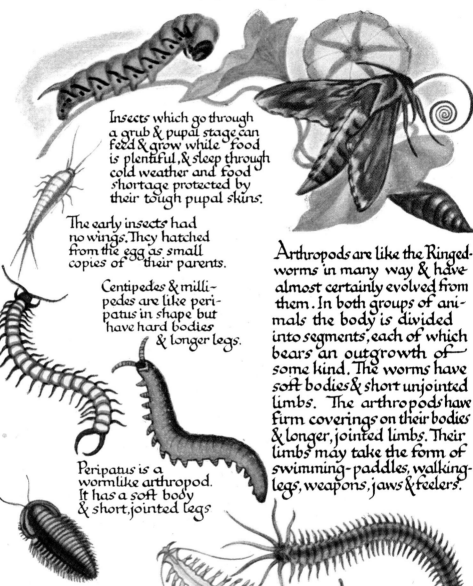

Insects which go through a grub & pupal stage can feed & grow while food is plentiful, & sleep through cold weather and food shortage protected by their tough pupal skins.

The early insects had no wings. They hatched from the egg as small copies of their parents.

Centipedes & millipedes are like peripatus in shape but have hard bodies & longer legs.

Arthropods are like the Ringed-worms in many way & have almost certainly evolved from them. In both groups of animals the body is divided into segments, each of which bears an outgrowth of some kind. The worms have soft bodies & short unjointed limbs. The arthropods have firm coverings on their bodies & longer, jointed limbs. Their limbs may take the form of swimming-paddles, walking-legs, weapons, jaws & feelers.

Peripatus is a wormlike arthropod. It has a soft body & short, jointed legs

Trilobites were among the earliest arthopods. They had 2 feelers, like insects, forked limbs like crustaceans, and like spiders had no mandibles.

Some sea-worms have segmented bodies, unjointed limb-like organs, and feelers.

66

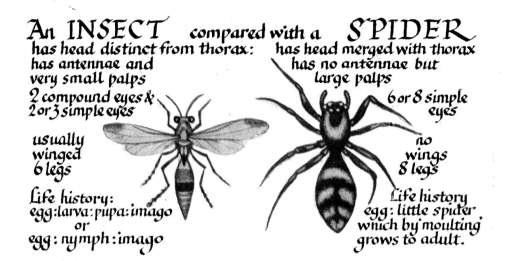

An INSECT compared with a SPIDER

has head distinct from thorax: has head merged with thorax

has antennae and very small palps

has no antennae but large palps

2 compound eyes & 2 or 3 simple eyes

6 or 8 simple eyes

usually winged 6 legs

no wings 8 legs

Life history: egg:larva:pupa:imago or egg:nymph:imago

Life history egg: little spider which by moulting grows to adult.

Section 3 — Arthropods

"JOINTED-LIMBED" ANIMALS

The great group of animals which include the crustaceans (crabs, lobsters, shrimps, etc.), the centipedes and millipedes, insects, spiders and scorpions, are called ARTHROPODS. This is an unfortunate name, as "arthropod" means "jointed limbed," and there are many animals outside this group which have jointed limbs also. All the arthropods have their skeletons outside their bodies. This armour, unlike the rigid shells of the molluscs, is delicately jointed so that the animal can move freely and quickly. The arthropods are alike in having bodies which are built in segments or rings, some of which may be fused together. They also have limbs which are divided into segments, and these may take the form of walking legs, swimming paddles, feelers and jaws. These animals with jointed armour vary in size from the microscopic mite which lives in the air tubes of bees (and causes Isle-of-Wight disease) to the Giant Japanese Crab, whose outstretched claws may span a distance of eleven feet.

WORM AND ARTHROPOD

It is difficult to trace the ancestry of boneless animals, whose soft and usually small bodies have not left such clear records in the rocks as those

head   thorax   abdomen

spiracles or breathing holes

A Grasshopper: showing the spiracles and the three main parts of an insect's body.

67

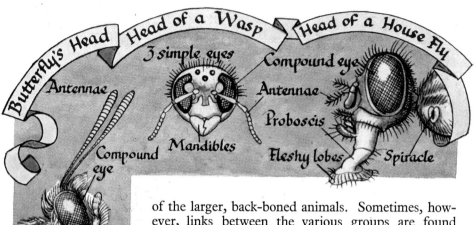

Butterfly's Head
Antennae
Compound eye

Head of a Wasp
3 simple eyes
Mandibles
Antennae

Head of a House Fly
Compound eye
Antennae
Proboscis
Fleshy lobes
Spiracle

Palp
Proboscis
Simple eyes
Jaws
S

Caterpillar's head, hard & horny. 'S' is the spinning-tube from which comes the silk for the cocoon

a   b

Caterpillar's feet: [a] One of the 6 front legs, which will remain when the caterpillar turns into a moth. [b] Cushion foot: these disappear when caterpillar changes

of the larger, back-boned animals. Sometimes, however, links between the various groups are found living to-day: animals which have not evolved, but have remained unchanged for perhaps many millions of years. Peripatus seems to be such an animal. Like a worm, it has a long, soft body ringed into many segments, though in its case the segments do not show very clearly. It has a pair of short legs on each segment, just as the more primitive arthropods; but the legs are unjointed, like the limb-like outgrowths of some of the sea-worms. On its head it has sensitive feelers, and when alarmed it shoots out long, white, sticky threads of a fluid similar to the silk which is spun by insects and spiders. Like the insects, it breathes by means of air-tubes. It may be through such a link as Peripatus that some of the arthropods have evolved from the higher worms.

In tracing the line of descent of any group of animals, it is helpful to study them in the earliest stages of their life histories. In its embryo stage, before it is born, every land vertebrate shows traces of its fish ancestors. Frogs and toads actually go through an active fish-like stage when they are tadpoles. Insects on hatching out of the egg, are in most cases grubs, maggots or caterpillars, creatures which are much more like worms than the fully developed beetles, flies or butterflies, into which they finally change. The change from a soft-bodied worm to an armoured insect, a change which took its ancestors millions of years to

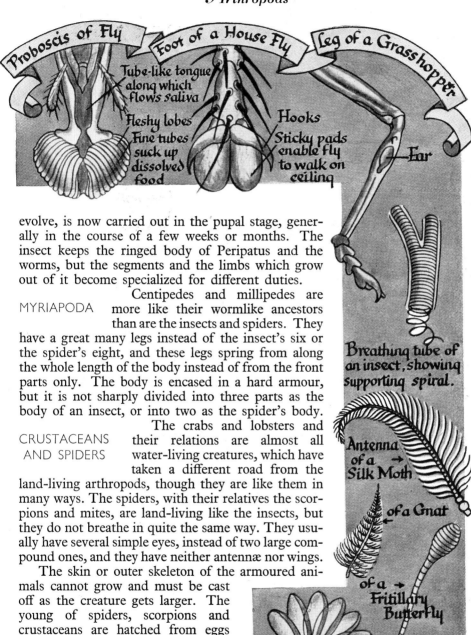

Proboscis of Fly

Tube-like tongue along which flows saliva

Fleshy lobes
Fine tubes suck up dissolved food

Foot of a House Fly

Hooks
Sticky pads enable fly to walk on ceiling

Leg of a Grasshopper

Ear

Breathing tube of an insect, showing supporting spiral.

Antenna of a → Silk Moth

of a Gnat →

of a → Fritillary Butterfly

← of a Cockchafer

evolve, is now carried out in the pupal stage, generally in the course of a few weeks or months. The insect keeps the ringed body of Peripatus and the worms, but the segments and the limbs which grow out of it become specialized for different duties.

MYRIAPODA   Centipedes and millipedes are more like their wormlike ancestors than are the insects and spiders. They have a great many legs instead of the insect's six or the spider's eight, and these legs spring from along the whole length of the body instead of from the front parts only. The body is encased in a hard armour, but it is not sharply divided into three parts as the body of an insect, or into two as the spider's body.

CRUSTACEANS AND SPIDERS   The crabs and lobsters and their relations are almost all water-living creatures, which have taken a different road from the land-living arthropods, though they are like them in many ways. The spiders, with their relatives the scorpions and mites, are land-living like the insects, but they do not breathe in quite the same way. They usually have several simple eyes, instead of two large compound ones, and they have neither antennæ nor wings.

The skin or outer skeleton of the armoured animals cannot grow and must be cast off as the creature gets larger. The young of spiders, scorpions and crustaceans are hatched from eggs or are born alive, and in the case of spiders and scorpions they are like their parents but much smaller. All

Life history of a Bluebottle

A. 500-1000 eggs are laid in decaying flesh.
B. Each soon turns into a larva and eats for about a week.

C. The larva then moults its outer skin, which instead of being cast off, hardens into a case, in which the pupa lies hidden.

D. After a time, varying from a week to the whole winter, the end of the case is burst open, & the fly comes out.

these creatures moult their outer coverings several or many times as they grow. Most insects do not grow quite in this way, though they moult in their early stages. When they hatch most of them are very different from the full-grown animal, and generally pass through two distinct phases before they reach maturity.

INSECTS The insects are the most numerous, and from man's point of view the most important of the arthropods. They are found in every part of the world wherever land-life is possible. Butterflies and mosquitoes have reached the extreme Arctic, other butterflies are found high up in the mountains. Some insects live in hot deserts, far from water; others live in fresh water and in hot springs. There are pale, blind cave-dwellers and insects of the seashore. Salt water does not seem to suit them on the whole, but there are insects called sea-skaters which run on the surface of the sea, and often live hundreds of miles from land.

Compared with the vertebrates, most insects are extremely small. Some of them could creep through the eye of a needle, yet their little bodies are far from simple. Each has a nervous and digestive system, a heart and blood. The eyes are "compound," being made up of thousands of similar parts, each one with its own lens. Hundreds of branching air tubes carry oxygen to every part of the insect's body, even to the tips of the wings and antennæ.

The body of an insect is made up of three distinct parts; a head; a front part or *thorax*; and a hind part or *abdomen*. The name "insect" is taken from the Latin word "insectum" meaning "cut into," because these animals look as though they were almost cut into three parts.

70

Life history of a Grasshopper

A

B. The insect which comes out of the egg is like a small adult without wings.

C. At the third moult appear the tiny leaf-like lobes which will grow into wings.

D. The wings are now larger. They will appear full-grown at the last moult.

A. The female of the Great Green Grasshopper lays her 20-30 eggs in the ground with her long, pointed ovipositor, or 'egg placer'. She covers them with a gummy fluid, which hardens and protects them.

The most noticeable things about an insect's head are the two large compound eyes and the feelers or antennæ. The thorax bears three pairs of legs and usually wings as well. The abdomen never bears any limbs, but it is sometimes armed with a sting. These few points about an insect are enough to distinguish it from other crawling creatures of similar size and appearance, such as spiders, woodlice, centipedes and millipedes.

INSECTS' LEGS The legs which the insect bears on the three rings of its thorax vary greatly according to its habits. In beetles which climb about the bark of trees, the front pair is much longer than the rest. In the burrowing mole-cricket, they are short and strong, with digging blades which look somewhat like the claws of a mole. The water-scorpion and praying-mantis have forelegs with pincer-like traps for seizing prey. The water-boatman's middle pair of legs have broadened into oars for rowing on the surface of the water. In many insects—grasshoppers, locusts, fleas and some beetles, the hind-legs are large and strong for jumping. Bees have a special pocket on their back legs in which they collect pollen. Some beetles, and bees, wasps and ants, have combs of bristles on their legs, and use these in cleaning themselves. They pass their fore-legs over their heads, and draw their dusty antennæ through the combs, much as a cat washes its ears with its paws.

INSECT TRAVEL Insects can travel in more ways than any other group of living things. They can walk, run and jump; they can swim under water and move on the surface, and when they are limbless larvæ they can jerk themselves along like clumsy snakes. They fly with limbs which have

71

Life history of the Peacock Butterfly.

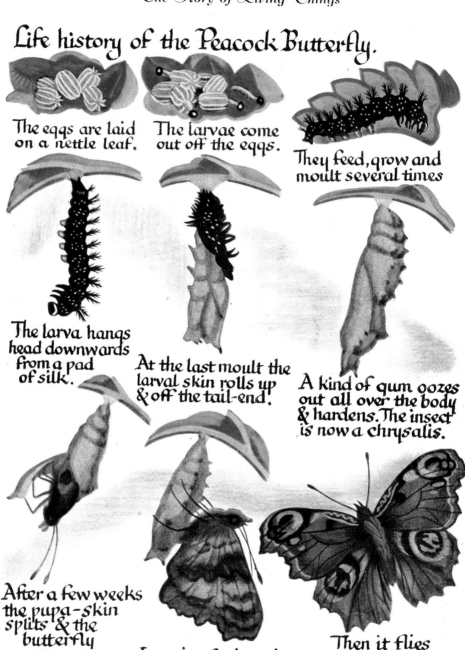

The eggs are laid on a nettle leaf.

The larvae come out off the eggs.

They feed, grow and moult several times

The larva hangs head downwards from a pad of silk.

At the last moult the larval skin rolls up & off the tail-end.

A kind of gum oozes out all over the body & hardens. The insect is now a chrysalis.

After a few weeks the pupa-skin splits & the butterfly appears.

It waits for its wings to get firm.

Then it flies away.

72

Life history of the Silk Moth [Bombyx mori]

Cocoon

Larva beginning to spin its cocoon which takes 3 or 4 days to finish.

Full grown Moth. Eggs. Caterpillar

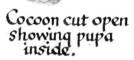

Cocoon cut open showing pupa inside.

[right] The Tusseh Silk Moth, whose cocoons are gathered in the wild state

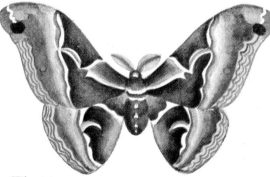

The Eri Silk Moth of S.& E. Asia, which feeds on the castor oil plant & spins a rough, strong silk.

Most of the silk we use here comes from the cocoon of the cultivated Chinese Silk Moth, Bombyx mori. The caterpillar is carefully reared in cool airy sheds, and fed on mulberry leaves. When it begins to spin, it dribbles out a sticky fluid from its spinning tube. This fluid sets as it comes into the air, & forms a thread of silk. The silk when unwound from the cocoon may be 1000 yards long.

73

been specially evolved for the purpose, unlike birds who have given up their fore-limbs to make organs of flight. Nearly all insects have wings, lightly built, transparent or covered with minute scales. These fragile and beautiful outgrowths often beat the air with extraordinary speed. A fly makes 330 wing-strokes in a second, a humble-bee 240, a wasp 110, a dragonfly 28 and a butterfly 9.

HOW INSECTS BREATHE   Although the young of some insects live in water and have gills, adult insects breathe by means of air tubes. They have no lungs, nor do they use their mouths in breathing. The air enters their bodies through small holes called *spiracles*. These lie along each side of the body, and are

The nest of a Tree Wasp, made of bits of wood chewed to a pulp, then flattened out into ribbons with the wasp's jaws and front pair of legs.

Many layers of wasp-paper to keep out wind and rain

The first cells, made by the queen alone.

All other cells contain eggs, grubs & cocoons.

worker wasp feeding larva

large cells containing pupae of the new queens

entrance to nest

Wasps' nest cut open to show the inside. The combs are like round plates, smooth above, and with many six-sided cells underneath, all of them opening downwards.

covered by flaps which open and close as the insect breathes. When a wasp moves its abdomen up and down and looks as though it were panting, it is driving the air out through the spiracles, and letting it flow in again. The air enters the insect's body and passes through air tubes, which branch again and again until every part of the body is supplied with oxygen. In order that these tubes shall not collapse under the pressure of other parts of the body, the larger ones are stiffened by a spiral thread which runs inside them, just as a rubber hosepipe

74

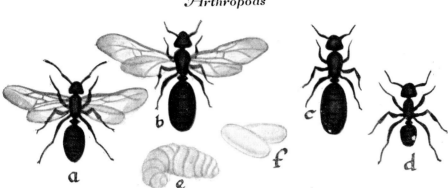

Nearly all ants have three distinct castes. The males [a] have wings & die after mating in the air with the winged female or queen [b]. She then strips off her wings [c] & after a time lays her eggs. She feeds them during the larval stage till they become pupae & finally workers [d], who then do all the work of the nest, while the queen devotes herself to the laying of eggs. [e] An ant larva. [f] Ant cocoons.

may have wire round it to prevent its being crushed.

EYES   Most insects have two kinds of eyes, compound and simple. The simple eyes are usually three in number and are arranged in a triangle on top of the head. They are not very noticeable, and probably do no more than distinguish dark from light. The compound eyes are more important, and can be clearly seen on each side of the insect's head. They are very large compared with the size of the insect, the eyes of a dragonfly are actually as big as those of a much larger creature, the mouse. They are called "compound" eyes because they are made up of many simple eyes. Each little eye has its own lens and separate nerve to the brain-centre in the head. The number of these eyes in a compound eye varies in different insects. The silverfish insect has twelve, the ant has fifty, the common house-fly four thousand, the swallowtail butterfly seventeen thousand, and the convolvulus hawk-moth twenty-seven thousand. Various experiments have been made to find out how much, and how far, insects can see with these eyes. It is known that many of them can see colours, and it seems likely that some of them can see clearly up to a distance of three feet, and can distinguish colours and movements at longer distances. It will perhaps never be known exactly what pictures an insect gets

An ant stroking & tickling an aphis to encourage it to yield its sweet honey-dew, which the ant likes to drink. Ants tend aphides carefully & often rear their larvae in their own nests.

The Harvester-ants live on the seeds of a grass called ant rice. They gather the grains from the plants & from the ground, and

after removing the husks they store the seeds underground. If they get damp, the ants spread them out to dry in the sun. Seeds which have sprouted are thrown away, and these probably form the fields of ant rice which are usually found growing round the nests of the harvesters. The ants make paths from 2" to 5" wide along which they carry their harvest home.

of its surroundings, for its eyes and brain are very different from those of a human being. It may be that each small part of the compound eye sees a piece of the surroundings, and the insect brain puts these pieces together to form a complete picture of the objects near it. Compound eyes are rarely found in insects before they have reached their final stage of development. In the early stages of their lives they have only simple eyes.

INSECTS' EARS Since some insects make sounds, and seem to send messages to one another in this way, it is likely that they can hear. No insect has ears at the sides of its head, but in the insects which "sing" and "chirrup," hearing organs are found on other parts of the body. Crickets and tree-grasshoppers have ears just below the knees on their front legs; meadow-grasshoppers, locusts and some moths, have ears on their bodies near the "waist." In gnats and midges the ears are at the bases of the feelers, and in the blowfly they are beneath the bases of the wings.

HOW INSECTS Few insects make sounds that can be heard by the human
"TALK" ear. It may be that they make and hear noises to which man is deaf, just as they see colours to which he is blind. It is certain that they have not voices, since "voice" is produced by expelling air

A termite soldier

Termites live in communities like ants, but they are not related to ants. They feed on wood, which is digested for them by the single-celled animals which live in their bodies. They do much damage to things which are made from wood, such as furniture and paper, but under natural conditions they eat up useless litter and turn it into material on which plants can feed.

from the lungs, through that part of the windpipe called the voice-box or larynx, and since insects have no lungs or windpipe, they must make sounds in other ways. The humming and buzzing sounds of insects are made by the beating of their wings against the air, or by a contrivance within some of the spiracles. Insects which belong to the grasshopper family rub one part of their body on another : some of them grate their wings together, others move the knobbed ridge on the back leg to and fro against a "vein" on the closed wing. Ants and butterflies seem to talk by gently touching one another's antennæ. When a bee wants to tell other bees in the hive that she has found a good place for gathering nectar, she "dances." She runs round in circles, while the other bees follow her and smell her with their feelers. When she flies off again, the other bees go out and search for the flowers about which she has told them. The scent which clings to her body gives them a clue, and they may find that she has marked some of the flowers with "bee-scent" from special glands in her body. The dance for pollen is quite different from the nectar-dance. When the bee wants to tell the others where this flower-dust is plentiful, she sways to and fro, and the scent of the pollen-grains which cling to her helps the bees in their search.

ANTENNÆ   The feelers or antennæ are set in sockets on the crown of the insect's head, and are of many different shapes. They are all many-jointed. Some are simple and thread-like, clubbed or pointed at the ends. Others are like tiny fans or plumes or fringes. They are

After mating, the queens of some kinds of termites swell to a great size. Their bodies become full of eggs of which they lay from 20,000 to 40,000 a day for many years. These queens cannot move and live in their royal cells tended by workers.

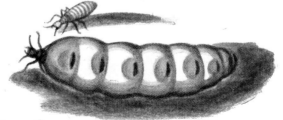

77

Honey Bees

Drone or male: big, with broad body & large eyes: mates with queen & is later killed by workers.

Queen: long, pointed body: does nothing but lay eggs: may live for five years.

Worker: small: short body: does all the work of the hive: lives for about 5 weeks

A bee hanging and making wax, which comes out in thin plates under her body.

of great use to the insect, who uses them to touch and find out whether things are good to eat or safe to walk on. Insects seem also to smell with their antennæ, and they may use them for tasting; but it is not easy to discover exactly what messages these delicate organs bring to their owners. Insects can see, smell, taste, touch and in some cases hear : but many of them seem to have extra senses which do not correspond to those of human beings, and these senses may be connected with the antennæ. (*See illustrations on page* 69.)

Insects have no mouths with lips and teeth, in which to chew their food. Some of them have jaws, usually three pairs one behind the other. These hang down in front of the mouth-opening and work from side to side. The first and largest pair of jaws are called *mandibles*. They are used to bite and tear the food, while the other jaws mince it up more finely. Beetles and wasps eat in this way. Other insects such as butterflies, moths, flies, greenflies and mosquitoes, feed only on liquid food and have various ways of sucking it up into their mouths.

The common house-fly has unpleasant feeding habits from man's point of view. It has under its head a short tube which FLIES AND MOSQUITOES broadens at the end into two lobes. When the fly feeds, it presses these lobes on whatever it is eating, pours out a liquid and sucks up the dissolved food. Flies are not particular in their feeding, as they may come straight from the dung-heap to the dining-table. They sometimes carry disease in the fluid which they pour on to their food, as well as on the hairs of their bodies and feet. Mosquitoes also carry disease, though the English varieties are usually harmless. These insects feed on blood, and their

78

mouth parts consist of sharp points for piercing their victims' skins, and a long tube through which the blood is sucked. When they have plunged this apparatus through the skin, they pour an irritant fluid into the wound to make the blood flow to that place and to prevent its clotting. If the fluid contains the microbes which cause disease, the animal or man who is stung becomes infected. When another mosquito sucks blood from the infected person, it will carry some of the microbes away in its body. Here they multiply, and in about ten days reach the glands of the mosquito which contain the irritant fluid. The man who is stung by this mosquito is infected by the disease when the insect injects the microbe-bearing fluid into his blood.

Bees, butterflies and moths have pleasanter ways of feeding. They drink the nectar of flowers by means of a long sucking-tube or *proboscis*. In butterflies and moths the proboscis is so long that it is kept coiled up like a watch-spring when not in use. (*See illustration on page* 68.)

LIFE HISTORY: Nearly all insects lay eggs, but the creature which hatches
    LARVA   out is usually quite unlike the parent. It is called a *larva* and
in most cases it is fat and wormlike. Only during this stage of its life does such an insect grow, and so it eats continuously. Soon it grows so fat that its skin becomes too small for it. Then it stops feeding, the skin splits down the back, and the grub comes out of the old skin with a new and larger skin on its body. It then begins to feed again until the new skin also becomes too small and is shed in its turn. This shedding of the outer skin is known as moulting, and the number of moults varies in different insects. Some larvæ moult only twice, others moult twenty

pollen brush
—with nine
rows of hairs

Inside of a
bee's back leg

front
wing

ridge
hooks
lump of pollen for
making 'bee-bread'

back
wing

The front & back
wings of bees are
hooked together
in flight. Here
they are shown
unhooked. Wasps
& ants have
the same hook-
and-bar
arrangement.

'basket'
formed of
hollow in leg
edged with
stiff hairs
Outside of
bee's hind legs

Each back leg of the
worker bee has a little
brush on the inside which
she uses to brush the
pollen off her coat after
visiting a flower. She
pushes the pollen into
the basket on the other
leg, & on reaching the
hive, she gets it out again
with the spike marked S

79

Red Admiral   Privet Hawk Moth

A BUTTERFLY

Antennae have knobs at ends
or are club-shaped, & are not
feathered. When resting, wings
are folded upwards with upper
sides together. Body slender,
not very hairy, thin waist.
Insect active in sunlight.

A MOTH

Antennae usually broad in
middle and pointed at ends
and are feathered. When
resting, wings are laid down
on back, with fore-wings
open. Body fat and hairy.
Insect active in evening.

times. When a larva has passed through its last moult, it has finished growing *for life.* If it has not been able to get enough food during the larval stage, it grows into a smaller insect than its brothers, but it can never become any larger.

PUPA The full-fed, full-grown larva usually makes some kind of covering to protect itself during the next stage of its life. Caterpillars form a chrysalis, or spin a cocoon; and in the larvæ of many flies the last skin becomes thickened and forms a hard, barrel-shaped case. Beetles, which generally spend this stage in the ground, do not protect themselves in this way but remain soft, with the limbs free of the body. At the stage between larva and perfect insect, the creature is called a *pupa.* Pupa is the Latin word for doll, and the stiff, unmoving chrysalis certainly looks somewhat doll-like. Although the pupa does not as a rule move outwardly, great changes are taking place inside it. When these changes are complete, the pupal skin is torn open and the perfect insect or *imago* appears. The wings are soft and limp at first, but

IMAGO after a short time they harden and stiffen, and the insect is ready for an active life. The time of development varies in different insects, and even in the same kinds it differs according to the climate and food supply. Some flies go through their larval and pupal stages in twelve days, but an American cicada spends seventeen years in an immature stage. An adult insect has generally a very short life, sometimes not more than two or three days. The mayflies which often spend three years in their development, have a winged life of only a few hours. Some ants and bees, on the other hand, live for years. Worker ants and queen bees have been known to live for two or three years, and queen ants have reached the age of fifteen.

Some insects do not go through the larval and pupal stages. They hatch from the eggs looking much like their parents, but are smaller and without

NYMPHS

wings. These insects grow and moult and at each moult the wings appear larger under the skin, until at the last moult they become free of their wrappings and quickly fill out to their full size. Grasshoppers, earwigs, cockroaches, mayflies and dragonflies grow in this way and are called *nymphs* until they reach their perfect, adult stage.

Most insects live by themselves, but some live with others of their kind. There are several sorts of caterpillars which spin a common dwelling place in which they live together for a short time. The small ermine-moth caterpillars

SOCIAL INSECTS

spin a tentlike web; they live inside it while they are young, but separate when they grow older. Other insects live together all their lives, and share the work of the community between them. Such are the social bees and wasps, and the ants and termites whose societies are often highly organized.

All communities of social insects are founded by the fertile queen. She chooses the site and begins the nest entirely by herself. Then she lays a few eggs and watches over them until they hatch, after which she feeds and tends the larvæ. She guards them when they turn into pupæ, and helps them out of their pupal cases when they are ready. The first eggs turn into workers, which are imperfect females who cannot lay eggs. The workers immediately busy themselves in building more rooms and corridors on to the nest, hunting for food, and looking after the queen. She does nothing now but lay eggs, which the workers feed and tend through the larval and pupal stages, until they too turn into adult insects. In ant colonies the eggs are taken from the queen and are put into nurseries. As they develop into larvæ and pupæ, they are kept separate from each other according to age. In wasp and bee colonies the queen lays the eggs in special cells. When they hatch, the larvæ remain in the cells and are fed by the workers, the bee larvæ on honey and pollen, and the wasp larvæ on animal food such as greenfly. Some bees store honey in the cells before the eggs are laid in them, so that the food is ready for the larvæ when they hatch.

A single scale

The wings of most butterflies and moths are covered with minute scales, which lie on the wing-surface like tiles on a roof. The scales themselves are like flattened bags and their various shapes and colours give a velvet richness or a metallic brilliance to the wings of these insects.

G

Though the first eggs are workers, males and egg-laying females appear later in the season. The male bees are called drones, and are of no use to the community except for mating purposes. Male wasps in some cases share in the work of the colony by cleaning the nest and removing the bodies of dead wasps. In many communities the males are driven out by the workers when cold weather comes and food is less plentiful.

Bees have only one queen for each colony, but wasps, termites and ants may have several queens in one nest. It is only among the termites that the queens' mates stay with them, the royal couples living in cells near the centre of the nest. The queen of the humble bees never becomes a mere egg-laying machine, such as the queens of the other social insects, but shares in the work of the nest all through her life. In the autumn she dies, and so do the others of the colony except a few young queens. These spend the cold months in some sheltered place, until the next year's warm weather awakens them to found new colonies.

Among wasps also, it is only the young queens who live through the winter. The rest of the colony dies with the first cold weather. If in autumn there are any larvæ still in the nest, the workers pull them out of the cells and kill them. In this way the larvæ do not die slowly of starvation, as they must when there were no workers left to feed them. The queens of ants and hive-bees live for several years, and their homes last for a long time. They do not have to build afresh each spring.

The social insects build their dwellings in many different ways and of various materials. Bees make "combs," built up of six-sided cells of wax, in which the young are reared. The cells are also used for storing honey on which the community feeds in winter when it cannot get its food directly from the flowers. In warm countries where flowers can be found all the year round, the bees store very little honey. The wax for the cells is made from honey in the bee's body, and comes out in eight flakes on the underside of the worker. Each bee, when her turn comes to build, makes the wax into a soft plaster in her mouth. When she has used up her building material, another bee takes her place. Bees are careful of their wax

BEES

2　　　　　　　　　　　　　　　1

and do not waste it, for each wax-maker has to eat from sixteen to twenty pounds of honey in order to produce one pound of wax.

WASPS　　　Wasps build their nests of a kind of paper, which they make by shaving dry wood from trees and fences with their strong cutting jaws. They grind the wood fragments into a pulp which they mould into the walls of the nest and the cells inside it. The wood-pulp dries and becomes a tough, thin sheet of paper. (*See illustration, p.* 74.)

TERMITES　　Termites are often called "white ants," but they are not related to the ants. They belong to the same group of insects as earwigs, cockroaches, grasshoppers and dragonflies. Some termites build tall nests or palaces, which are from ten to twenty-five feet high. The nests are made of fine earth and bits of wood, mixed with fluid from the insects' bodies. This forms a kind of cement, which sometimes becomes so hard that it can only be broken by means of an explosive.

1 Actias selene
2 d'Urville's
　Bird-wing
3 Swallow-tail
4 Large Copper
5 Orange Tip
6 Clifden Blue

Most ants live underground, where they tunnel passages and dig out many little rooms, each of which is used for a different purpose. Some of them are nurseries, some house the ants' "cows." The "cows" are other insects, usually greenfly, which give out a sweet liquid when the ants stroke them. The honey-ant keeps her "honey-pots" in a special room in the nest. They are ants of her own community, who are fed continually with honey dew until they become swollen with it. When the outside food supply fails, these living honey-pots

83

This Mantis is a near relative of grasshoppers, cockroaches & earwigs. It poses to look like a flower & thus attracts other insects which it eats.

yield up their stores to the rest of the colony. The harvester-ants use one of their rooms as a granary for storing seeds of various kinds. They take care that the seeds shall not sprout by biting through the radicles or by keeping them quite dry. The Leaf-cutting or Saüba ants grow mushrooms in their nests. They cut pieces of leaf about the size of a sixpence from surrounding plants, and take them back to the colony. There the leaves are chewed to a pulp, and used as leaf mould on which to grow a fungus which is like a very small mushroom. In human society mushrooms are grown in cellars, so that they may be harvested all the year round. In much the same way, these ants make sure of a supply of their favourite food by cultivating it underground.

ANTS

The Amazon-ants raid the nests of other ants and carry off their cocoons. When the pupæ hatch, they do the work of the nest for their captors. The Spinning-ants use their larvæ in sewing their leafy homes together, for the larvæ give off a sticky fluid which hardens into a thread of silk. There are "farming" ants which weed a space near their nest and only allow plants with edible seeds to grow there. When the seeds are ripe, the ants gather them and chew them into a dough. They make the dough into little biscuits, which are dried in the sun and then stored. Among ants the workers are divided up according to their different duties. There are soldiers, nursemaids, builders, repairers, sentries, foragers and milkmaids. Their societies are organized to such a degree that the thousands of creatures in a colony are but small parts of one large body. They have no life except in that of the community.

More than half the insects in the world are beetles. Some of them, from man's standpoint, are harmful: the destructive wireworm is the larva of the skipjack-beetle: the cockchafer's grub can destroy a whole crop of corn or beet:

BEETLES the Colorado potato-beetle is dreaded in all countries where potatoes are grown: the "snout-bearing" beetles or weevils are some of the worst of insect pests. Most beetles, however, are harmless, while some are of great use as scavengers or as eaters of insects harmful to plants. In common with most insects, beetles have wings; the front pair called *elytra*, are hard and thick, often very glossy, and lie closed over the back. The transparent hind wings are folded beneath them, and can only be seen when the insect is flying.

The ladybirds are the best known and most welcome of the beetles. They are not only pretty, with their vermilion and black-spotted wings, but they are useful also. They have cleared many lemon and orange groves of the scale-insects which were destroying them: and they also feed on the greenfly which do so much damage to rose bushes.

GREENFLY The greenfly or aphis is one of the commonest of all insects. It belongs to that group which feeds entirely on plant juices by sucking them up through a delicate hollow beak. These insects do much harm to farm and garden crops, but are themselves eaten by many other kinds of insects. Wasps, lacewings, hover flies and ladybirds all feed on them. The eggs of greenflies are laid in the autumn and in the spring they hatch out into fully formed but wingless insects. These soon produce young ones which instead of being in the form of eggs, are small but perfect images of their parents. Soon these daughters in their turn give birth to young, which quickly grow up and produce more

A servant bringing cooked locusts to the table of Ashur-bani-pal, King of Assyria from 668 to 625 B.C. The bodies of locusts contain fat & protein & are very nourishing. They are still eaten by natives of the countries which they infest.

1. The stick-like caterpillar of the Oak Beauty Moth

2 The Leaf Butterfly is very conspicuous when flying, but when pursued it can disappear by closing its wings.

3 The Leaf Insect not only imitates the green leaf, but also its imperfections such as holes and spots.

4 A Tree-hopper which looks like a thorn.

Insects have many enemies & protect themselves, not only by stinging & biting, but also by the shapes & colours of their bodies. They may look so much like their surroundings that by keeping quite still they become indistinguishable from them. Or they may be boldly patterned and

86

5

6 The White Ermine Moth is not good to taste, & advertises the fact by its strongly contrasted colouring. Its caterpillar is protected by long hairs which make it almost impossible for birds to swallow.

5 The Cocktail Beetle tries to frighten its enemies by curling up its abdomen, rearing its head & snapping its jaws.

7 The Puss Moth caterpillar defends itself with its frightening mask and lashing tail-whips.

8 The Hornet warns by its bold pattern & colour that it has an unpleasant taste.

9 The harmless Hornet Clearwing Moth, quite good as food, mimics the distasteful hornet.

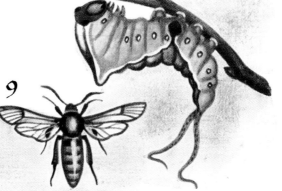

8   9

[continued] brightly coloured, & thus warn their enemies that for some reason they are not good to eat. Sometimes these showy insects are mimicked in colour, pattern and habit by other insects which are edible and defenceless.

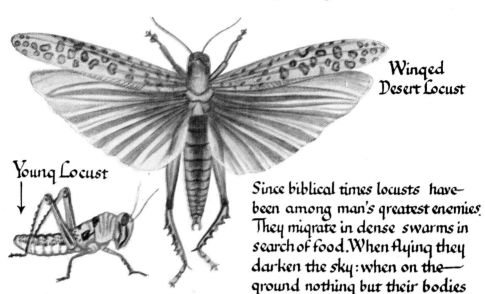

Winged Desert Locust

Young Locust

Since biblical times locusts have been among man's greatest enemies. They migrate in dense swarms in search of food. When flying they darken the sky: when on the ground nothing but their bodies can be seen; & when they rise again not a leaf remains. The young wingless locusts, known as 'hoppers' or 'voet-gangers' [foot-goers] are just as destructive, but can be trapped with barriers and pits.

greenfly, and so on all through the summer. Just before the cold weather returns, winged males and females are born. These mate and the females lay eggs, which lie dormant all through the winter and hatch in the spring. There are many kinds of greenflies, besides their relations the leaf-suckers, white-flies, plant-lice and scale-insects. Nearly all of them are serious pests.

EARWIGS   The earwig is usually looked upon as a pest, and it can certainly do much damage in a garden, but although it is often found inside flowers and fruit, it may sometimes be there to eat greenfly or the eggs of other harmful insects. The female is a good mother, and broods her eggs like a bird. If the eggs become scattered, she collects them together again. When they hatch into little earwigs, for like grasshoppers they do not go through larval and pupal stages, the young insects creep under their mother's body and she covers them for some hours. Earwigs have large hind wings which are carefully folded fanwise and crosswise, and packed under the small wing-covers with the help of the pincers at the end of the body.

USEFUL INSECTS   Although many insects can be harmful to man and his interests, there are also some which are helpful. Silk-moths give him the threads for making the softest and most beautiful cloth. Honey-bees provide him with a sweet food, and fertilize the flowers which give him fruit. One of the tropical scale-insects is cultivated for the sake of the *lac* which it makes. Lac is a gummy substance used in the manufacture of sealing wax, dyes, varnishes, lacquers, and various moulded products such as gramophone records and electrical fittings. Another scale-insect provided cochineal, a red colouring matter, until it was discovered that a dye of similar colour could be made from coal-tar. Since then the cochineal-insect has had a more important use. It has saved huge tracts of land in Australia from becoming jungles of prickly pear. This cactus was spreading rapidly and could not be checked, but the imported cochineal-insects quickly killed the plants by sucking their sap from them. Insects are being used more and more by man to keep down plants and other insects which have become pests. The enemies of the pests are searched for, and when found are bred in large quantities and sent to the places where their services are required.

Although they are small creatures on the whole the arthropods, especially

female
Cross-spider

male
Cross-spider

Spiders, scorpions and mites are arachnids. Most of these arthropods live on land, and unlike insects they breathe by means of lunglike organs. None of them has wings. Only the mites go through a larval stage: the other arachnids hatch from the egg as small copies of their parents. Spiders produce silk, with which they spin webs, make cocoons for their eggs and, when young, form threadlike parachutes on which they are carried for many miles.

Wanted in the garden

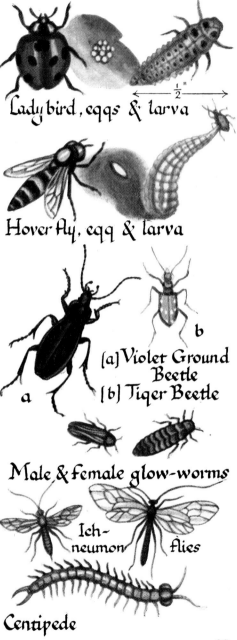

Lady bird, eggs & larva

Hover fly, egg & larva

[a] Violet Ground Beetle
[b] Tiger Beetle

a

b

Male & female glow-worms

Ichneumon flies

Centipede

Both lady bird & larva feed on greenflies; the larva eats 30 to 40 in an hour.

The Hover Fly feeds at flowers & so helps to pollinate them. For 10 days & nights the larva feeds greedily on greenfly, draining them of their juices & flinging the skins away.

The Violet Ground Beetle [a] eats wireworms & other harmful insects, as well as small slugs and snails.
The Tiger Beetle [b] feeds on weevil & cockchafer grubs, wireworms & caterpillars.

Glow-worms eat snails and slugs. The larva works its way into the shells of small snails and feeds on them.
The larvae of ichneumon flies live inside the bodies of many kinds of plant-eating insects & destroy large numbers of them.

The centipede eats grubs & insects. It is flatter and redder than the millipede. It has longer feelers, about 15 pairs of legs, & moves quickly.

NOT wanted in the garden

¼"

Larva
[leatherjacket]
and
Daddy longlegs

[below] Skipjack &
larva [wireworm]

Larva of Cockchafer & adult

Apple-blossom Weevil
actual size

Millipede

The Daddy longlegs lays 200 to 300 black eggs. In about 14 days the larvae hatch out, bury themselves in the soil & feed on the roots of grass & other crops, doing a great deal of damage.

The larva of the Skipjack or Click Beetle is the harmful wireworm, which for 3 to 5 years feeds on the roots of plants and ruins crops of potatoes.

The Cockchafer's grub lives in the ground for three years doing much damage to grass, corn & vegetables.

Weevils are the most harmful of all beetles. They & their larvae feed on all parts of plants, & there is scarcely a tree or plant which is not attacked by them.

The millipede feeds on the underground parts of plants. It is darker and more rounded than the centipede, has many more legs, and moves slowly.

the insects, are of great importance in the world. The humble-bees, for example, can maintain vast flocks of sheep by pollinating, and so increasing, the clover on which the sheep feed. Another group, the blowflies, can destroy the flock by laying their eggs in the skins of the animals. Mosquitoes have played a part in the history of man by spreading malaria, a disease which has wiped out whole armies, and which may have been partly responsible for the downfall of the Greek and Roman civilizations. For thousands of years, locusts have fallen in swarms on growing crops and caused men to die of hunger. On the other hand, the many minute crustaceans which form the food of fish such as herring and mackerel are arthropods. These creatures are also the main food supply of the great whalebone whales which are hunted and killed for their oil.

ARTHROPODS AND VERTEBRATES

In these and many other ways the arthropods can influence the lives of men and beasts. These jointed, armoured animals have adapted their bodies in varied and wonderful fashions to every condition of life : from intense heat to bitter cold : from a small space under a stone to the freedom of the air : from the parched desert to a home in the river or under the sea. In difficult conditions, their powers of adaptation are often greater even than those of the vertebrates.

lungs and legs

AMPHIBIANS
AND
REPTILES

tough skins and eggs with shells

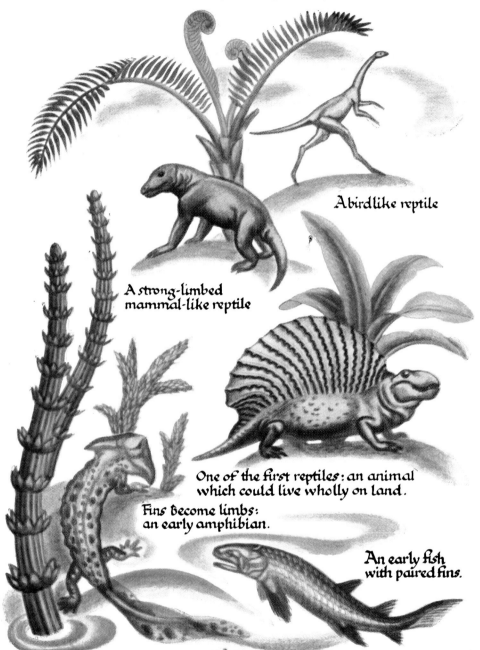

A birdlike reptile

A strong-limbed
mammal-like reptile

One of the first reptiles: an animal
which could live wholly on land.

Fins become limbs:
an early amphibian.

An early fish
with paired fins.

THE BEGINNING OF LIFE ON LAND

94

Lung-fishes use their air-bladders as lungs & can live in mud or sand during times of drought. Their fins are long and flipperlike but they cannot walk on land. The ancestors of the lung-fishes were closely related to the fishes which developed legs and lungs and became land animals.

Section 4—Amphibians and Reptiles

In the study of the history of man, time is conveniently divided into centuries and years. In studying the history of the earth, as it is written in the layers of rock which cover its surface, time has to be divided into periods of millions of years. During these periods, the climate of the earth has changed many times, and each change has had its effect on the evolution of living things.

THE FIRST LIFE

More than a thousand million years ago, while the dry land of the world was still thick with volcanic gases, the first life began in the sea. It may have begun as microscopic specks of protoplasm, and have evolved into cells which were neither animal nor plant. Through hundreds of millions of years these cells evolved, until the sea contained water-plants, invertebrate animals, and animals with backbones but without skulls. As the stifling gases cleared from the land, plants began to grow there, mosses, ferns and horse-tails, fossil remains of which are now found in coal beds deep in the earth.

FISHES

By this time true fishes had appeared in the waters. They were backboned animals with skulls, but otherwise unlike the thin-scaled fishes of to-day. They had heavy bony scales, bony plates on their heads, and unequally divided tails. Those who lived in fresh water developed air-bladders, so that when their stagnant lakes or pools became short of oxygen, they could eke out the supply by taking gulps of air at the surface. The air would be forced down into the air-sac, and the blood which flowed

Pterodactyls were the first flying vertebrates.

Plesiosaurus went back to the sea & developed flippers.

Ichthyosaurus (fish-lizard) reached the length of 30'.

Brontosaurus (thunder-lizard) 50'-70' long, lived in swamps.

Four reptiles of the Age of Reptiles, when they were masters of the animal world on land and in the sea and air.

There are a few amphibians which keep their gills all their lives. The Olm, or Proteus, is only found in certain underground waters, & as it lives in darkness it has become blind and colourless.

in its walls could absorb the oxygen there instead of finding the gas in the water which passed through the gills. When the backboned animals learnt to live on land, this air-sac developed into a lung.

As the climate of the earth became drier and many of the pools disappeared, the early fishes took two different lines of development. Some of them went back to the sea and became more fishlike. Others overcame the difficulties of drought by learning to breathe air and to drag their bodies across dry land from pool AMPHIBIANS to pool. The paired fins became limbs. The webbed rays of the fins became fewer until there were five, and the ends of the rays became fingers and toes. The tongue became movable. Slowly the gills disappeared and lungs were formed. For the first time living things gave voice in a world which for hundreds of millions of years had known only the noise of wind and water, thunder and avalanche, and the humming and scraping of insects. This change from water-living to land-living animal is seen to-day in the lives of *amphibians*—newts, frogs and toads, who in a few weeks go through a process which took their ancestors countless centuries to evolve.

The first land vertebrates were flesh-eaters like their fish ancestors. As there were as yet few land creatures for them to feed on, they lived mostly in the water, using their short limbs for journeys from one pool to another. Gradually they learnt to feed on the plentiful land-plants, and became more adapted for life on land. They developed longer legs and grew stronger and larger. Some of them no longer went back to, or started life in the water, as modern amphibians do. They lost their gills completely and became true land-living *reptiles*. As a cooler and drier period followed the hot, damp, luxuriant times of the coal-bearing forests, the amphibians became scarcer and smaller, while the more hardy reptiles survived.

AGE OF When warmer weather returned to the earth and plants became REPTILES more abundant, the reptiles grew large and plentiful. By the time that plant-life had developed as far as the conifers, reptiles dominated the animal life of the world. This was the Age of Reptiles, and it lasted for many millions of years during which time were evolved some of the largest and most fantastic of animal forms.

H 97

DINOSAURS   The most important group of land-living reptiles of this age were the dinosaurs, the "terrible lizards." Some of them were no bigger than rabbits, but many of them were gigantic. The Brontosaurus, the "thunder lizard," was about sixty-five feet long, with a body like an elephant's, and a head and tail like those of a huge snake. It weighed about forty tons and lived in swamps. The Tyrannosaurus, the "lord-" or "tyrant-lizard," the largest of flesh-eating land reptiles, was forty-seven feet long and stood twenty feet high. Some of these giant reptiles went back to the water and, as in whales and seals, their limbs became flippers. Having given up their gills, they could not regain them and they had to come to

PTERODACTYLS   the surface to breathe. Other reptiles took to the air. The pterodactyls, the "wing-fingered," had wings which were formed by a great sheet of skin running from the side of the body along the arm to the end of a very long fourth or fifth finger. They had large heads and their teeth were sharp, as those of crocodiles. Some pterodactyls had a wing-spread of twenty feet, while others were the size of a robin.

Towards the end of the Age of Reptiles, mammals first came into being. They probably evolved from some of the small mammal-like animals which appeared early in the evolution of reptiles. The first mammals

MAMMALS   were not much bigger than rats, yet these insignificant creatures survived to develop into larger and more varied forms, while the huge reptiles died out.

There were several reasons for this, one of them being a change in the world's climate. Reptiles are cold-blooded animals; that is, their temperature varies with the temperature of the air or water in which they live. As their surroundings get colder, they become less and less able to move until at freezing point they are frozen to death. When the earth's climate changed, and became again drier and cooler, only those reptiles survived who were small enough to creep into holes and crevices. The great size of the giant reptiles had other disadvantages. It made them slow and clumsy in their movements and this, with their small brain-development, laid them open to attack from the smaller, swifter and larger-

The Axolotl, like the Olm, may keep its larval form, or it may develop into its adult state. As an adult it is the Tiger Salamander, which looks rather like the Spotted Salamander. It breeds in either form, the young always being axolotls

1. Spotted Salamander [6"-10"] lives on land in damp places & produces its young alive.
2. Female Crested Newt
3. Male Crested Newt. [5"-6"] These newts have warty skins.
4. Common Smooth Newt [3"] with crest & bright colours worn in breeding season.
5. Egg of newt.
6-10. Newts growing up

Life History of a Frog [The dates are taken from an actual experience.]

The eggs as they are inside the mother.

After they are laid in water, the outer coat swells & becomes a jelly. Mar. 20

A larva inside the egg. March 26

Larvae hatch & stay fixed to water-weeds by means of their holders. Mar. 29

holders

The larva grows external gills. April 2

gill-opening

Front legs developing inside here

The hind legs appear & lungs for breathing air begin to develop. May 27

The true tadpole stage. The animal has internal gills & a gill-opening, and breathes water like a fish. April 6

The fore legs appear. The tail is absorbed into the body & there used as food. June 10.

The tadpole begins to look like a frog. June 15

The small but perfect frog is ready for life on land. June 20

The full grown frog, which feeds chiefly on garden pests.

In some tree frogs both back and front feet are fully webbed & very large. By spreading them out, the frog is able to glide through the air as it leaps from tree to tree.

brained mammals. Their great bodies needed much food which grew scarcer as the weather became cold and dry. It is possible also that the mammals helped to put an end to the giant reptiles by feeding on their eggs.

To-day, except in the warmest parts of the earth, there are com-

AMPHIBIANS AND REPTILES OF TO-DAY

paratively few reptiles left, and even fewer amphibians, They are too dependent on their surroundings—the reptiles on warmth and the amphibians on warmth and water, to compete with the more adaptable mammals. The old masters of the earth, with their long pedigrees, have been beaten in the struggle for existence by opportunist upstarts.

The amphibians of to-day consist of the rare Caecilians, the newts and salamanders, frogs and toads. They are called amphi-bians, "double-life" animals, because most of them start life in the water, where they breathe by means of gills; and later develop lungs and spend at least some of their time on land.

The reptiles include crocodiles and alligators, tortoises and turtles, lizards and snakes, and a little creature in an order by itself, the Tuatera. The word "reptile" means creeping, and though it is not descriptive of the towering reptiles of the past, it fits them well enough to-day. Except for a few tree-living lizards and some which at times run on their hind-legs, modern reptiles carry their bodies close to or touching the ground. They are different from amphibians in several ways.

The Fire-bellied Toad is not good for other animals to eat. When it is swimming, the bright red, black & white of its under parts can easily be seen by its enemies, and when alarmed on land, it turns up its limbs to show these warning colours.

101

They breathe air by means of lungs all their lives, and undergo little change but increase in size after they leave the egg. They have horny plates or scales on their skins which protect them from the effects of dry air on the body. Most amphibians have smooth skins provided with glands which keep the skin continually soft and moist, so that they are still, in a way, surrounded by water even when on land. This moisture makes it possible for the animal to breathe through the skin as well as through the lungs; but it has the disadvantage of letting too much water escape from the body, if the creature remains long on dry land. So the moist-skinned frogs and newts, unlike the dry-skinned toads, cannot live far from water. The amphibians, like the reptiles, are cold-blooded animals; neither of them can stand extremes of heat or cold. They usually AMPHIBIANS hibernate when they live in countries which have cold winters; and snakes which live in very hot deserts have to find a sunless hiding place during the day and come out in the cooler evening.

Crocodiles have snouts which are longer and more pointed than those of alligators. Crocodiles live in many warm parts of the world, but alligators are found only in America and China.

Nearly all the amphibians are small, feeble creatures, with few means of defending themselves. Some of them secrete poison in glands under their skin, but most of them rely for their safety on hiding or running away. They rarely live far from stagnant or slowly moving water, and most of them lay their eggs in ponds or lakes. They lay a great many eggs at a time, generally once a year in the spring. Water which contains even a trace of salt is fatal to all amphibians, as well as to their eggs and larvæ. It is thought that the first land-living animals evolved from those which had become used to living in fresh water, and this may be the reason why salt water kills their direct descendants.

Most of the larvæ of amphibians spend their lives in water, breathing by means of gills. They generally look quite unlike their parents. At first they feed almost entirely on plant food, but as they grow older they become eaters of other animals, such as insects, spiders, worms, snails, and small fishes. They have very large mouths, often with a tongue, and sometimes with small, sharp teeth. A fully grown amphibian generally has four legs, but in some cases there are only two, while a few of them have no legs at all.

CAECILIANS   The legless amphibians belong to a small group called Caecilians, which burrow in the soil, and look somewhat like big, bluish-grey earthworms. They live in a few tropical parts of the world, and since they are rare and their way of living difficult to watch, little is known about them. They are near relatives of the newts.

All the amphibians with tails are either newts or salamanders. They look much like lizards but, unlike the reptiles, they have smooth, moist skins. There are few differences between them except that of size. The name of "newt" or "eft" is usually given to the smaller kinds, while the larger are called "salamanders." In America most of these animals are called

NEWTS AND   salamanders whatever their size, the word newt being used
SALAMANDERS   only for two or three kinds which spend all their lives in water. From early times many stories have been told about salamanders, particularly of those coloured black with yellow spots. It was said that these animals could live in fire and not be burnt. It was also believed that in their bite was a deadly poison, and that if a salamander crawled over an apple tree, the fruit would surely wither. In reality salamanders are timid creatures, merely giving off a milky fluid through the skin in self-defence. This would certainly poison any animal taking them in the mouth, but otherwise they are quite harmless.

Except for the Giant-salamanders of China and Japan, which grow to a length of five feet, these animals are small and weak, their short limbs scarcely adapted for life on land. Most of them are much more at home in the water, and some live permanently in ponds and streams. Those which live in still water do not change from the fishlike tadpole stage to that of the air-breathing land animals, but keep their gills throughout their lives.

BREATHING   All amphibians can breathe to some extent through their skins, but unless they are in water in which there is a large amount of extra air or oxygen, they must use lungs or gills as well. But there

Millions of years ago Giant Tortoises lived all over the world, but now they are only found in the Galapagos Islands. They feed chiefly on cactus, which supplies them with both food and water: they may weigh 500 lbs., measure 4' in length & live for 300 or 400 yrs. The newly-hatched tortoise is at first quite soft: the egg is about the size of a tennis ball and has a hard brittle shell.

are a few exceptions to this rule. The Red-eft of North America loses its gills and, like nearly all newts and salamanders, develops lungs : but after living on land for about a year, this animal goes back to live in the water. It cannot regain the gills which it has lost, but instead a very rich blood supply develops in the lining of its mouth. This blood acts in the same way as the blood in the gills, it absorbs the oxygen in the water through the thin skin which covers it : so that by taking mouthful after mouthful of water, this newt is able to breathe without gills or lungs.

Certain kinds of salamanders which live in turbulent mountain streams breathe entirely through their skins. In these surroundings lungs would be a drawback, for their air-filled spaces would make the animal too buoyant to control its movements. The fast-flowing water is so full of air bubbles that there is always enough oxygen in it for the salamander to breathe through its skin : so lungs are either very small or absent altogether. On the whole, the tailed amphibians show very clearly the link between water-living and land-living animals : for they vary from the gilled Mud eel of North America, which has only two limbs and lives in swamps and ditches, to the lunged Spotted-salamander, which is more at home on land than in the water, and whose eggs are hatched inside the mother's body, so that she gives birth to four-limbed offspring.

Most of the tailed amphibians lay their eggs in water. The eggs are often fixed to the leaves of water-plants, which the mother folds over to give them some protection. Sometimes she or the father guards them until the young

REPRODUCTION
hatch out. The young larvæ are generally limbless, tadpole-like creatures with tufted gills. At first they hang by their mouths to the water-plants, but after a few days they begin to swim about. Slowly the limbs appear, the fore-legs first, the hind-legs later. Lungs are developed, the gills and finlike membrane of the tail disappear, and the animal is ready to leave the water. In a few cases the eggs are laid on land, and the larva goes through its water-life within the egg.

FROGS AND TOADS
The frogs and toads are the most numerous and best known of amphibians. They differ from newts and salamanders in having no tails, in being short and stout in body, and in having very long back legs. They are better adapted to life on land, for although they do not walk well, they can take very long jumps. Their eyes are large and prominent and, with their nostrils, are set near the tops of their heads, so that they can be almost completely hidden in water, and yet see and breathe above it. The eyes of man and other mammals are focused mainly by changing the shape of the lens inside the eye. The frog cannot do this, but has to move the lens for-

EYES AND EARS
wards or backwards to see clearly : so that when it is looking at something near, its eyes bulge out of its head, and when it looks into the distance they sink back again. Both the tailed and tail-less amphibians have good ears. These can be seen quite clearly on the head of the common British frog. Behind each eye there is a dark, round patch of skin, which shows where the ear-drum lies just under

MOUTHS AND BREATHING
the surface. The large mouths of frogs and toads are set with teeth, but these are used more for holding their prey than for chewing it. These animals catch their food either by a quick snap of the mouth or with their tongues. The tongue is generally long, slightly forked,

The Loggerhead Turtle reaches the same size & weight as the Giant Tortoise. It walks with difficulty but is a graceful swimmer & never leaves the water except to lay its 50 — 1000 soft shelled eggs in a hole in the sand.

105

sticky at the end, and is joined to the front of the mouth. It is shot out with unerring aim at passing insects.

Since these animals have no ribs, they cannot breathe in the same way as other land vertebrates. Instead, they pump air in and out of their bodies by moving the floor of the mouth up and down. The air is drawn in through the nostrils, and then, with nostrils closed, it is forced down into the lungs.

Many frogs can croak or bellow, and they use their voices to call to their mates in springtime, when pairing and egg-laying take place. The eggs are nearly always laid in water. They are small and black, and each is embedded in a ball of clear jelly. The frog lays her eggs in great shapeless masses, but the toad sheds hers in long glassy ropes, twisted about the stems of water-plants. After a week or so, the eggs hatch into little black creatures, with tails and tufted

1. This lizard runs on its hind legs & can hop like a frog over rocky places.
2. This is one of the two known poisonous lizards: its tail is a food reserve.
3. Desert-dwellers are generally flat and sand-coloured.
4. Lizards who burrow underground or who hide under grass or stones usually have only 2 legs or none at all. This one has two hind flaps.

5. ARABIAN CHAMELEON
6. LICHEN BARK-GECKO

gills but no mouths. At first they crowd together, hanging on to waterweeds by the suckers under their heads; but in a few days their mouths appear, and they swim about to look TADPOLES for food. Soon they lose their external gills and reach a fishlike stage. They have internal gills covered by a flap, and like a fish they have the lateral line sense-organs. They swim, fishlike, by means of their tails. Instead of the large eyes and mouths of their parents, they have small, beady eyes beneath the skin. Their tiny mouths have six hundred and forty horny, clawlike teeth. Their bodies are black, beautifully spangled with gold.

When the tadpoles are two or three months old, their legs begin to show, at first the hind-legs (unlike the newt) and later the fore-legs. As the legs grow longer, the gills wither away and lungs are developed. The animals must now come to the surface for air, and if they cannot find some solid thing to rest on while they keep their nostrils out of the water, they must soon drown. At this time they begin to get a taste for animal food, for as their bodies change inside, pond weeds do not

5. Most tree-dwellers have high, narrow bodies & long legs. The chameleon has a prehensile tail, feet adapted for grasping & a long sticky tongue.
6. Trunk & wall-dwellers often have flat bodies. Geckos have pads or *suckers* on their toes.

107

The Iguanas are the great lizards of the New World. This one, the Common Iguana, lives in trees, & feeds chiefly on plant food. It is 4′ to 6′ long.

satisfy them any longer. As their legs grow, their tails become shorter. Their eyes grow large and bulge from the top of the head. The mouth becomes wide and the tongue grows longer. When the animal is about three months old, the tail finally disappears, and the small but perfectly formed frog is ready to leave the water. (*See illustration p.* 100.)

Frogs and toads cannot be separated into two sharply divided groups, for they are all very much alike. The name of "frog" is usually given to the slender, lively, smooth-skinned animals, and "toads" are generally the squat, dry, rough-skinned kinds, which crawl rather than leap.

FROG *VERSUS* TOAD

Some frogs live in trees and are of a brilliant green, or striped and patterned in other bright colours. They have discs at the ends of their fingers and toes which, being moist, stick like suckers when they are pressed against any smooth surface. By this means the frogs are able to climb the trunks of trees. Some of these frogs have large, webbed hands and feet. When these are spread out, they act as planes and the animals can glide from one bough to another, or from a high branch to the ground.

The toad sheds its skin at regular intervals. The skin splits down the back, and is pulled downwards and forwards by the hind-limbs. When it has come off altogether it is taken up by the fore-limbs and pushed into the mouth and swallowed. Although many stories are told about the harmful and poisonous qualities of toads, these creatures are in fact gentle and harmless. In extreme distress they may defend themselves by giving off a little milky poison from glands under the skin, but if left undisturbed they do only good, by eating up flies, caterpillars, and other REPTILES unwanted small animals.

During the time when the English climate was tropical, reptiles of all sizes stalked and crept about the land. In the cooler world of to-day, their descendants prefer countries which lie nearer the equator. Originally the reptiles were all four-footed creatures with four or five toes on each foot. In course of time, some of them lost one pair of legs, and there are now a great number with no legs at all. The limbless reptiles include all the snakes and some of the burrowing lizards.

Most reptiles lay eggs, but some of them hatch their eggs inside their bodies and produce their young alive. Reptiles' REPRODUCTION eggs have soft or hard shells, unlike the shell-less eggs of the amphibians. The shell protects the egg from loss of the moisture inside it, and allows the parent to be independent of water when she wants to lay. The shell is to the egg what the scaled or horny skin is to the grown animals, and both shell and skin make a complete land-life possible. Reptiles generally leave their eggs to be hatched by the heat of the sun, but some of them make simple nests of dead leaves, or scoop out a hole in sandy soil, or bury their eggs.

Although reptiles have changed greatly since the time when THE they were masters of the TUATERA earth, there is one living to-day which is much like some of the reptiles of that Age. This is the tuatera, a lizard-like animal about two

3.

2.

1.

The Frilled Lizard 1. At rest 2. Running away 3. Unable to escape, it tries to frighten its foe by spreading its umbrella-like frill.

109

feet long, which lives only in New Zealand. (*See illustration, p.* 266.) Its head is large, with heavy ridges above the eyes. The body is flattened from side to side so that the animal can slip easily into the burrows in which it lives. Besides its two large bright eyes, the tuatera has traces at the top of its head of a third rather simpler eye, which may have been an important sense organ in some of the early backboned animals. This third, or pineal, eye can also be seen in most lizards and also in those primitive fishlike animals, the lampreys. In other backboned animals, including man, it has become a little stalked knob in the brain, and is known as the pineal gland. Tuateras lay leathery-shelled eggs, which the mother buries a few inches below the ground. She does not look after them but leaves them to hatch by the heat of the sun. In about thirteen months the young ones come out of the eggs and are able to look after themselves.

CROCODILES AND ALLIGATORS

The crocodiles and alligators are the largest living reptiles and also, except for the tuatera, the most unchanged since prehistoric times. Although they spend most of their lives in water, only one, the twenty to thirty-foot saltwater crocodile, ever enters the sea.

There is little difference between a crocodile and an alligator. In the crocodile the large teeth of the lower jaw shut into shallow notches in the upper jaw; in the alligator they fit right up into pits. The crocodile's snout is generally long and pointed, while that of the alligator is blunter and more rounded. True alligators are only found in China and in the basin of the Mississippi. Both crocodiles and alligators lay hard-shelled eggs about twice as large as a hen's egg. These are laid on land, and there are from twenty to ninety in a clutch. Crocodiles swim fast and gracefully by means of their powerful tails, but on land

The Basilisk runs swiftly on its hind legs & can even dash across the surface of water. 2'-3' including tail.

they can only drag their bodies awkwardly along the ground; so although their hard skins and hard-shelled eggs give them liberty to live on the dry earth, their short, weak legs restrict them to a life in the water.

TORTOISES AND TURTLES Like the crocodiles, tortoises and turtles have changed little since the very early days, perhaps because their bodies are almost entirely enclosed in a thick, unyielding shell. The outer part of the shell probably developed from the same kind of horny scales as are found on other reptiles. The shell is in two halves, an upper and a lower, which are joined at the sides, but are open at the back and

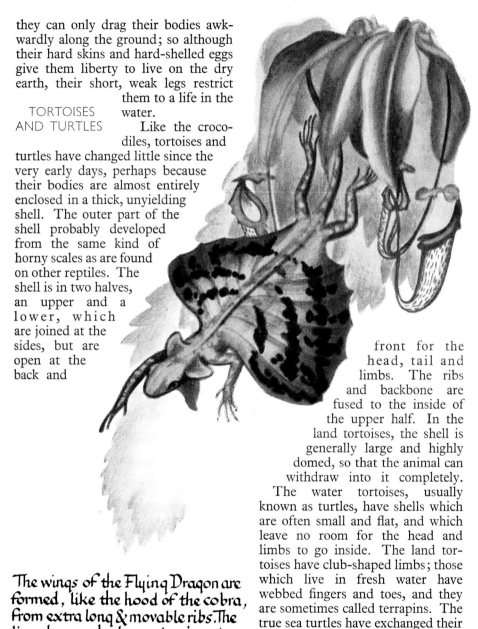

front for the head, tail and limbs. The ribs and backbone are fused to the inside of the upper half. In the land tortoises, the shell is generally large and highly domed, so that the animal can withdraw into it completely. The water tortoises, usually known as turtles, have shells which are often small and flat, and which leave no room for the head and limbs to go inside. The land tortoises have club-shaped limbs; those which live in fresh water have webbed fingers and toes, and they are sometimes called terrapins. The true sea turtles have exchanged their toed limbs for flippers. (*See illustrations, pages* 104 *and* 105.)

No present-day tortoise or turtle

The wings of the Flying Dragon are formed, like the hood of the cobra, from extra long & movable ribs. The lizard spreads them when jumping from tree to tree and uses them like a parachute. 8″–11″.

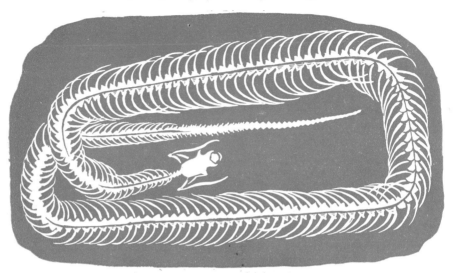

A snake's skeleton, showing the long backbone & numerous ribs. These move the horny plates underneath the body, by which the snake pushes itself along. The separated lower jaws can also be seen: in life these are connected by an elastic ligament, & as the bones supporting the lower jaw are movable, the mouth can be opened very wide.

has teeth, but the jaws are covered with a horny beak, which generally has sharp cutting edges. Some tortoises feed only on plants; others, more often the water dwellers, are flesh-eaters. The females have no voice and can only hiss, but the males, especially in the mating season, can pipe or bellow according to their size. As their ribs are immovable, the tortoises cannot breath in the same way as the other reptiles, who draw air into their lungs, and drive it out again, by outward and inward movements of the ribs. The tortoises have to pump air in and out of their bodies in much the same way as the amphibians, by movements of the throat and floor of the mouth. They lay round eggs, which have either a leathery or a hard, brittle shell. These are generally buried in sand or loose earth, and hatch in a few months. Tortoises grow very slowly and live to a great age. Some of the giant tortoises have reached at least two hundred years.

THE SCALED REPTILES: LIZARDS AND SNAKES   Both snakes and lizards belong to the order of the "scaled reptiles." They are not such ancient types as the crocodiles and tortoises; the first lizards appeared at much the same time as the toothed and long-tailed bird, Archæopteryx. Snakes were evolved even later, at the end of the Age of Reptiles and the beginning of the Age of Mammals. The scaled reptiles are more truly land animals than either of the older groups of reptiles, though the snakes and a few of the lizards have given up their land limbs, and creep along the ground on their bellies.

HOW SNAKES MOVE

Most of the legless reptiles burrow into the earth, or lurk under stones or in the undergrowth, where legs would be both useless and inconvenient. The snakes have evolved a very special way of moving over the ground. They have ribs along almost the whole length of their bodies, and each of these ribs ends against one of the broad, horny, overlapping plates which lie on the skin of the underside. By bringing these plates forward and then pushing them back against the unevennesses of the ground, the snake can glide along at a great speed. Some of the snakes still bear small, clawlike traces of their hind-limbs.

Although the legless lizards look much like snakes, there are several differences between the two groups of animals. In the legless lizards there are traces inside the body of the original *fore*-limbs, which are never found in snakes. The lizards have lower jaws which are fused into one piece in front; in the snake, the jaw is formed of two almost straight bones, which are joined in front by an elastic ligament. As

JAWS, TEETH AND FANGS

snakes swallow their food whole, this is a useful development, for the mouth can be stretched to a great size if the prey is rather large. The backward-curving teeth are useful for the same reason, for they can be pushed forward over the food and hooked into it, while the long swallowing process is taking place. In the poisonous snakes, some of the upper teeth are developed into fangs, down which poison runs, either in a groove or through an enclosed channel. In

Snakes do not chew their food but swallow it whole. This snake eats birds' eggs, which are broken up in its gullet. The yolk & white then flow into the stomach, while the shell is vomited up as a small pellet.

J

some cases the fangs are at the back of the mouth, but in the most dangerous snakes they grow at the front. If the teeth or fangs get broken, they are replaced by reserve teeth.

Snakes cannot "sting" with their tongues, nor can they use them for covering their prey with slime before it is swallowed. The snake's tongue is a sense-organ, and is used somewhat in the same way as the antennæ of an insect, for tasting, smelling and touching. Like the insect's antennæ, it is wonderfully

1. Corn Snake 5'
2. Bushmaster 12'
3. Harlequin Snake 3'
4. Rhinocerous Viper 4'

5. Boa Constrictor 12'
6 Anaconda 20'-30'
7 Indian
        Python 17'

sensitive, and may be connected with senses which are unknown to human beings.

Snakes have no external ears and no ear-drums, yet they seem to be able to hear. Their sense of hearing may be attuned to sound-waves TONGUES, EARS which travel AND EYES through the earth instead of through the air. Most lizards have quite good ears, though in the burrowing and more snake-like kinds the ears may be completely covered. Some of the

115

burrowing lizards have developed a transparent window in, or of, the lower eyelid. This protects the eye from soil and sand while allowing the animal to see. In snakes there are no eyelids at all, but the eye is covered with a transparent cap which may have been evolved from the "third eyelid." Most vertebrates have this third eyelid, though in man it is only a small piece of skin in the corner of the eye nearest to the nose. It can be seen quite clearly in the cat, and is probably used for keeping the eye moist and free from dust. When a bird closes its eyes, the third eyelid moves across the eyeball like a shutter, but the transparent third eyelid of the snake is immovable. It is shed at each casting of the skin.

SLOUGHING   The casting of the dead outer part of the skin is known as sloughing. It takes place in all reptiles and amphibians, and in many other animals, including man; though in most creatures the process is so gradual that it is scarcely heeded. It is most noticeable in snakes because they shed the whole of the outer skin at once. The skin loosens first at the lips, and the snake slowly works its way out, turning the cast skin inside out as it does so. Before sloughing, oil comes out of the body underneath the old skin, and helps to loosen it. Healthy snakes shed their skins every month or so.

Snakes and lizards either lay eggs or produce their young alive. Most of them

Many snakes shake their tails if they are angry or alarmed. The rattlesnake has at the end of its tail hollow horny rings fitting into one another, and when these are shaken they make a sharp rattling sound. A young rattlesnake has only a small ring at the end of its tail, but a new ring is uncovered at each moult.

GRASS SNAKE

VIPER OR ADDER
male [patterned] & female

The Grass Snake is harmless
It has usually a yellow
collar. It is more slender
than the adder and is
narrower behind the ears.
It is from 3' to 4' long.
It likes water & damp places.

The Viper is poisonous. It
generally has a V on its head
& a zig-zag line down its
back, though sometimes the
markings do not show.
It is only about 18" long.
It prefers dry & stony heaths.

show little care for their eggs and none for their offspring; but the female python coils herself round her clutch of a hundred eggs until they are hatched.

Snakes do not need so much warmth as lizards, though like all reptiles and amphibians, they prefer warm climates, and have to hibernate in cooler weather.

SHAPES AND COLOURS Both snakes and lizards live hidden lives, on the ground or in holes and crevices, in trees, or under the earth, or partly in water. The lizards which live in trees are generally narrow from side to side, while ground dwellers are squat and flattened, and the burrowing kinds are long, thin, and sometimes legless. As in most animals their colouring, unless it is of a "warning" nature, harmonizes with their surroundings. Desert reptiles are generally pale and sand-coloured. Ground dwellers are grey, brown and black. The forest snakes have rich colours and bold markings which, however striking they may appear away from the animal's natural surroundings, take their place in the dappled sunlight and shadow of the trees. There are only two poisonous lizards, and they are "warningly" coloured, with rings of black and either yellow or salmon-pink.

Most scaled reptiles have no voice and can only hiss, but a few lizards can make a chirping noise. The geckos, small soft-skinned lizards with suckers on their toes, given gentle chirps or clicks which sound like "gec-ko."

Snakes and lizards are timid and secretive animals, who prefer DEFENCE to hide or run away rather than turn and defend themselves. Their poisonous fangs are used chiefly in getting their food, but are sometimes used in self-defence. The lizards rely on their tails, either dealing lashing blows with them, or leaving them in the grasp of their attacker. As the tail goes on moving violently after it has been broken off, the pursuer thinks that he has caught his prey; and while he is dealing with the wriggling tail, the lizard slips off unnoticed. A new tail soon grows in place of the lost one.

The amphibians and reptiles are very ancient forms of life; some of them, such as crocodiles and tortoises, lingering on although not well fitted for the world of to-day. The climate is too cold for them to spread themselves, as they once did, all over the earth; and they have not evolved a body-covering which would enable them to withstand low temperatures. The pace of modern, mammalian life is too fast for them, and they fall before their swifter foes. Their numbers, compared with those in the Age of Reptiles, are small. Yet it was these slow-moving creatures which made the great adventure of leaving the water completely to found the mighty races of land-living, air-breathing animals. Hundreds of millions of years ago, these lowly crawlers first lifted the body from the ground on legs. Some of these ancient beasts grew hair and became mammals. Others learnt to travel through the air : these animals grew feathers and became birds.

BIRDS

WINGS AND FEATHERS

Archeopteryx was covered with feathers but had teeth and a long tail. Its arms had become wings, but they still had three clawed fingers.

In modern birds the finger bones are welded together to make the wing stronger. The nestling hoatzin has clawed thumbs & second fingers which it uses to clamber about the branches.

As the world grew colder, the scales of these reptiles became feathers which gave both warmth & lightness to the body.

Birds may have evolved from reptiles which ran on two legs, beating the air with their forelimbs; or from those which lived in trees and glided from branch to branch.

Wings and feathers have given birds the power to rise high up into the air, to move quickly and to travel for long distances. Flight gives them escape from their ground-living enemies: and feathers help to keep their bodies at an even temperature in all climates. The young can be kept in high, safe places and tended with care.

Section 5—Birds

"A bird is a transformed . . . and glorified reptile." It is difficult at first to believe that these creatures of the air, whose movements are freer than those of any other animal, should be near relatives of such lowly, earth-bound crawlers as snakes and crocodiles. Yet birds have evolved directly from reptiles, and are still like them in many ways. The feathers lie on their bodies like overlapping scales. The combs and wattles of farmyard fowls are like the crests and dewlaps of certain lizards. There are scales on the "legs" and toes, and the bird's bill is not unlike the toothless beaks of tortoises and turtles. The toes and claws are similar to those of lizards, though the feet have changed greatly in shape. There is often a lizard-like claw on the thumb of the bird's forelimb, or wing, and there is sometimes a claw on the first finger as well. The chick of the South American Hoatzin actually clambers about the branches on all fours, using the well-developed clawed fingers on its wings. Birds and reptiles lay eggs which are very similar in size and appearance. In their unhatched state the young of both have "egg-teeth," with which they break out of their

BIRDS AND REPTILES

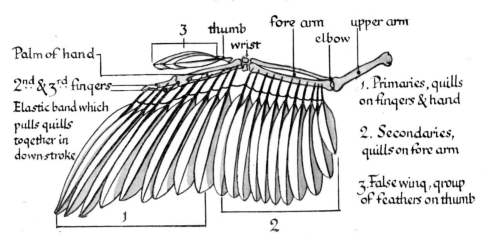

3 thumb
fore arm   upper arm
wrist   elbow

Palm of hand

2nd & 3rd fingers
Elastic band which
pulls quills
together in
downstroke

1. Primaries, quills
on fingers & hand

2. Secondaries,
quills on fore arm

3. False wing, group
of feathers on thumb

1

2

Wing of a bird, showing how the quills grow out from the arm
bones. The whole arm & the spaces between the roots of the quills
are covered with small feathers, to make the wing a solid oar with
which to push back the air in flight. All feathers grow out of the skin.

shells. The air-sacs, which are so characteristic of birds, are also found in the
chameleon. The blood-cells of the two groups of animals are much the same,
and in several ways their skeletons and certain inside organs are alike.

HOW BIRDS MAY
HAVE EVOLVED

The first birds of whom there is any fossil record
appeared in the Age of Reptiles. The link between the
reptiles and these lizard-like birds has not been found, but
they may have evolved from small, kangaroo-like dino-
saurs, which stood and ran on their hind legs. Perhaps these little creatures,
constantly running from their huge enemies, and beating the air with their
forelimbs, developed a fringe of scales on their arms. Such primitive wings
would make for faster running, as they helped to take the weight of the body
off the ground. As the wings grew larger, they would lift the body more and
more, until they could raise it from the ground; at first a little height for a
short time only, and finally right up into the air. On the other hand birds may
have evolved from tree-living reptiles who developed parachutes of scales as
they leapt, and then glided from branch to branch. Gradually, through millions
of years, these small forest-dwellers may have learned, not only to float through
the air, but to fly in it as well.

ARCHÆOPTERYX

The early birds were not at all like the birds which
are living now. They were much more like their rep-
tile ancestors, with long, jointed tails and three claws on their wings.
They had sharp teeth in their jaws, which were unlike the toothless
beaks of modern birds : but they had birdlike feet and instead of being

Although most humming birds are very small, they can fly for short distances at 60 m.p.h. Their wings beat the air so quickly that they make a humming sound and form a haze round the body. The birds can hold themselves steady in mid-air as they feed.

covered with scales, they had feathers.

THE FIRST FEATHERS It is not known how scales evolved into feathers, but it is possible that the bird-reptile's scales became finer and thinner, and split up from the edges to form barbs. However they may have come about, feathers have played a most important part in the evolution of birds. Their lightness and resistance to air made the feathered wing the most perfect flying apparatus, while the warmth of feathers made it possible for birds to take full advantage of their powers of flight. Without a warm covering for the body, no creature could move quickly through the cold upper air. Scales keep out damp, and protect their wearer from the claws of enemies, but they do not resist the cold. Feathers and fur hold layers of air between the animal's body and the outer air, and this helps to keep the body at an even temperature. Towards the end of the Age of Reptiles, when the world's climate became cooler, these fur and feather coverings kept the small mammals and birds warm and nimble, while

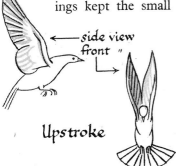

←— side view
front "

Upstroke

side view —→
front "

Downstroke

When a bird flies, it not only flaps its wings up and down but also gives them a slight twist before the upstroke. The tips of the wings make a series of figure eights in the air.

DODO

KIWI

Any part of the body which is not used, gradually gets weaker and smaller & finally disappears. The ostrich still has wings but can only flap them as it runs. The kiwi's wings are very small & quite useless. The dodo gave up flight, and since it could not escape from its enemies, it became extinct.

the great scale-covered reptiles grew cold and numb, and eventually died out.

Birds have improved on their reptile ancestors in many ways. They are warm-blooded and keep the same temperature summer and winter. Their feathers help to keep this heat in, and so they can remain active all the year round. The cold-blooded reptiles are dependent on the weather for their body temperature, and though lively enough in the warm days, must hibernate or die when winter comes. The cold makes them too sluggish to search for food, even if it were to be found : but when a bird is faced with food shortage, its wings will carry it to some place, perhaps thousands of miles away, where weather is kind and food is plentiful. The power of rising suddenly into the air gives the bird more freedom from its enemies which have no wings, and eggs and young can be kept high up out of their reach.

HOW BIRDS DIFFER FROM REPTILES

Only four kinds of animals have ever learnt to fly. Three of them, the bats, insects and birds, are living to-day : the fourth was the extinct pterodactyl.

These flying dragons or lizards were not forerunners of the birds, since their wings were developed on quite a different plan, more like those of the bat.

FLYING
ANIMALS
The so-called flying "lemurs" and squirrels are not fliers but parachutists. They cannot soar into the air, but only glide from one branch to another, held up by the web of skin which is stretched between their fore and hind limbs. In these animals, as in the true fliers, the bats and pterodactyls, all four limbs become parts of the flying apparatus. In birds the fore limbs only are used; the hind limbs are kept free for use on tree or ground, so that birds can run as well as fly. Since their wings fold so neatly to their sides, they can even dive and swim under water.

Birds are perfectly adapted for flying. Their small bodies are light for their size, and many of them have some bones filled with air instead of marrow. Just as the fish is streamlined for its passage through water, birds are similarly built for their passage through air. Their feathers lie closely to the body, pointing backwards so that they offer as little resistance as possible to the air. In flight the feet are generally tucked up. Only the wings break the smooth sweep from bill to tail.

WINGS
The wings of the bird have been evolved from the fore-limbs, and the bones are built on the same plan as in the forelegs of beasts and the arms of man. If the human arm were bent up close to the side, and if the hand could turn so that the little finger touched the outside edge of the forearm, the arm would then be in the same position as a folded wing. Stretched out, slightly bent at the elbow and wrist, it would be in the position of the bird's wing in flight. The bird's arm is the framework supporting the feathers which make the wing. Large strong quills grow out of the hand and forearm, and are held together by an elastic band near their bases. As the bird makes an up-stroke in flight, this band stretches, and lets air pass between the loosened quills. On the down-stroke it tightens, holding the feathers closely together, so that the bird can push against the air. The gaps between the bases of the wing quills are filled in with little feathers to make this

Penguins also lost the use of their wings for flight, but developed them as flippers for swimming.

125

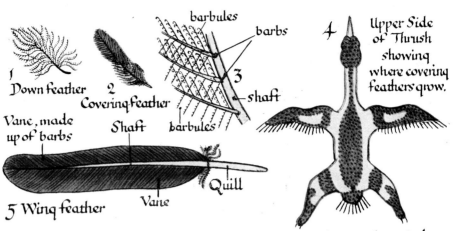

1. Down feather

2. Covering feather

Vane, made up of barbs

Shaft

barbules

barbs

3

shaft

4

Upper Side of Thrush showing where covering feathers grow.

5 Wing feather

Vane

Quill

Vane

1. There are two kinds of down feathers, those of the nestling & those under the coverts of the adult bird. 2. These coverts grow in definite patterns or feather-tracts. 3. A feather enlarged to show how the barbs are hooked into each other to make feathers air-tight. In birds which do not fly the barbs do not interlock. 4. Showing the feather-tracts: the spaces between them are covered with down feathers. 5. The shaft is hollow at the end & solid where the barbs grow.

down-stroke effective, for the same reason as the feet of frogs and ducks are webbed in order to push back the water. It is with the down-stroke that the bird "rows" itself through the air, much as a frog swims through water or a boat is pushed along the surface with oars. (*See illus. p.* 123.)

HOW BIRDS FLY
A great effort is needed to push the air down strongly enough to raise a solid body from the ground. The muscle which does this work is the largest in the bird's body. This big flight-muscle is fixed at one end to the upper arm bone, and at the other end to the high ridge of bone called the "keel" of the breast-bone. When this muscle contracts, it pulls the arm towards the breast, lowering the wing and making the difficult downward thrust. The hollowed undersides of the wings help to force the air out backwards on the down stroke, thus pushing the bird forwards. The arched upper sides let the air glance off easily in the upstroke. On windy days the wings are used as planes, the bird gliding on the air, and frequently changing the tilt of its body to take advantage of the air currents. The primary feathers, those which grow from the hand of the bird, are of great use in steering; and for that reason they are especially long in birds such as swallows and swifts, who catch insects as they are flying.

TAILS
Steering is also done by means of the tail feathers, which serve besides as brakes. As a bird lands, it spreads its tail fanwise, and turns the feathers downwards. The tail is always short and stumpy, though the

quill feathers which are rooted in it often make it look very long. The trailing "tails" of birds such as peacocks, are not made up of tail feathers, but of the covering-feathers of "coverts" above the tail.

FEATHERS   Birds are the only animals which have feathers. These grow out of the skin much as hair does, but feathers are more complicated than hairs. Some birds, particularly those which are hatched in nests on the ground, come out of the egg covered in soft down feathers. Tree and cliff dwellers, on the other hand, are often almost naked when they are hatched, but they soon begin to grow limp down feathers. Many birds, especially water birds, keep these soft coats beneath the outer feathers all their lives. The down holds layers of air next to the bird's body and keeps it warm, and it may also help swimming birds to float. In winter, birds fluff up their feathers to make the layers of warm air as thick as possible. The outer feathers do not grow all over the body, like the fur of mammals, but in certain definite areas. From these feather-tracts they spread out so that, with the help of the down feathers, the whole of the skin is covered. All birds moult once, twice, or three times a year. Their moulting is not like the sloughing of reptiles, where only the outer layer of skin is cast. The whole feather is lost, in much the same way as the hairs of mammals are shed.

The feathers of some birds are brilliantly coloured, & others are made in such a way that they change from one colour to another as the light falls on them at different angles. The brightest colours are found in the male birds especially during the pairing season. The duller colours of the hen birds hide them when they are sitting on their eggs. Young birds also are usually protectively coloured.

Quetzals:
cock and hen

PREENING   Birds preen themselves by drawing each feather separately through the bill. It is said that birds oil their feathers with a clear liquid which they get with their beaks from the preening gland at the base of the tail. This is not altogether certain, for some birds have no such gland and yet keep their feathers glossy. Other birds have beaks so shaped that they could not take up the oil and spread it on their feathers. It may be that the liquid from this gland increases the flow of some juice in the mouth, which is used in keeping the feathers clean.

HOW BIRDS   Birds, like insects, are intensely active animals, and
BREATHE   to keep up this energy much oxygen is needed. Insects have a very efficient breathing apparatus, which supplies oxygen quickly to the whole body. Birds breathe much like reptiles and mammals, by means of lungs: but beyond their lungs run air-sacs, which in some birds pass right into the bones. When the bird breathes in, air rushes through the lungs into the air-sacs. When it breathes out, the air passes out of the air-sacs through the lungs again. It is in the lungs that the blood picks up its oxygen, and gets rid of its waste gas, carbon-dioxide. A bird's lungs get a double amount of fresh air with each breath. The lungs are fixed to the bird's ribs, and the movement of the ribs in flight helps to expel and draw in the air. Instead of getting out of breath when moving quickly, as mammals do, a bird is actually helped to breathe by the action of its flying. The good supply of air in the air-sacs is useful to the bird when diving and when in full song, but it has small effect in buoying the body up in flight.

The humming birds are near relations of the swifts. Some of them are only 2½" from beak to tail. They build nests which are about the size of half a walnut shell & their eggs are no larger than peas. The young of the small humming birds are the same size as humble bees.

LEGS AND
FEET

Birds walk on their hind-legs, like man; but like cats and dogs they have only their toes on the ground. The parts of the bird's hind-limbs which are generally seen are the foot and the toes. Except in the long-legged waders, the leg with knee much bent is hidden under the feathers. No birds have more than four toes, sometimes there are only three. The ostrich, with its one large and one very small toe, has developed its feet along the same lines as the horse, which runs on only one toe of each foot. Both horse and ostrich are swift runners, which in their wild state live on the open plains. The shape of a bird's foot depends upon whether it is a percher, climber, swimmer, walker or runner, scratcher or bird of prey. Large birds generally walk or run: small birds run and hop.

BEAKS   Although a bird, like man and the apes, uses only its hind-legs for walking, its fore-limbs are so completely adapted for flight that they are useless for anything else, except occasionally for sheltering the young. The mouth has had to take the place of a hand, and this has led to the evolution of a long, flexible neck and a hard beak or bill. In past ages birds had teeth, but there are no toothed birds living to-day. The modern birds have horny bills, often with a sharp cutting edge. The nostrils are in the beak, generally at the end nearest the face, but sometimes they are in the middle, and in the kiwi they are at the extreme tip. (*See illustrations pages* 132 *and* 133).

Beaks are variously adapted for each bird's particular needs, though it is not easy to see the reasons for some of them, which are of huge size and brilliant

Swimming Foot

e.q. ducks: geese: gulls: pelicans

Foot for Walking & Scratching
e.q. fowls: pheasants

Perching Foot
e.q. crows: larks:
& most of the
small birds.

Climbing Foot
e.q. woodpeckers:
parrots: cuckoos:
toucans.

Foot for Seizing
and Holding

e.q. eagles: hawks: owls.

colour. Toucans and hornbills have great beaks which are almost as large as their bodies. These growths are not as heavy as they look, for they are made up of a thin horny shell, covering a delicate mesh-work of bone. The shape of the beak is largely determined by the food which the bird eats. Birds which crack open hard seeds have short, thick bills. The beaks of birds of prey are curved for seizing, carry-ing and tearing their food. Birds such as swallows which catch insects on the wing, have short, broad beaks with a wide gape and bristles at the base, while those which pick up small insects from plants or from the ground, have slender, pointed beaks. The broad bills of ducks and geese have hard, hooked tips and hard edges, but the rest of the beak is covered with a soft, sen-sitive skin. Such beaks are well suited for nosing in the mud, where food must be found by a sense of touch alone. The beaks and tongues of these mud-feeders are fitted with horny fringes, so that the bird can strain out the water and mud, leaving the food in the mouth. The long, slender bills of humming birds are well fitted for finding nectar deeply hidden in trumpet-shaped flowers, and similar beaks are seen in birds such as the curlew and woodcock, which search for worms in the soft earth and sand.

FOOD   The food of birds is very varied. Some birds are almost entirely vegetarian, and feed on fruit and seeds; but most of them are carni-vorous, and do much good by keeping down the numbers of insects. Every insect probably has its bird-enemy; even the hairy caterpillars, which most birds will not touch, are sought after by the cuckoos. Some birds eat snails and slugs, others full-grown insects, others again prefer eggs and larvæ. Although most of them work by day, a few hunt by night.

GREBE

JACANA

AVOCET

MALLARD

Wading birds have stilt-like legs & feet with strongly developed toes which are sometimes webbed. In birds which spend much time swimming, the legs are placed far back so as to make them more effective as oars & rudders. Most of these birds have webbed feet, but sometimes the toes have leaf-like lobes. The Jacana has very long toes, so that it can walk on the surface of floating leaves.

Birds should be welcomed if only for the help they give in checking farm and garden pests. The harm they may do to fruit and seeds is more than balanced by the services which they render in this way. The chaffinch destroys chickweed and groundsel: the goldfinch eats the seeds of the troublesome dandelion and thistle. Rooks sometimes eat a few freshly sown seeds of wheat, but they save whole crops by killing wireworms and cockchafer grubs. Larger birds such as owls keep a check on small mammals, for they feed on rats, mice and moles, though some of the flesh-eating birds eat other birds and their eggs. Swallows help to keep down swarms of flies and mosquitoes in the summer. In hot countries vultures are useful scavengers, for they eat up refuse which would otherwise become the breeding ground for disease.

Since birds generally eat in a hurry, always on the look-out for possible

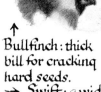

Bullfinch: thick
bill for cracking
hard seeds.
→ Swift: a wide gape for
catching insects in mid-air.

Fire Crested Wren:
slender bill for
picking up
small insects.

Crow: typical bill
suited for many
different purposes.

Golden Eagle;
the hooked beak
of the bird of prey.

Drake: flattened
bill with sifting
apparatus.

Woodcock:
long, slender bill
for feeling
underground for food.

enemies, they have no time to taste and chew their food, so their sense of taste is poorly developed, though not entirely absent. Only a few birds, magpies, blackbirds, rooks, owls and night-hawks, are known to have a sense of smell. In most birds this sense is probably lacking, since there is little need for it.

SMELL AND TASTE

The scents of possible prey or of other birds would soon be lost up in the air among the various cross-currents of wind. Few birds seem to find their prey by scent. They rely on their eyes, and keep to the foods which they recognize by sight as having been good in the past. They do not as a rule experiment with new forms of food unless pressed by hunger. Birds which search for food in mud or earth, or in the hidden parts of trees and flowers, cannot use their eyes; but they depend on their sense of touch rather than on smell or taste.

SIGHT

The sense of sight is more keenly developed in the bird than in any other animal, and the focus of its eye can be more quickly adjusted. The eyes are not movable in the sockets as they are in mammals, but instead the neck can be bent in almost any direction. As the eyes are placed on each side of the head, the bird cannot look forwards with both together. It uses one at a time, turning the side of its head to face the direction in which it wants to see. Then it concentrates the sight of the one eye on whatever it is looking at. Birds have a good colour sense: they are often brightly coloured themselves, and so it seems likely that they recognize their friends and enemies by their hue. Penguins steal brightly

132

With his sharp
straight bill the
←male Huia chisels
away the bark of trees
containing grubs, then the
hen gets them out with
her very long curved beak.

In winter the
Puffin sheds its
coloured eye-& beak-plates.

Hornbills
& Toucans
have large
beaks which are
light for their size. Some
hornbills have a great
'helmet' above the beak.

The Flamingo thrusts its
bent beak upside down
into the mud from which
it sifts out its food.

coloured pebbles from each other's nests. Bower-birds decorate their bowers with gaily coloured objects—feathers, shells, insects and flowers. The Satin bower-bird prefers blue ornaments, and refuses anything orange or red. (*See p. 144*).

EARS   In accordance with the streamlined shape of their bodies, birds have no ear-trumpets on the outside of their heads, but in spite of this they have a sharp sense of hearing. With their long, flexible necks they can move their heads in any direction, to pick up the slightest sound. The opening of the ear lies behind and below the eye, and is generally covered with feathers. Owls hunt at night, and depend more than the day birds on their ears. They have tufts of feathers above the ear opening, which may help to collect sound-waves as do the ear-trumpets of mammals.

VOICES AND SONG   The first voices ever to break the silence of the earth were the croaks of amphibians as they called to their mates. Their descendants, the reptiles, probably made sounds similar to those which they make to-day—roaring, hissing and chirping. The first birds, who were so nearly related to the reptiles, may have had harsh croaks which were used only in the mating season. As time passed, and the birds' powers of flight gave them more safety from their enemies, they were able to build nests and stay with their young. There was some sort of family and social life, and voices came to be used apart from mating calls. There was an ever-growing number of emotions which the birds wanted to express, and this led to

hip —
bone
/ \
thigh

muscles that
make the —
toes curl
round the
perch —

knee

ankle —

foot ———
toes

Bird's leg in
ordinary standing
position

As a bird settles down on a branch to sleep, it bends its legs at the knees & ankles. This pulls the muscles which curl the toes, so that they clasp the perch tightly & cannot be loosened until the bird wakes up & straightens its legs.

the rich and beautiful sound-language which many birds have to-day.

BIRD LANGUAGE — The males sing when paying court to the females, the father bird entertains the brooding mother with his song. The young ones cheep excitedly as the parents bring them food, and the older birds call to them when danger is near. Birds cry out when frightened or distressed, and chatter and scream angrily at their rivals. The voice is used as a means of keeping birds of the same kind together in the dark, or in the thickly leaved forest. There is a hunger-cry, and a call when food is found. There is the song which claims a tree or piece of ground for the bird's own, and warns off all intruders : and there is the song which seems to spring from the pure joy of being alive and able to sing. Such song is best heard in the very early mornings of April and May. As the first pale light shows in the east, scattered chirps and twitterings are heard. When dawn breaks, there is a great burst of song as every bird sings its reveille.

BIRD VOICES — The clear notes of the songsters are not given to all birds. Some are silent, particularly the females, and others give harsh, discordant cries. The deep and loud call of the ostrich is like the roar of a lion : the wild shriek of the barn-owl sounds almost human. The lapwing utters a plaintive "pee-wit," the duck a robust "quack-quack," and the jay makes a sound like wood being sawn amongst the trees. Sometimes the voice changes with the season; the bubbling spring notes of the nightingale give place in early summer to the anxious croak of the father with a nestful of hungry children. The voices of mammals and amphibians come from the larynx, which is in the upper part of the windpipe. Birds have a larynx but it is voiceless. The song-box or syrinx is at the lower end of the windpipe, in the chest and just above the lungs.

SLEEP — After the last song at sunset, most birds go to sleep. They do not sleep in their nests unless they are brooding their eggs or young, for nests are not homes, but nurseries. Birds generally sleep perched on twigs and branches, their heads tucked under the plumage of the shoulder, their feathers

Most birds have the ear-
opening well hidden by
feathers, but in a few, such as
the Cassowaries, Ostriches &
Vultures, this hole is uncovered

The Cuckoo arrives about April 15th and leaves for Africa in August

The Swallow arrives about April 11th & leaves for S. Africa in October.

The Nightingale arrives about April 17th & leaves for N. & Central Africa at the same time as the swallow

⌐ Birds which visit England in summer

Birds which visit England in winter ⌐

The Snow-bunting arrives at the end of October & goes in the middle of April.

The Fieldfare arrives from Scandinavia in November and leaves England in May.

The Goosander & many other ducks arrive from the North in November & leave England in March. When migrating, ducks fly in arrow-head formation fluffed out to keep them warm. There is no danger of a bird's relaxing its toes while asleep, or of its falling off its perch. When it grasps the branch with its feet and settles down, tendons which run round the knee and ankle joints pull the joints of the toes so that they curl tightly round the branch. The more the bird relaxes, and the more the knees are bent, the tighter the grip on the perch. In winter many birds find sheltered places to sleep in : holes in trees or in haystacks, old nests, barns and church towers. Other birds go abroad and spend the winter season in a warmer country. (*See page* 136.)

MIGRATION   This yearly travelling, from a cold country to a warmer one and back again, is called "migration." It takes place regularly at more or less set times, among the "migratory" birds. These usually travel in large or small flocks, but sometimes over short distances they fly alone. The migration may be local, from high ground to low, or from an exposed place to one more sheltered. It may be from the cold part of a continent to a part nearer the equator, or the birds may travel thousands of miles from one hemisphere to the other. The advantages gained by such journeys are easy to see in most cases : but it is hard to understand how the bird has a foreboding of a food shortage and cold which it has never experienced. Nor is it easy to explain how the flights are made, often across hundreds of miles of sea, with not a landmark to serve as guide, and in many hours of utter darkness. There is much still to be learnt about bird migration, but a few facts are certain. Breeding takes place in the spring and summer of the cooler of the two climates. The adult male birds usually arrive first, followed by the adult females, the younger birds bringing up the rear. In autumn the young birds leave first as a rule, though the cuckoo goes about three months later than its parents. The older birds, other than cuckoos, stay on for a short time, perhaps to rest a

Like many of the long-legged birds, the stork when resting, stands on one leg, its neck doubled back, and its head resting on its shoulders.

little after working so hard during the months of nest-building and bringing up a family.

Little is known about the height and speed of flying during these long journeys. The height probably varies with the weather, and though birds have been found flying singly at over ten thousand feet, they are rarely met above five thousand. In migration the greater part of the flight probably takes place within two thousand feet of the ground. The average speed seems to be between thirty and forty miles per hour. With the wind behind them, some birds can fly at fifty and sixty miles, and eagles and duck-hawks can travel at over one hundred and ten miles per hour, but long flights would not be made at this speed.

HEIGHT AND SPEED OF FLIGHT

The practice of "ringing" birds has done much towards adding to man's knowledge. Ringing is done by snaring birds in specially built traps, driving them gently into "catching boxes," then slipping on to each bird's foot a light metal ring, stamped with a number and address. All this is done without hurting or unduly frightening the bird ; and if it is again caught, perhaps some thousands of miles away, the ring may be returned to the marking station with details of the date and place of capture. In this way, and by the constant observation of naturalists, lighthouse keepers and other people, much has been learned about birds in the last fifty years, but even more remains to be discovered.

THE RINGING OF BIRDS

The first birds probably laid their

1. The Arctic tern migrates for a longer distance than any other bird. It breeds in the Arctic & spends the non-breeding season in the Antarctic seas. 2. The Long-tailed cuckoo is a New Zealand bird which flies northwards toward the equator in the winter.

3. The Rufous humming bird migrates from north-west Canada to Mexico. 4. The White capped redstart breeds high up in the Himalayas & winters in the warmer foot-hills.

1

2

eggs, like reptiles, on or in the ground. In warm countries they could then be left to hatch by the heat of the sun, or of decaying vegetable matter. Perhaps the parent watched near by, as the mother crocodile does to-day. In cooler countries, the eggs would have to be kept warm by heat from the bird's body, so rough collections of sticks would be made to keep the eggs and brooding hen bird from the cold and damp of the ground. As birds became more at home in the air, they built their nests higher up, and by degrees they made them safer and more comfortable for mother and young. Although some birds still lay their eggs on the bare ground, and others are content with a rough heap of sticks or stones, many of them, especially the passerine or perching birds, build finely fashioned nests of various shapes and materials. In most cases there is a warm, soft lining for the eggs, made of small feathers, wool, cotton-fibres, or down plucked from the mother's breast. The outside is often disguised with bits of lichen, moss and spiders' webs. The hen bird generally weaves the nest, while the cock bird brings her materials, but sometimes both kinds of work are shared equally between the pair. Nests may be made of mud, as the swallows' and martins', or roughly built of sticks, as those of the rooks and pigeons. Holes in trees and disused rabbit-burrows are used by many birds as cradles for their young, while others lay their eggs on ledges of bare rock or on pebbly beaches.

NESTS

EGGS   By building nests birds safeguard their eggs; and since most birds are careful parents, they need lay fewer eggs than those animals who leave eggs and young to look after themselves. The reptiles lay from twenty to ninety eggs in a clutch, but few birds lay more than twelve, the usual number being

In China a soup is made from the nests of the Sea Swift. The bird makes the nest out of its own saliva, sometimes mixed with a little seaweed. It builds on the upright sides of cliffs.

The hen & cock Tailor-birds help each other to sew the edges of leaves together to make a pocket, in which they build a nest of fine grass, cotton-down, and hair.

The nest of the Oven-bird is made of mud mixed with a few sticks & straws. It has two rooms, an ante-room and an egg-room.

four or five. Birds' eggs are similar to those of reptiles both inside and outside; the eggs of pigeons and of geese might be mistaken for those of tortoises and crocodiles. Reptiles' eggs are white or cream-coloured. They are round or plum-shaped, but never *oval*, that is, with one end narrower than the other like a hen's egg. Birds' eggs vary in shape, but are generally oval. This saves room in the nest, where the eggs can lie neatly in a circle, the narrow ends towards the middle. It is not known why birds' eggs are sometimes so gaily coloured, but it seems to be a general rule that the eggs of ground-nesting birds are green or brown, speckled and streaked to make them less noticeable against the grass and undergrowth : while those laid in holes or which are otherwise well hidden are often pure white. The texture of the shell ranges from pearly smoothness to a pitted roughness. The size of the egg varies with the size of the bird, though it depends in some cases on the number of eggs laid. The hen bird must be

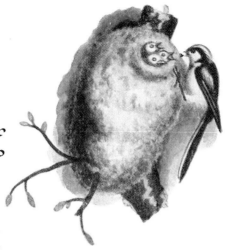

The House Martin's nest is built of daubs of clay, each one being left to harden before the next is added. It is lined with feathers & straw, and has only one small opening.

able to cover her eggs, so if they are large compared with her body, there can be only one or two of them. The birds which are hatched ready to leave the nest and look after themselves, come out of larger eggs than those which arrive in the world naked, blind and helpless. The first do much of their growing inside the egg, and so they need more food stored there than the little birds which are fed by their parents after they are hatched. The undeveloped birds are generally found in high or well-hidden nests: those who hatch covered in down and able to run about are the young of ground-nesting birds.

SEED AND EGG   The inside of an egg is in some ways like that of a seed. There is the small embryo, or beginning of new life, and the food which it will need for its growth before breaking out into the world. In the egg, food and water is contained in the yolk and white, the embryo or future chick being at first a tiny reddish speck on one side of the

The nest of the Long-tailed Tit is a feltwork of moss, wool, lichen & spiders' webs: it is lined with hundreds of feathers.

The Reed-warbler weaves her deep, cup-shaped nest round the stems of three or more reeds.

yolk. The yolk is hung in the white by means of two "ropes" of thicker white, which are fixed to the lining of the egg shell. These keep the yolk safely cushioned in the middle of the egg, and however the egg is turned, the embryo always lies uppermost, nearest to the warm body of the brooding mother. All over the shell there are minute pores through which comes air for the developing chick to breathe, and at the broad end there is a large, air-filled space. The time taken for the chick to develop within the egg varies with the different kinds of birds; robins take thirteen days, the swallow fifteen days. Farmyard hens sit for twenty-one days, and ducks for twenty-eight. Swans brood for forty-two days. At the end of this time, the young bird has used up all its food, and is ready to come into the world. It takes a deep breath of the air in the air-chamber at the broad end of the egg, and chips its way out of the shell. It does this with a horny tip at the end of its beak. This is called the egg-tooth, and it falls off soon after the bird has left the egg. Young crocodiles also have an egg-tooth, and cheep before breaking their shells in the same way as an unhatched bird.

YOUNG BIRDS When their young family is hatched, there comes a very busy time for the parent birds. Each day from dawn to dusk they must find food to fill the open beaks of their nestlings. Like human babies, young birds are generally fed on a different food from that of their parents. The food of young creatures must be quite soft and easily digested. Babies have milk at first.

Flamingoes breed in colonies and build their nests of mud in swamps or shallow water. The nests are about twelve inches high and are hollowed on top for the eggs.

142

Young birds sometimes have food which has been partly digested by the parents and brought up again. Pigeons make a kind of creamy food in their crops for their young squabs. Other nestlings are fed on grubs and caterpillars and small pieces of earthworm. Many young birds have bright yellow or orange mouths, which probably help their parents to see quickly where to put the food, especially if the nest is in a rather dark place. Most parent birds are particular about keeping the nest clean, and remove every day the mess which the young ones make. Sometimes they hold them in such a position over the side of the nest that the nursery is not dirtied at all.

LEARNING TO FLY AND TO SWIM

When the little birds are feathered and strong, they are taught to fly. It is frightening, when they have only known the firmness of the nest under them, to let themselves fall into space, but they usually learn to fly by easy stages. Sometimes the older bird hops with the young ones from branch to branch, gradually increasing the distance until they have to use their wings. The parents are very patient with their fluttering, piping brood, and often reward a successful little flight with a juicy caterpillar. In a few cases, water birds have to be taught to swim. Some parents do this gently, taking each baby on their backs into the water, then slowly diving down, leaving the young one on the surface. Others are not so kind. The razor-bill holds its chick by the scruff of the neck and pulls it under the water, and some wild ducks push their young over the edge of the nest into the

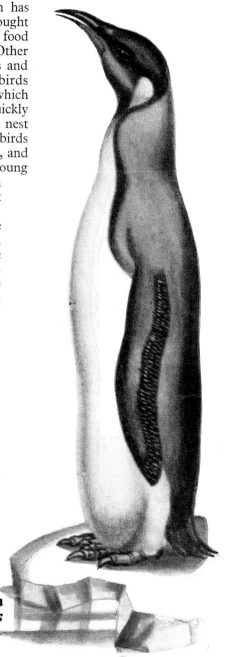

The Emperor penguins, which live in the Antarctic, keep their eggs from freezing by placing them on the backs of their feet & covering them with the loose fold of skin on their abdomens.

The Bower Birds, besides building nests for their eggs, also make bowers of twigs, which they decorate with flowers & bright objects such as berries, shells, beetle-wings, bits of moss & lichen. These places are used as playgrounds during courtship. There are several kinds of these birds, all building bowers of different design, each with its own form of decoration.

pool beneath. Hawks and eagles teach their young ones to swoop on their prey by dropping a small dead animal from the nest, and urging them to catch it in mid-air. Insect-catching birds such as the swallows do the same with an insect.

FAMILY LIFE Birds generally take the duties of parenthood seriously, and put the welfare of their offspring before all things, even before their own safety. Some birds—storks and parrots, eagles and ravens—mate for life and tend and feed each other for years. It may be true enough to say that birds are but transformed reptiles, but in their evolution from those lowly creatures, they have developed something more than bodily fitness for a freer and fuller life. In them are found for the first time in the upward trend of evolution, the beginnings of friendship and of true family life, with their bonds of tenderness and unselfishness.

MAMMALS

Man developed his brain & hands and learned to speak. He became master of the other mammals.

Ape-man: a mammal who stood upright & used his hands for making weapons & tools.

Other mammals developed larger brains & sharper senses: and continued to evolve.

Some mammals developed huge bodies heavily armed with tusks & horns: but their brains remained small & they died out.

The placental mammals kept their young inside their bodies until they were almost ready to look after themselves.

Eggs were broken & stolen by other animals. The marsupial mammals gave birth to undeveloped young & kept them safely in pouches.

The early mammals were small. They laid eggs like reptiles, but instead of scales they had a warm covering of fur.

Mammals evolved from reptiles, probably from the simple strong-legged theromorphs.

146

The duckbilled platypus is a reptile-like mammal. It lays two leathery-shelled eggs but it feeds its young on milk. It is covered with fur but it cannot keep its temperature as constant as that of other mammals.

Section 6 — Mammals

The age of the earth is not known, but it may be between one and a half thousand million and three thousand million years old. If the age is taken to be two thousand million years, land vertebrates have existed only during the last sixth of its history. Mammals, birds and flowering plants have been on earth about one thirteenth part of the time. The most recently evolved mammal is man, who began to be different from the apes perhaps ten million years ago. He became manlike less than one million years ago, and has worn his present form for only a few score thousand years.

Mammals are up to the present the most highly evolved of all living things. They grow hair or fur, and they feed their young ones on milk. Their name lays stress on this last quality, for it comes from the Latin word "mamma" which means breast. All mammals, except two who lay eggs, produce their young alive. Like birds, they usually take care of their young, and like birds also, they are descended from reptiles.

THE FIRST MAMMALS The first mammals began to emerge towards the end of the great Age of Reptiles. They may have descended from the very early reptiles known as theromorphs, the "beast-formed" animals. These simple, rather dog-shaped creatures probably gave rise also to the dinosaurs which became birds, as well as to many kinds of reptiles of those and later days. The earliest fossil traces of the mammals show that they were small animals. Few of them were as large as rabbits, most of them were rat-sized, and many were smaller still. It was possibly their small size which at first gave them

The spiny ant-eater is covered with spines and hair, and like the duckbill is not perfectly warm-blooded. The female. lays eggs & carries them in a pocket of skin on her under side until they are hatched. The young one stays in the pouch for some weeks.

the chance to survive and multiply. They could live unnoticed by the large flesh-eating reptiles, and needed only a small amount of food. They could probably eat food of any kind, such as roots, leaves, insects, grubs or worms. Like those strange mammals of to-day, the duckbill and echidna, the first mammals laid eggs; but while their eggs lay hidden in burrows, safe from their great reptile enemies, the little mammals dug up and smashed and ate the eggs of the reptiles. So the numbers of these big creatures grew less and less.

GREAT REPTILES DIE OUT   As the climate of the world became cooler and drier, food became less plentiful, and the struggle for life grew harder. The great reptiles became sluggish with cold, for they had neither fur nor feathers to keep their body-temperature stable. They were clumsy in movement and so large that they could not hide. They fell as easy prey even to creatures smaller than themselves. They needed a great deal of food, but it no longer grew amply about them, and they had neither the swiftness nor the skill to hunt far for it. Their brains were too small to direct and control the huge bulk of their bodies. One of the great reptiles called Diplodocus was over sixty feet long, yet its brain was only the size of a walnut.

THE MAMMALS LIVE ON   The mammals on the other hand were nimble, and so small that they could lie hidden in burrows in the ground. They did not fear the cold, for they had grown a coat of hair and had become warm-blooded. Their body-temperatures did not vary, like the reptiles', with every change in their surroundings, but remained constant. After a time the mammals ceased to lay eggs, which could be stolen or broken by other animals. Instead, they carried their young ones in a pouch, like a kangaroo, until they were ready to come into the world. Later they evolved a still safer shelter for their offspring and carried them inside their bodies. When the young were born, the mammals did not leave them as the reptiles left their eggs. They fed them with a special liquid from their own bodies, the liquid known as milk, until they were strong enough to look after themselves.

The first mammals, like the early reptiles, looked very much alike; but as the lands and seas and climate of the world changed from age to age, their bodies became different as they adapted themselves to every kind of condition. Through millions of years they grew bigger and more varied, until they became the most important animals in the world. Some of them made the same mistake as the reptiles : they increased in size until they were larger than the animals living to-day. Their bodies became too big for the size of their brains, and their undeveloped senses failed to warn them of danger or guide them to food and safety. So they too died out, while smaller mammals lived on, and evolved into the forms of present-day animals. Living things still tend to increase in size. The mammals of to-day are larger than their ancient ancestors, and man himself is bigger than he was five hundred years ago. The next few million years may bring changes in the shape and size of man and beast as great as those which have taken place in the past.

There are several differences between the milk-giving mammals and their reptilian ancestors. The former have fur instead of horny plates and scales. They have a constant instead of a changeable body-temperature. Like all land

The pouched mammals are a link between the egg-laying mammals & the placentals, which carry their young in their bodies until they are almost completely formed. The young kangaroo is barely 1" long when born & makes its way to its mother's pouch where it feeds on milk for 4 months.

GLYPTODONT　CORYPHODON

EARLY MAMMALS WHICH HAD DISAPPEARED
1. An armadillo as big as an ox. 2 An animal like the tapir.
4 . A forerunner of the hoofed mammals.
6. A strong-limbed beast, the size of an elephant.

vertebrates they breathe by means of lungs, but in a different way from birds or reptiles. In man and the other mammals the breathing apparatus is separated from the digestive organs by the diaphragm. This is a thin sheet of muscle which is fixed at its edges so as to form the up-curved floor of a box or *chest*. The ribs, the backbone and the breastbone make the walls of the chest, and the heart and lungs lie inside it. When mammals breathe *in*, their muscles pull the ribs upwards and outwards. At the same time the diaphragm contracts, and the humped-up floor of the chest is flattened downwards. This makes the chest larger, and air is sucked down the windpipe into the lungs. The lungs are full

MAMMALS AND
REPTILES

MACRAUCHENIA　GIANT SLOTH

3 PALEOMASTODON   4 PHENACODUS

FROM THE EARTH BEFORE THE COMING OF MAN
3. An early elephant, about the size of a large horse.
5. A camel-like animal which browsed on the leaves of trees.
7. A toothed whale, the first mammal to take to life in water.

of branching air-tubes, which divide again and again, until they become extremely small and end in minute air-sacs. About one fifth of the air is made of oxygen, a gas which living creatures need for the working of their bodies. In insects, oxygen is taken to all parts of their small frames by means of air-tubes. In vertebrates the gas joins with the red blood cells, and is carried in the blood along tubes of various sizes called blood-vessels. Blood travels in a continuous stream, from the lungs to the heart, from the heart all over the body, and back to the heart and lungs again. In the lungs it joins with the oxygen through the walls of the air-sacs, and from the heart it is pumped along the blood-vessels. In its passage round the body the blood gives up its oxygen, which helps to make the energy that keeps the body working, moving and warm. As the oxygen is used up another gas, carbon-dioxide, is produced and given off. This passes from the body into the blood and is taken back to the lungs, where it goes through the walls of the air-sacs, into the air-tubes, and is breathed out. When a mammal breathes *out*, the ribs and breastbone sink, and the diaphragm humps up again. This makes the chest smaller and drives the used air out through the

7 ZEUGLODONT

Man was the last mammal to evolve. Although he was physically defenceless and smaller than many of the other animals, he was able to hunt them and later to tame some of them to be of use to him.

windpipe. All mammals breathe in this way, even the whale, which though it can stay under water for some time, must come at length to the surface to breathe or it would drown.

HIBERNATION   A few mammals have kept the reptilian habit of lying dormant during the cold weather. Some of them, such as the Spiny-anteater or Echidna and the hedgehog, are not perfectly warm-blooded. Their temperatures vary, though not so much as the reptiles', with the heat or cold of the weather. So, like the reptiles, they curl up in some small space and "sleep" through the winter. Winter-sleep, or hibernation, is much deeper than sleep, for the animal's body almost stops working altogether. Its heart scarcely beats, and it almost ceases to breathe. Some animals doze, more or less soundly, because there is a shortage of their food in the winter months. There is no fuel to keep their body machinery working, so the machine slows down and draws what little energy it needs from the fat stored in the body during the spring and summer. The English bats, like the swallows, feed on insects. In the cold weather the insects die. The swallows fly away to a warmer country where insects are plentiful. The bats go into a sleepy condition which lasts through the cold weather. Dormice and squirrels sleep a great deal in the winter, though they occasionally wake up to eat some of their stored nuts and acorns. Bears which feed on fruits, insects and honey, stay in their dens in a dull, sleepy state from the end of October to the middle of April.

Most mammals are able to get enough to eat all the year round. Some of them, including man, eat both plant and flesh food, but most of them eat either the one or the other. Their bodies are adapted, both inside and outside, to deal with the different foods. Even the main shape of them differs. The plant-eaters, from rabbits to horses and elephants, have somewhat barrel-shaped bodies : the flesh-eaters, from stoats and weasles to tigers and wolves, have lean, limber figures. This is because the food of the flesh-eaters or *carnivores* is highly

nourishing and easily digested. They do not have to eat much

FLESH-EATERS
AND
PLANT-EATERS

of it, nor do they need a long food canal to deal with it. In plant food, on the other hand, the small nourishing part has to be taken out of a great deal of stringy, indigestible matter.

So the plant-eaters or *herbivorous* animals have to eat more food than the flesh-eaters, and they must also have a longer food canal to digest it. This greater length of gut makes the plant-eater's body stick out at each side, instead of being nipped-in like the body of a carnivore.

Teeth, tongues, snouts and feet may all vary with different ways of feeding. Animals which live on insects, such as moles, shrews, ant-eaters and armadillos, have long pointed snouts with which they can dig out their small prey. The ant-eaters have long, sticky tongues which whip out and draw hundreds of insects at a time into their toothless mouths. Flesh-eating mammals, like birds of prey, have sharp curved claws for getting their food. The teeth of flesh-eaters are

The Mammoth, Irish Elk and Woolly Rhinoceros had de-veloped thick coats to with-stand the intense cold of the Great Ice Age. Cave Bears, Bison, Reindeer & Wild Ponies also lived during this time.

SEAL

All these mammals have adapted themselves along similar lines to life in water, although they are not related to each other, except the Dolphin & Porpoise which are little whales. The Seal is one of the 'flesheaters' and the Manatee is distantly related to the Elephant. All their bodies are fish-like, with flipper-limbs & no external ear.

different from those of plant-eaters. At the back of its mouth, the plant-eater has flat-topped, ridged teeth, suitable for grinding the grass or leaves or tree bark on which it feeds. The carnivore's back teeth have high, sharp points for cutting and tearing its food instead of grinding it. At the sides of the mouth there are four pointed "dog-teeth" or canines, with which the animal fights and catches its prey. In some animals these canine teeth grow very long and become tusks, as in the walrus and the wild boar. The tusks of the elephant and narwhal are overgrown front cutting-teeth, or incisors.

RUMINANTS

One group of plant-eating animals, the ruminants, have evolved a peculiar way of eating. They "chew the cud." The beasts which eat in this way are sheep and oxen, goats, antelopes, giraffes and all kinds of deer. After eating at a great rate and swallowing its food almost whole, the ruminant finds some quiet spot where it can lie down undisturbed. There it brings its unchewed food back into

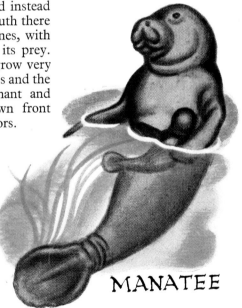

MANATEE

its mouth from the first division of its stomach, which is in four baglike parts. Then it re-chews the food until it has ground it to a pulp and mixed it thoroughly with saliva. There is good reason for this strange way of eating. The cud-chewers feed chiefly on grass, which usually grows out in the open away from the pro-tection of trees. The animals need to eat a great deal of grass in order to get enough nourishment, and if they were to stay where the grass grew, slowly chewing each mouthful, they would be exposed for a long time to the carnivorous animals which prey upon them. So they have evolved the useful

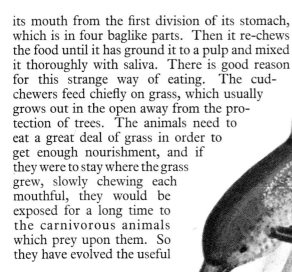

DOLPHIN
PORPOISE

habit of swallowing as much food as possible in a short time, and then chewing, re-swallowing and digesting it in some safe place. Though the danger from flesh-eating beasts no longer exists for tame cattle and sheep and goats, they still chew the cud in the safety of their fields and stalls.

Varied surroundings have pro-duced through the long ages thousands of different forms from the simple reptilian mammals of early days. Many strange-looking animals have died out, but there is still much variety among the mammals living in all parts of the world to-day.

Some mammals, whose ancestors once lived on land, have taken to a life in the sea. They are the seals and walruses; and the whales, which include the porpoises and dolphins. These animals have

The claws of the sloth are long & curved. The animal hangs upside down from the branches of trees & pulls itself along on them. Its fur is coloured green by the single-celled plants which grow in special crevices in the hairs, so the sloth is well-hidden in the green light of the forests in which it lives.

become streamlined like fishes, and their limbs have grown finlike. The seals are fur-covered and come ashore to breed, but the whales have entirely given up life on land. Their skin has lost its hair. The tail has changed

WATER MAMMALS

into two flattened lobes, which are used somewhat like the tail of a fish, to drive the body through the water. These sea-beasts have become very unlike land-mammals, though they still breathe air, and give birth to living young, which they feed on milk. The otter and the polar bear, the beaver and the water-vole, are as much at home in the water as on dry land. They have the streamlined figures of the other water animals, but they have not changed their limbs into flippers. (*See illustrations pages* 154 *and* 155.)

AIR MAMMALS

A few mammals spend much of their time in the air, though it is only the bats which can actually fly. The flying-squirrels and the so-called flying "lemurs" only glide from a high branch to a lower one, spreading out their limbs on which are stretched parachutes of skin. The bat is a true flier and has wings instead of mere parachutes. Its wings are different in several ways from those of the bird. They are, like the bird's, made from the forelimb; but as the bat is a furred animal it cannot grow long, firm feathers from its hand and arm, to make a vane with which to beat the air. Instead, its four

156

fingers have grown extremely long and a web of skin is stretched between them, and from them to the arms, body, legs and feet and tail. With such wings the bat flies quite ably and often at a high speed, but its body, though light, is heavy compared with the bird's. It has none of the bird's hollow, air-filled bones, and it has to use much more energy to keep itself up in the air. (*See illustration page* 161.)

UNDERGROUND MAMMALS   Some mammals live underground, and just as the water animals are streamlined for their passage through water, so the bodies of these creatures have taken a similar shape for their passage through earth. The mole is particularly suited for this kind of life. It has very large fore paws, with big, strong, flattened nails, turned in such a way as to make digging easier. With this shovel-like hand the animal tunnels through the earth. The eyes are small and are hidden beneath the fur, and even when open they are of little use. The ears do not stick out from the head, for there is no ear-trumpet. The fur, unlike the fur of other mammals, grows in no particular direction, so that it lies smoothly whichever way the animal twists and turns in its tunnel. Armadillos and pangolins also burrow into the ground, and for this purpose they are encased in earth-resisting scaly or shield-like armour.

The sand-rat, in its thousands of years of tunnelling in the hot desert sand, has not only lost the use of its eyes and ears, but is almost completely hairless.

Most mammals live on the surface of the

The zebra's stripes blend with tall grasses in strong sunlight and hide it from its enemies. When the animal is in the open plains, the stripes break up the outline of its body so that it cannot be seen at a distance.

The Giraffe's long neck & long, sensitive tongue enable it to feed on the tender shoots of the trees' upper branches. Its spotted coat makes it almost invisible in the dappled shadows of leaves and sunlight

earth, and adapt themselves to the varying conditions of climate, food and surroundings. They may live in the jungle, the prairie, in sandy or snowy deserts : some of them live in trees and rear their young in nests like the birds, others leap from narrow rock to rock among the mountains.

ON THE EARTH

Mammals are less brilliantly coloured than any other group of living things. They are sometimes boldly striped and patterned, but except in a few cases, there is nothing among them to compare with the glowing colours of flowers, insects, reptiles and birds. There are no "warning" colours such as those found in other animals. Even the seemingly conspicuous spots and stripes of the leopard and tiger, serve but to hide the animal in the streaked and dappled sunlight of the forest and grassy jungle. Among beasts of prey this camouflage is not worn for reasons of defence, but to enable the animals to stalk

COLOUR

158

their quarry unseen. The non-flesh-eaters such as the giraffe and zebra, find it equally useful to be hidden from such enemies by coats of similar design. Animals which live in snowy regions are usually white, and others can change their brown summer coats to white in the winter.

Though there seem to be no warning *colours* among the mammals, a few of them use strongly contrasted markings or signs of other kinds. The bold black and white stripes of the skunk warn its enemies to keep away or be sprayed with the evil-smelling fluid which it can eject from glands near its tail. The sharpness of the porcupine's quills is a warning in itself, but the effect is heightened by their black and white bands.

Rabbits and several kinds of deer have light or dark markings on the hind parts or sides of their bodies. These markings show up strongly at a distance, and probably serve to keep members of a group together, especially when they are fleeing from enemies.

HOOFS The limbs of mammals vary with their surroundings and ways of living. While all birds walk on their hind legs, using their fore-limbs as wings, most mammals walk on all fours. The very earliest mammals probably

Although they are often strikingly marked, few mammals are brightly coloured. Only the Mandrill has colours, on his face & hindquarters, which can compare with the vivid tints of birds, reptiles & insects.

159

Lizard
It is probably from a simple hand like this that the following forelimbs have been evolved.

Ape
Grasping

Man
Holding and Manipulating

Flesheater
Catching & tearing

Armadillo
Digging

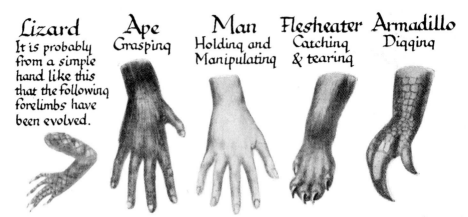

From the simple five-fingered reptilian hand, the fore-limbs of mammals have developed according to their different ways of life.

had five toes, but there are many now which walk on two toes or on one toe only. Such animals specialize in walking and running, and have great nails called hoofs to protect their feet from the hard ground. One group is made up of those hoofed mammals which have two or four toes on each foot : the oxen, sheep, goats, deer, giraffes, camels, pigs and hippopotamuses. In a second group the toes are one or three in number. These animals include the horses, asses, zebras, tapirs and rhinoceroses. The elephants, and small creatures called dassies, are in the two remaining groups of hoofed mammals. Elephants have five toes enclosed in a common covering of skin instead of being separate from each other. The hoofed animals have tended to lessen the numbers of their toes, and make their feet strong and hard with hoofs, because they took to living in

Otter
Walking in soft mud, & swimming

Seal
Swimming

Camel
Walking on soft ground

Horse
Running on hard ground

Bat
Flying

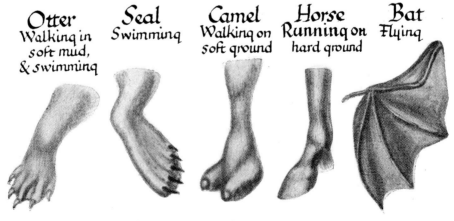

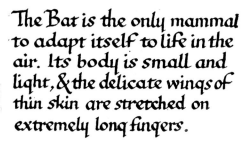

The Bat is the only mammal to adapt itself to life in the air. Its body is small and light, & the delicate wings of thin skin are stretched on extremely long fingers.

the open, where great speed was possible and often needful. They often had to trek long distances in search of their green food, and are constantly being hunted by the flesh-eaters. The cloven-hoofed animals walk upon *two* toes instead of on *one* toe as the horse does. The pig has, besides the two toes of its cleft hoof, two shorter toes which are useful in broadening the foot when the beast walks on swampy ground. The feet of the camel are well adapted for walking on the loose, dry soil of the desert. The two toes of each foot are very broad and spreading, and have soft wide cushions underneath, which enable the animal to keep a foothold in the shifting sands.

Flesh-eaters have four or five toes all furnished with strong, sharp claws for catching, holding and dragging their prey. Sea mammals have changed their hands and feet for flippers. In the mole the hand has become PAWS, CLAWS, a powerful digging claw, and in the bat it has grown into a AND FLIPPERS wing. Apes and monkeys, and their relatives the lemurs, have taken to life in the trees, and their hands and feet have evolved in such a way that the thumbs and first toes are separated from the other digits, so that they can grasp the branches. In a few cases the thumbs are missing, but on the whole the fore-paws of these animals are very like the hands of man. Like him they have changed their hands and feet from those of their five-toed reptilian ancestors less than the other mammals.

All the backboned creatures have their eyes built on the same general plan, but the eye of the furred animal is the most like the human eye. In man the eyes are placed rather close together in front of the head. The eyes of EYES lions and other flesh-eaters, as well as those of monkeys, are in this position. Other animals, such as rabbits and horses, have their eyes on each side of their heads. This frontal position of the eye is usually found in beasts which hunt, and the side position in those which feed on plant food. Eyes in front of the head give the power of judging distances accurately, and this is important to the carnivores who get their food by springing quickly upon it.

THE EVOLUTION OF THE HORSE

The evolution of the horse from a small four-toed mammal
to the horse of today took about 40 million years.
The numbers on the figures below correspond
to the numbers of the fingers on the hands of man.
Opposite: 1. Eohippus [size of a fox]
2. Mesohippus [size of a sheep]
3. Merychippus [size of an ass]
4. The Modern Horse—

The
Modern
Horse
runs on
1

Merychippus
had 3 toes
but only
ran on
1
toe

toe:
the 2nd & 4th
have become
'splint bones'

Mesohippus
ran on
3
toes

Eohippus
ran on
4
toes

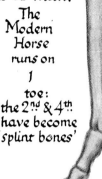

They cannot afford to miss their aim. Nor must the monkey misjudge its distance as it leaps from branch to branch. On the other hand, eyes at the side of the head give a very wide if somewhat hazy view of the animal's surroundings. The horse or deer or rabbit, grazing in open country, can see almost all the way round at the same time, and the slightest movement warns it of danger.

Animals which live underground, where eyes are not only useless but might be damaged by the earth, have very small eyes which are sometimes buried in the fur. Lemurs, which live in trees and come out at dusk, have huge eyes in order to gather what little light may be left in the tropical night. Those night-living animals which have small eyes, such as mice and most bats, depend more on their senses of smell, hearing and touch than on sight.

HAIR   The sense of touch is present all over the skin in mammals as in other animals, but in mammals it is often transferred through the hair or fur. No other animals have hair, but it is found in all mammals, even though it may not be easy to see. The whale seems to be hairless, and it still bears traces of its furred ancestors in the bristles on its snout. Man has lost his hairy coat, though he is still covered on most parts of his body with short, fine hairs. These hairs, on man and all other mammals, are connected with sensitive touch-spots in the skin. The hairs themselves are not sensitive, they are only horny out-growths of the skin, like scales, feathers, claws and nails. Some animals have long thick hairs which stand out beyond their fur. They are usually on the head, and are called whiskers. These stiff hairs are of special value to creatures such as cats who hunt in the dark. The whiskers on a cat's head WHISKERS tell him, when he cannot see, whether he can get through some small opening in the undergrowth. If his whiskers touch the sides of the hole, then he knows that it will be too narrow to take his body.

Dogs are noted for their keen sense of smell, and man makes use of them to find travellers lost in the snow, and to track other animals. Most SMELL mammals seem to have a well-developed smell-sense, which warns them of approaching danger from other animals, or guides them towards their prey. Elephants can smell a white man when he is several miles away.

In man the sense of smell is probably less developed than in the other mammals : nor is his sense of hearing so acute as theirs. Animals such as the dog and horse

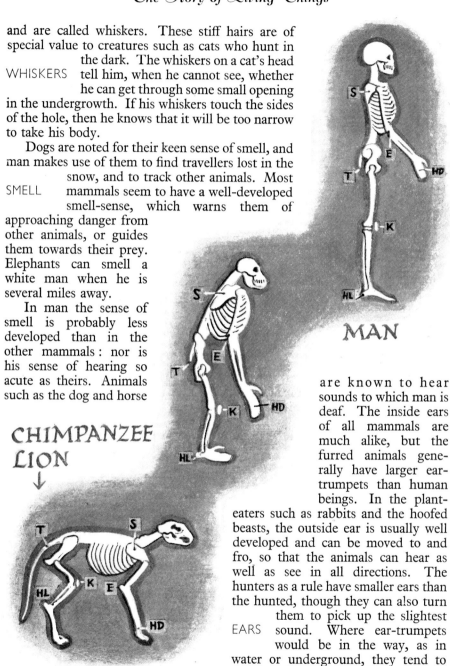

MAN

CHIMPANZEE
LION
↓

are known to hear sounds to which man is deaf. The inside ears of all mammals are much alike, but the furred animals generally have larger ear-trumpets than human beings. In the plant-eaters such as rabbits and the hoofed beasts, the outside ear is usually well developed and can be moved to and fro, so that the animals can hear as well as see in all directions. The hunters as a rule have smaller ears than the hunted, though they can also turn them to pick up the slightest EARS sound. Where ear-trumpets would be in the way, as in water or underground, they tend to grow small, like those of the hippopo-

164

The diagrams opposite—
show how man's skeleton
is like that of apes & four-
footed beasts though he has
learned to walk upright. The
drawing on this page shows
how birds walk on two legs
also, using their arms as wings.
S=shoulder blade E=elbow
HD= hand K=knee T=tail BIRD
HL= heel

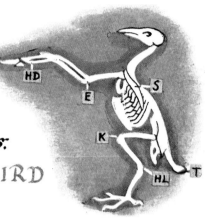

tamus and pygmy-armadillo or to disappear altogether like the whale's and the seal's. The bat, on the other hand, sees little in the dusk with its small eyes, but its huge ears are sensitive to the sound of a moth's flight.

Living things have been classed into different groups according to their likeness to each other, and these groups are divided and sub-divided. Sometimes it is easy to see the relationship between animals of the same order, sometimes it is more difficult. The hoofed animals are quite clearly alike in many ways. They all have horny growths, or hoofs, on their feet. They are almost all grass or leaf eaters, and they are the only mammals to have horns. They tend to be large animals and generally live in open ground or on mountains. It is plainly not at all difficult to group such beasts under one heading. There are, however, creatures such as the sloths, ant-eaters and armadillos, which do not look at all alike. Yet these three kinds of animals belong to the same order of the "toothless" mammals, and are like each other in having either no front teeth or no teeth at all. When there are any teeth in the mouth, they have no roots, and go on growing, like finger-nails, throughout the animal's life.

ORDERS OF THE MAMMALS

Mammals have been grouped in the following orders. Starting from the point at which they are most nearly like their reptilian ancestors, there are in the first group the two egg-laying mammals, the duckbill and the spiny ant-eater or echidna. From these there is a step up to the *marsupials* or pouch-bearers, which give birth to their young in a very undeveloped state, and carry them in a pocket or fold of skin outside their bodies. Kangaroos, wallabies, opossums and koalas belong to this order. All the remaining mammals are *placentals*, animals which nourish their offspring for varying lengths of time inside their bodies, and do not bring them into the world until they are fairly well developed. There are a great many orders under this heading, from ant-eaters and armadillos

EGG-LAYERS AND POUCH-BEARERS

165

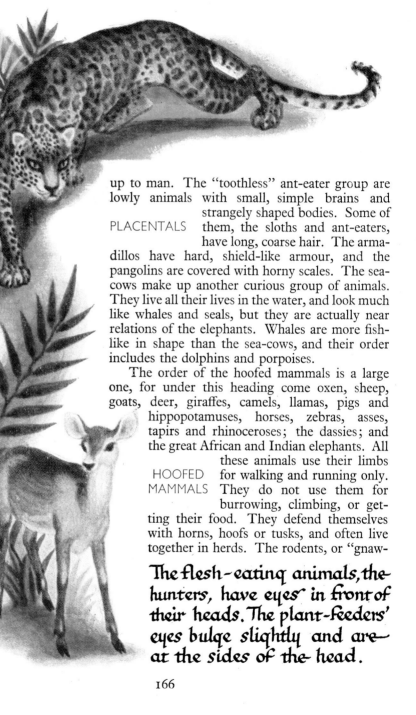

up to man. The "toothless" ant-eater group are lowly animals with small, simple brains and strangely shaped bodies. Some of PLACENTALS them, the sloths and ant-eaters, have long, coarse hair. The armadillos have hard, shield-like armour, and the pangolins are covered with horny scales. The sea-cows make up another curious group of animals. They live all their lives in the water, and look much like whales and seals, but they are actually near relations of the elephants. Whales are more fish-like in shape than the sea-cows, and their order includes the dolphins and porpoises.

The order of the hoofed mammals is a large one, for under this heading come oxen, sheep, goats, deer, giraffes, camels, llamas, pigs and hippopotamuses, horses, zebras, asses, tapirs and rhinoceroses; the dassies; and the great African and Indian elephants. All these animals use their limbs HOOFED for walking and running only. MAMMALS They do not use them for burrowing, climbing, or getting their food. They defend themselves with horns, hoofs or tusks, and often live together in herds. The rodents, or "gnaw-

The flesh-eating animals, the hunters, have eyes in front of their heads. The plant-feeders' eyes bulge slightly and are at the sides of the head.

166

ing" animals, have large, chisel-shaped incisor teeth, which grow all the time and are only kept at the right length by constant use. Rats and mice, squirrels, rabbits, porcupines and beavers are all rodents.

The carnivores, or beasts of prey, make up another large order. They rely on teeth and claws, alert senses and quick movements.

CARNIVORES Those which live on land include the Cat group—lions, tigers, leopards, mongooses, and hyenas; the Dogs—wolves, jackals and foxes; the Bears—including pandas, weasels, badgers and otters; and lastly the seals, walruses and sea-lions. These sea-carnivores have become adapted for life in the water, although they can push themselves along the ground on their flippers, and always come on land to have their young.

The animals which belong to the order of insect-eaters are small, and have long snouts and sharp teeth. They live in trees, or in the ground, in water or under the earth, and include the shrews, moles and

The Mole's eyes have almost disappeared, since they are useless to it in its life underground. The eyes of the Tarsier, like those of most nocturnal creatures, are very large so that they may collect all the light possible.

The Star-nosed Mole has tentacles on its nose so that it may feel instead of see.

167

hedgehogs. The "finger-winged" beasts—the bats—
are the only mammals which can fly : the small bats
eat insects and the larger ones
INSECT-EATERS   eat fruit.

These orders of placental
mammals cannot be arranged one above the other,
like steps on a ladder. The plan is rather that of a
many-branched tree, with some orders higher than
others, and some on equal levels though growing in
different directions. Only one group, the primates,
have reached a higher branch than any other animal.
To this order belong the lemurs, monkeys, apes and
man.

THE PRIMATES   Unlike other mammals, monkeys, apes and man have not
specialized rigidly along set paths. While their brains
have evolved, their bodies have remained adaptable.
Man, with his five fingers and toes and unfurred
body, is physically more like his remote reptilian

forbears than, for example, the horse which runs on one toe on each foot, or the bat which flies with a web on its long fingers. It is this very lack of specialization which has given man the freedom to evolve in the direction which he has taken. While the other mammals specialized in running, swimming, digging, flying or climbing, man and his ape-like ancestors specialized in brain-development. Man's ancestors, who were of the same stock as the apes, having neither large teeth nor claws nor horns with which to defend themselves, took to the safety of the trees. This brought about the development of thumbs and first toes which

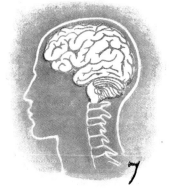

BRAINS

were set at an angle to the hand and foot; for these animals' lives depended on their power to take hold of the branches as they leaped from tree to tree. Their lack of physical defences made these creatures rely on the sharpness of their wits to save them from their enemies. After long ages some of them developed a way of walking on their hind limbs, which let free their fore limbs for grasping and throwing. So the hand and the brain evolved together.

MAN   The human mammal, physically defenceless, puny in size and strength compared with many of the beasts, has yet surpassed them and become their master by developing his brain and hands, and adapting himself to all sorts of conditions. Evolution does not stand still, and there is no reason why there should not be evolved in the future beings as superior to man as he is to his far-off reptilian ancestors. Compared with the age of the world he is young, and may still have millions of years before him. In the long ages which lie ahead he will have time to reach undreamed heights, in the direction to which he set his face ten million years ago. The evolution of man is not only an achievement of the past, but also a promise for the future.

These are some of the ways in which mammals can defend themselves. 1. The porcupine has the hairs on its back developed into spines. 2. The armadillo is covered with horny plates. 3. The Cats, & other beasts of prey, have large canine teeth, which in other animals [the walrus, 4, and some Pigs & Deer] have grown into tusks. 5. Many of the hoofed mammals have bony growths or 'horns' on their heads. The horn of the rhinoceros [6] is not true horn but consists of highly compressed hair. 7. Man uses his brain & his hands to invent & manipulate means of defence.

HOW ANIMALS BEHAVE

BEHAVE

FORM AND
COLOUR

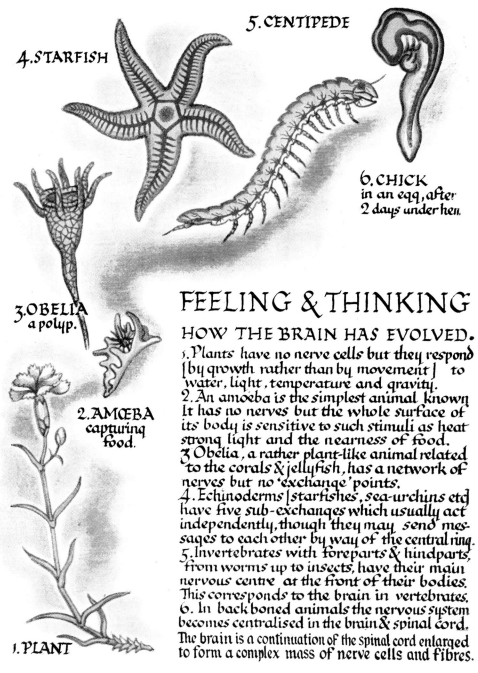

5. CENTIPEDE

4. STARFISH

6. CHICK
in an egg, after
2 days under hen.

3. OBELIA
a polyp.

2. AMŒBA
capturing
food.

1. PLANT

FEELING & THINKING

HOW THE BRAIN HAS EVOLVED.

1. Plants have no nerve cells but they respond [by growth rather than by movement] to water, light, temperature and gravity.
2. An amœba is the simplest animal known It has no nerves but the whole surface of its body is sensitive to such stimuli as heat strong light and the nearness of food.
3 Obelia, a rather plant-like animal related to the corals & jellyfish, has a network of nerves but no 'exchange' points.
4. Echinoderms [starfishes, sea-urchins etc] have five sub-exchanges which usually act independently, though they may send messages to each other by way of the central ring.
5. Invertebrates with foreparts & hindparts, from worms up to insects, have their main nervous centre at the front of their bodies. This corresponds to the brain in vertebrates.
6. In back boned animals the nervous system becomes centralised in the brain & spinal cord.
The brain is a continuation of the spinal cord enlarged to form a complex mass of nerve cells and fibres.

172

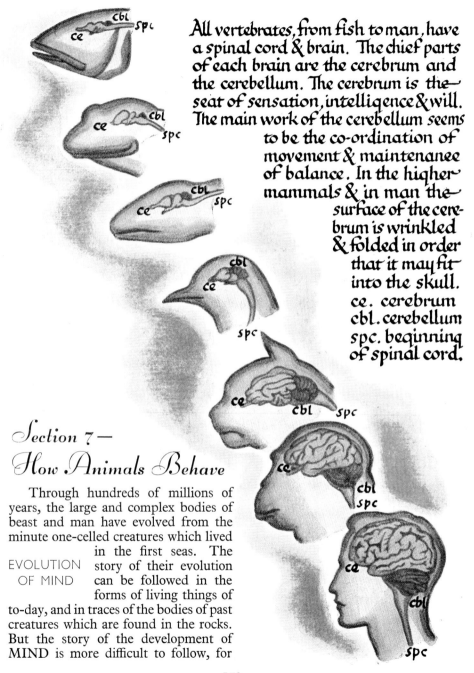

All vertebrates, from fish to man, have a spinal cord & brain. The chief parts of each brain are the cerebrum and the cerebellum. The cerebrum is the seat of sensation, intelligence & will. The main work of the cerebellum seems to be the co-ordination of movement & maintenance of balance. In the higher mammals & in man the surface of the cerebrum is wrinkled & folded in order that it may fit into the skull.
ce. cerebrum
cbl. cerebellum
spc. beginning of spinal cord.

Section 7 —
How Animals Behave

Through hundreds of millions of years, the large and complex bodies of beast and man have evolved from the minute one-celled creatures which lived in the first seas. The story of their evolution can be followed in the forms of living things of to-day, and in traces of the bodies of past creatures which are found in the rocks. But the story of the development of MIND is more difficult to follow, for

EVOLUTION OF MIND

173

mind cannot be seen or measured; much can be learnt, however, by studying the means by which animals, from the simplest to the most complex, receive their sensations, and by watching the ways in which they respond to their surroundings, or *behave*.

The behaviour of a living creature depends on the impressions which it receives from the outside world. An animal gets information by means of its senses, and if these are lacking or undeveloped it behaves in a *sense*-less way.

SENSES Among the senses are those of sight, hearing, smell, and taste, touch (including the senses of pain and change of temperature) and the senses of movement and position. As a rule the senses become keener as living things become more highly evolved, though in some animals one sense may be strongly developed while others are still unformed. The seeing powers of birds and the smelling powers of dogs are far sharper than those of man, though their other senses are not equally advanced. Man's senses are on the whole more highly developed than those of the other animals.

Except in the case of plants and very lowly animals, the stimuli which give the various sensations are received by the sense organs. In man and the higher animals the chief sense organs are contained in the skin, the THE NERVOUS eye, the ear and semi-SYSTEM circular canals and the membranes of the nose and tongue. These are connected to the brain by white threads called nerves, From the brain, nerve fibres run to all the muscles of the body, and when the brain receives any message from a sense organ.

Plants have no need to travel to find food, and movements of their leaves & petals are slow & limited. But some of them must add insects to their diet. The Venus fly trap behaves like an animal when it snaps its leaves on food & rejects indigestible things such as small stones.

174

One-celled animals, like the Slipper Animalcule, which can move about, react by trial and error until they find themselves in favourable surroundings. Some have the beginnings of sense organs, such as eye spots.

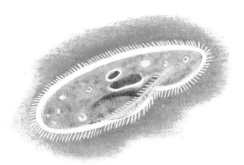

it sends out directions to the muscles telling them how to act. If a child touches a hot coal, it immediately drops it, and probably cries out and runs away. The touch organs in the skin have sent a message through the nerves to the brain at a speed of 400 feet per second. The message says "too hot, painful." The brain flashes back orders to the muscles which control the hand, voice and legs, saying "drop coal, cry for help, run from source of pain." It is the brain of the child which has felt the pain, and it is the brain which makes it behave in the way it does.

This sending in and giving out of messages along lines of communication suggests the telephone, and the nervous system of the backboned animals works on much the same plan. The nerves may be compared to telephone wires, by means of which the various parts of the body communicate with each other and act together in harmony. Just as a telephone subscriber must first get through to the exchange before he can be connected with another subscriber, so the nerve messages of the body must go through the spinal cord and brain. The brain does the work of the great central telephone exchange, while in the spinal cord there are groups of nerve cells which act as local exchanges. The brain, the spinal cord and the nerves given off from both of them, are together known as the central nervous system.

Plants and the simplest animals, such as the minute one-celled amœba, have no nerve cells, but they are sensitive to certain stimuli, including heat and light and the nearness of food. They respond in a limited way—

PLANTS AND ANIMALS plants by growth rather than by movement. In the case of the one-celled animals, the whole body acts as a nerve cell, just as it acts as a muscle cell or any other kind of cell. It holds within itself all the possibilities of the complex body of the higher animal, with its many different kinds of cells.

One of the simplest of the many-celled animals is the small, plant-like Hydra. This is a green, freshwater polyp, about half an inch long, with a tube-like body. There is a single opening at one end; this is the mouth and it is surrounded by a ring of tentacles. The hydra is related to the jelly-fishes, sea-anemones and corals. Like them it has several kinds of cells in its body, each sort carrying out a different duty. Some cells specialize in digestion, some in

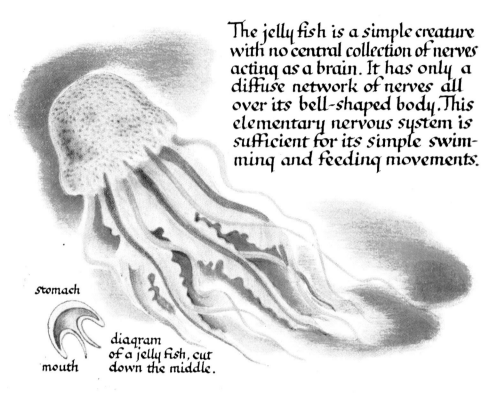

The jelly fish is a simple creature with no central collection of nerves acting as a brain. It has only a diffuse network of nerves all over its bell-shaped body. This elementary nervous system is sufficient for its simple swimming and feeding movements.

stomach

mouth

diagram of a jelly fish, cut down the middle.

reproduction, some in movement. Certain of them have become very sensitive, and developed into sense cells : others, which are the nerve cells, carry messages from one part of the body to another. In the hydra these are scattered all over the body in a kind of irregular network. In the jelly-fish, the nerve HYDRA cells form, besides a network, a denser ring round the edge of its bell-shaped body. This is the beginning of a centralized nervous system, but the tangled network of nerves, connecting each part of the body directly with every other part, is a long way from the orderly nerve paths of the higher animals. It limits the actions of such creatures to little more than a few simple swimming and feeding movements.

The starfish, one of the "spiny-skinned" animals (which include the sea-urchins and sea-cucumbers), behaves less simply than the jelly-fish. It can move over the sea floor by the combined action of the muscles of its rays and the tube-feet on the undersides of them. The starfish can defend itself and STARFISH keep itself clean with the little stalked pincers on various parts of its body. Its feeding movements are quite elaborate. This more advanced behaviour corresponds with an advance in the arrangement of the nervous system. In the starfish each ray has its own nervous system, and can act independently of the other four rays. It can even walk away from the rest of the

176

The starfish has a nervous system for each separate arm, but these are connected together by a nerve ring. The arms may act as separate individuals or they may work together as a whole.

A starfish tries →
to turn over.
Each arm pulls
in a different
direction until
one of them
gets a hold.
An arm which
is cut off walks
away by itself. →

A starfish
opening a
cockle. The
arms work
together.

body if it is torn off. But there is a ring of nervous tissue round the creature's mouth through which the five rays can communicate with each other. The starfish can act as five separate animals, but its rays can also work together as a whole.

None of these animals has a forepart or a hindpart, a left side or a right side. They are the same all round, with nothing which could be called a head, and they can move equally well in any direction. Worms, however, although fairly simple creatures, usually move with one end in front. This way of moving brings with it the development of the head. As the head evolves with its important organ the mouth, sense organs are developed upon it.

THE CENTRAL They act as scouts to collect information in advance of the
EXCHANGE body following behind, and also search for, and help to capture and test, the food which is put into the mouth. With the coming of the head, the brain appears, and the two organs evolve together, but the brain does not dominate the other nerve centres until the backbone and the spinal cord come into being.

In the worm the brain is in two parts, one just above and in front of the mouth and the other just below and behind it. The two parts are joined together by thick nerves which form a ring round the animal's gullet. From this ring a double cord runs down the underside of the body. The worm's body is

N

i The moth gathers pollen.
ii She makes it into a ball
and flies to another flower.
iii After laying her eggs in the ovary of this
flower, she pushes the pollen into the pistil.

made up of many segments, and in each segment the cord swells out into a little knot of nerve cells. Each of these knots acts as a small brain for its particular part of the body. This arrangement of the nervous system is also found, with slight variations, in the arthropods These are the "jointed-limbed" animals, and include the insects, centipedes, crabs, lobsters and spiders. Sometimes the sub-brains do not swell into small knots from the main nerve cord, but form one large mass which in many cases is bigger than the head-brain. House-flies and crabs both have large sub-brains in the middle of their bodies. Some of the great prehistoric reptiles had tiny head-brains but larger nerve centres in their spines.

The central nervous systems of backboned animals are built on a different plan from those of the invertebrates. In the backboned creatures—fishes, amphibians, reptiles, birds and

Some instincts are shown only once in a lifetime. The Yucca-moth has an elaborate way of securing food for her future offspring. She lays her eggs in the seed-boxes of the Yucca, & by pollinating the flowers herself, ensures the development of the seeds.

178

mammals—the double cord along the undersides of the worm and the insect becomes a long tube of nervous tissue. This is the spinal cord, which lies inside and is protected by the backbone. At the head end, the spinal cord becomes

NERVOUS SYSTEM
OF VERTEBRATES

larger and more intricate, forming the soft mass of nerve cells and nerve fibres known as the brain. In simple vertebrates such as the lancelet and fishes, the front or head end of the spinal cord differs little from the rest. As animals evolve, the brain becomes larger and yet larger as it has more work to do. Sense organs become more numerous and more sensitive, bringing the brain more reports of the outside world. The brain has to control more varied and more exact muscular actions, as the animals explore and experiment.

The development of the sense organs and consequent growth of the brain has been of the greatest importance in the evolution of animals. Developing brains has given the animals more power to act in accordance with the fuller knowledge of their surroundings, which developing sense organs has made possible. Creatures who can feel, smell and taste, see and hear well, have a great advantage over those which are almost deaf, as insects are, or almost blind like worms and starfishes. They are more aware of the nearness of food, of danger, of their fellows and can suit their behaviour to varying conditions. In this way *intelligence* has slowly evolved. Mammals have become the highest group among animals because their sense organs and nervous systems are more highly developed, and because this development has brought with it the growth of *mind*. Man, though smaller than many animals, defenceless and unprotected by fur or scales, slow-footed, unable to fly or to burrow, has overcome these disadvantages by using his brain, and is learning to control the other living things also.

Size limits brain power. Insects are too small to have much intelligence The smallest warmblooded vertebrate is the humming bird. Though it has a brain, it behaves so much like an insect that this Hawk-moth has been mistaken for it.

179

Insects have reached the same high position among the invertebrates as mammals have in the vertebrates, but these two great divisions of the animal world have evolved along very different paths. The ways in which they breathe have had much to do with their two lines of evolution. Land-living, air-breathing arthropods generally breathe by means of air-tubes, which open out along their sides like little port-holes. This method is only possible in bodies up to a certain size, just as simple port-hole ventilation can only be used on small ships. Large ships have to have some system of forced ventilation, and animal bodies over a certain size must have their oxygen pumped through them by a complicated system of lungs, heart and blood vessels. Insects have to stay small because they have no air-pumping apparatus such as lungs, and their blood does not catch up the oxygen and take it to all parts of the body. If they grew beyond a certain size, they would suffocate, for some parts of their bodies would be without oxygen. Although large bodies do not always contain large brains, small bodies can only hold small brains. The largest insect does not weigh as much as the harvest mouse, and its brain is

SMALL BODIES AND LARGE BODIES

4

5. The eel becomes needle-shaped and shrinks to 2½ ins. It is now called an elver & needs fresh water. It swims up rivers & travels over moist land to pools & lakes.

3

2

Bermudas
SARGASSO SEA

4. By the third year it has swum three thousand miles, and is about 3" long. Its shape begins to change.

3. With millions of other eels it swims a few miles a day.

2. The little fish rises to the surface & begins to travel eastward.

1. The eel is hatched in the depths of the Atlantic Ocean. It is a small flat transparent creature.

1

180

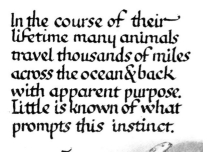

In the course of their lifetime many animals travel thousands of miles across the ocean & back with apparent purpose. Little is known of what prompts this instinct.

5

6

6. It lives in fresh water for five to eight years, by which time it is full grown and from 2 to 3 feet long.

7. Then it changes colour, its snout becomes pointed, its eyes larger. It finds its way back to the sea & re-crosses the Atlantic to its birthplace. There it lays its eggs & dies.

7

smaller than the brain of the tiniest humming bird.

As land creatures evolved from their back-boned ancestors the fishes, they developed a way of forcing oxygen quickly to every part of the body. They were thus able to grow large and strong, and a larger body brings with it the chance to develop a bigger brain. Since such a body takes longer to grow, and usually gives a longer life than the smaller body, there is more time for experiment and learning. The small size and short life of an insect deprive it of these advantages. Its undeveloped sense organs prevent it from having a clear idea of the world about it. Its undeveloped nervous system with a correspondingly small brain gives it no power to learn by experience. So the insect relies on its highly developed *instincts* to see it through both the expected and unexpected adventures of life.

Instinct is an inborn urge in an animal to do the kind of things necessary for its everyday life. It sets going an action or series of actions whenever a given situation is met. The mind and body of an instinctive creature are in some ways like a piece of machinery, which works in a pre-ordered way when a button is pressed or a trigger pulled. Instinct does not vary, but is set like a machine to

181

Many animals have a migratory instinct, some at regular, others at irregular intervals. The salmon is hatched in shallow, fast-running water at the head of a river. When 2 years old, the fish swims down to the sea. It feeds there for 2 or 3 years until it is full-grown. Then it returns to the river where it started life, sometimes travelling hundreds of miles & passing many river-mouths on its way. There it lays its eggs,

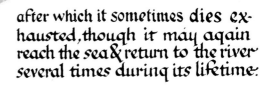

after which it sometimes dies exhausted, though it may again reach the sea & return to the river several times during its lifetime.

work in one way only. The instinctive animal does from the beginning and without having to be taught, all those actions necessary for its way of living. The larger-brained animals have a number of useful instincts, too, but they also learn to do new things. They can invent ways out of difficulties which they have never met before and which their parents never had to face. They behave *intelligently*.

INSTINCT v. INTELLIGENCE

The smaller a creature's brain, the less it learns and the more it acts by instinct. On the whole the instincts of each group of animals are those which meet the usual

Some creatures have sense organs whose uses we do not understand. Fishes have a 'lateral line' running along their sides. It is thought that this sense organ may record changes in pressure & direction.

conditions of their lives. It is only when something unusual happens that instinct fails. If the small-brained, instinctive animal is faced with the problem of doing anything different from that which it and its parents have always done, it cannot as a rule *think* of a way out of the difficulty. If, for instance, the eggs of a brooding pigeon are moved a few inches to one side of the nest, the bird looks uneasy and feels under her body with her beak for the missing eggs. Then she goes on brooding on the empty nest. She does not try to put the eggs under her again although she can see them only a few inches away. Her instinct tells her only to sit on something in the middle of the nest. Under usual conditions the eggs would not be moved, and all would be well. When the unusual happens, the bird does not vary her behaviour to suit the altered state of things. She behaves instinctively, not intelligently.

The lives of most animals are more or less ruled by their instincts. Some of these are fairly simple, such as that which prompts a young mammal to suck the milk of its mother. Others are complex, and call for a chain of connected actions. There are instincts to migrate, to build a home and to look after a family : there are the instincts of courtship and of community life. Although INSTINCT PLUS the instinctive behaviour of an animal may sometimes lead to INTELLIGENCE its undoing, in most cases it is enough for its needs. However, even a lowly animal may sometimes vary its instinctive behaviour by what seems to be intelligence, so that no hard and fast line can be drawn between instinctive and intelligent actions. Living things differ from the non-living in several ways. One of their peculiar qualities is that there can be no certainty about their behaviour. Even a small and comparatively simple creature may suddenly do something wayward or unusual. A non-living machine, how-

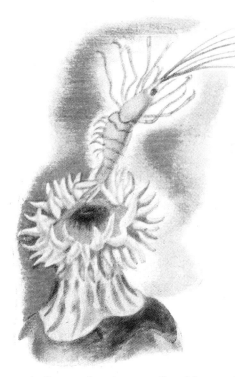

A sea anemone, whose nervous system is similar to that of the jelly fish, can learn & remember for a short time. If given pieces of blotting paper soaked in beef juice, it takes them at first but soon learns to reject them. After a short pause, it will still reject the blotting paper but after a long pause it will accept it again.

ever large and complicated, always behaves according to physical laws.

When comparing one kind of behaviour with another, it must be remembered that different creatures live in widely differing worlds. Their surroundings may be the same, but their knowledge of them may be very unequal. To some animals the world must be a dark, silent, scentless place, known only by a sense of touch; while to others, such as the dog, it must be largely built up of various smells. Man probably gets the most balanced picture of the world about him, though each of his senses may be surpassed in keenness by that of some lower animal. He lacks some of the senses which other creatures have, and in most cases he can only guess what these sense organs tell their owners. The lateral line of the fish and the antennæ of insects do not correspond with any of man's sense organs, and they probably pick up sensations which he cannot even imagine. Man's nose is much less sensitive than a dog's, and some insects can see colours beyond the violet edge of the rainbow, which the human eye has never seen. Many sounds are quite outside the range of his hearing. There is a special kind of whistle which cannot be heard by the human ear, yet a dog will come running when it is blown. The shrill voice of the bat can be heard only by people with sensitive hearing.

ANIMALS LIVE IN
DIFFERENT WORLDS

The simplest animals, the single-celled protozoa, have no special sense cells, but they are sensitive to light, heat, cold, to salt, acid and alkali. They can distinguish "hard" from "soft," and "up" from "down." They behave almost as the higher animals when they chase their prey, lose it, chase it again and recapture it: but they have few actions beyond swimming towards food, and avoiding solid objects, or chemical conditions of the water which would hurt them.

In most of the invertebrates the senses are both few and dim. When these animals see at all, most of them probably perceive objects only as flat, vague shapes, or as shadows between themselves and the light. Full grown insects have better sight than the other invertebrates, for many of them can see solid shapes and various colours. Bees can see colours which are invisible to man, but they cannot tell the difference between yellow and orange, blue and purple, or red and dark grey. Many insects have a good sense of smell; some of them seem to smell their fellows when over a mile away. It is thought that they INSECTS do this by means of their antennæ, extremely sensitive organs which also give the insect a delicate sense of touch. When they hear at all, insects probably hear only one or two tones, usually the notes made by another creature of their own kind. In many cases when they seem to hear, they may be feeling the sound waves beating against their bodies.

The insect's world is almost silent, sometimes scented by its kindred and its favourite food, full of different touch sensations, and made up of vague, sometimes coloured shapes. Although their lives are almost completely ruled by instincts, insects do occasionally vary their behaviour to suit an unusual condition. A certain colony of leaf-cutting ants had their nest near a small railway, which was used for taking away earth from a mine. The ants had to cross the rails continually on their way to and from gathering leaves. Many of them were killed by the wagons. After a few days they dug a tunnel under each rail, and went on their errands in safety. When the tunnels were blocked up with stones, the ants made no attempt to go across the rails, although there were no wagons running at the time. They dropped their leaves and set to work to dig fresh tunnels. Insects and other invertebrates can learn and remember for varying lengths of time. Worms and crayfish quickly learn to choose between a path

Frogs quickly learn to avoid disagreeable things, like hairy caterpillars, & remember the lesson for as long as ten days. Bees have a strong instinct to store honey for winter food: but when they are taken to a warm climate where flowers are plentiful all the year round, they alter their instinctive behaviour & only gather enough for each day's needs.

185

along which they meet with an electric shock, and a path which is not so unpleasant. Bees show that they can learn when they remember the colour of their hive, and its surrounding landmarks.

It is difficult for human beings to imagine the life and feelings of a fish. Instead of moving over solid ground on long, jointed limbs, the fish has to push against the water which supports it and surrounds it on every side. The eyes of the fish are not so well developed as those of the land vertebrate, for good eyes would be wasted in a dim world of water, through which even the highly developed human eye cannot see clearly. The fish's eye sees better than that of most invertebrates: it can be focused on near or distant objects, and can distinguish different colours. The senses of smell and taste are well developed, and
FISHES are not only in the mouth and nostrils, but are found in the fins, in little feelers under the chin, or all over the skin. A fish hears either faintly or not at all. The ear is probably used more as a balancing organ than for picking up sound waves. It may work together with the lateral line, which lies along each side of the fish's body. The lateral line is known to be a sense organ, but what it tells the fish is not clear. It may be sensitive to currents in the water, or to changes in the pressure against the creature's flanks. The instinctive behaviour of fishes is far less varied than that of the insects. They lead dull lives on the whole, though the salmon and the eel make adventurous migrations, while some fishes show care for their eggs and young families. Experiments have proved that fishes learn slowly and with difficulty.

The amphibian brain is much the same as that of the fish, and its behaviour shows the same lack of variety. Frogs and toads can learn simple facts connected with food. For example, a certain frog learnt to find its way to a tank of water
AMPHIBIANS through a simple maze, in which the wrong path was marked with a red card, and the right path with a blue card. When the cards were changed the frog was confused, but whether it could see the colours as red and blue, or whether it merely saw two tones of the same colour, is not certainly known. Some amphibians, like frogs and toads, have well-developed ear drums, and can hear the voices of their kindred—the first voices ever to break the silence of the world.

When the vertebrates became true land animals, life became richer, more varied and more difficult. Animals who made this adventure had to learn to walk, run, jump, climb, or fly. These movements needed greater muscular control than the simpler motions of swimming and crawling. Life on land and air-breathing on a large scale demanded the development of lungs,
LAND heart and blood-vessels. Increasing competition with other
VERTEBRATES creatures called for the keeping of a sharper watch for food and enemies. This brought about improvements in the sense organs. All these changes made for development of the spinal cord and brain. Bodies grew stronger and more active and elaborate. More messages came in from the outside world as senses grew sharper, and more directions had to be given to the muscles which controlled the body's increased activities. As the brain grew larger and more elaborate, it developed in such a way that intelligent behaviour

Different kinds of behaviour are shown here. The hen sees only one way to get to the corn, straight through the netting. The dog at first tries to get through the wire, then realises that it must go round it. The child thinks before she acts: she knows that she must first walk away from the sweets in order to get them.

187

became possible. Mammals were the only creatures who took full advantage of life on land. Reptiles progressed only a little way from the amphibians and their sluggishness cost them their position as lords of the earth.

Birds are creatures of many and varied instincts, though they have less ready-made behaviour than the insects, and while young have to learn to do a number of things necessary to their later life. Their parents BIRDS often help them to learn to fly and swim, and to catch prey : but instinct alone teaches them to build their nests. It is instinct which urges them to fly to warmer countries, when the cold weather of their native land would kill the insects on which they feed : and instinct leads them back to the cooler land, when the spring comes bringing with it the long hours of daylight, which they need in order to find enough food for their young. When birds are grown-up, they learn less quickly than while they are young, and their behaviour becomes more set. Yet they sometimes vary their behaviour slightly to suit changed circumstances; as when they make a nest out of new materials, or turn to some fresh kind of food, if these things are more plentiful than those which they generally use.

Touch, taste and smell are senses which most birds have scarcely developed, but their ears are sharp and can distinguish clearly one sound from another. The bird's eyes are in

Protective colouring is useless without some sort of suitable behaviour. Most animals keep perfectly still when alarmed. The Little Bittern takes up a rigid pose with its beak pointing upwards and becomes almost invisible among the reeds in which it lives. It turns so that it always faces the enemy.

188

some ways better than those of any other animal. Not only can it see for a great distance, but the bird notices the smallest movement, and can focus its eyes very quickly from a far object to a near one. Birds seem to have a good colour sense, which is useful to them in several ways. Many of them are brightly hued, and so they can recognize their friends and enemies by their colour. The female is attracted by the gay, courting dress of the male, and an eye for colour helps the birds to find the fruits and berries on which many of them feed. They seem to be particularly excited by the colour red, and many fruits and bird-pollinated flowers are of this colour.

The minds and behaviour of mammals vary greatly from the almost reptilian dullness of the kangaroo to the quickness and curiosity of the monkey,

Protective poses are as important as protective colouring. All
these insects take up different
attitudes when threatened by
danger. Each particular pose
corresponds with the shape or
colour of the animal concerned.

189

Most animals are darker above than below. This colouring
cancels the effects of strong light on the back & dark shadow
underneath, so that the animal tends to merge with the
background. Spots & stripes break up the form of the body.
The animal on the right shows the effect of a coat of one tone.

and the intelligence of man. The senses of
mammals vary also, but less than their
intelligences. Most of them except man
have a keen sense of smell, so sensitive that
it warns them of enemies while they are still
some distance away. Their ears catch the
faintest noise, and they can
MAMMALS hear sounds which are pitched
too high for the human ear.
Each hair on their furry bodies is connected
with an organ of touch, and many mammals have whiskers which are especially
sensitive in this way. The cat's whiskers
stand out from each side of his head and
above the forehead. They help to guide

Strong colours, sharply divided, also
break up the shape of the body &
make it indistinct at a distance.

190

him at night when he is creeping through the undergrowth. The highly developed senses of mammals have given them an advantage over less sensitive creatures. They have been able to find out about, and make the best use of, their surroundings, until they have outstripped all rivals. Their sense of sight is good as a rule, though not so penetrating as that of the birds. The eyes of all mammals, including man, are similar, though some of them, such as the dog, are colour-blind. Those animals whose eyes are set closely together in front of their heads, see shapes more solidly and judge distances more accurately, than those who have eyes at the sides of their heads. The power of focusing both eyes on one object has helped in the development of the hand. The use of hands and the power of speech have helped man to his present position among animals.

Most animals learn their lessons by muddling aimlessly, and remembering which actions had pleasant and which had unpleasant results. Those low down in the scale may muddle all their lives and never remember at all, or remember for a short time only. As they evolve, they learn more quickly and remember for

LEARNING a longer period, perhaps for a lifetime. Animals are rarely cleverer than they need be. They have the instincts which are normally useful to them, and sometimes just enough intelligence to vary their instinctive behaviour if necessity arises. As a rule they can learn and remember only if the lesson is connected with food or something useful to them.

Even the higher mammals usually learn to do things by the same method of trial and error as that used by the lowest creatures. It is rare to find any animal thinking out a problem before tackling it. Dogs can be taught to open the door of a box containing food, by pushing back a bolt or pulling a loop of string. They learn to do this, not by understanding the simple mechanism, but by clawing about until by chance they come upon the right method. Then they remember, and the trick is learnt. If the box is turned round, they still go on scrabbling at the place where the lock used to be, until, perhaps after a long time, they accidentally rediscover the lock and learn their trick again. Sometimes, however, a mammal at about the same stage of development as the dog, will show signs of reasoning power. It will pause before an action, and in that pause will think out, however dimly, some plan to carry out that action.

Among the mammals below man, apes show the most advanced powers of reasoning, though even the cleverest ape is far less intelligent than the dullest human being. Emotionally they are much like man. They show anger, jealousy,

APES class-consciousness, fear of the strange and uncanny, and a liking for teasing animals which are weaker or simpler than themselves. They also show man's better qualities of sociability, friendship and parental care : but intellectually they remain far below him. Their language is merely a collection of sounds expressing various feelings. Like the lower animals they live mainly in the present, with little memory of the past and no hope for the future. Yet they occasionally show that they can work out in their minds the answer to a problem before taking any action; and in the solution of the problem they often use a tool, though it may be only a stick. A chimpanzee will plan how to reach a banana by piling up boxes and standing on them, or by fitting one stick into another to make a pole long enough to hit the fruit down. In thinking out these simple pieces of construction before making and using them, the ape is really doing a little elementary engineering. But the tools have to be under his eyes before he can make his plans. He cannot think of an object which is out of sight, and go and look for it.

Man alone has the power to see things in the mind's eye, and to ponder on such abstract ideas as Truth and Beauty. He alone can hope and plan for the future and remember long years back into the past. He alone can speak and use his hands with skill. His well developed brain gives him choice of action instead of unthinking bondage to his instincts. He can plan his way of life as no other creature can, and through his actions can direct the development of other living things. Yet his brain has evolved, together with the rest of his body, along a path which began with the lowliest creatures. With the growth of the brain and development of the senses, has come the unfolding of the mind.

MAN

The intelligence of man is the highest point which has, as yet, been reached by tendencies the early stages of which can be seen in the simplest animals. From amœba to man, there is an almost continuous flow of increased nervous and mental activity.

Sometimes this takes a certain direction and comes to a dead end, as in the case of insects, who it would seem have reached the limit of their development. In the vertebrates it moves onwards and upwards, always increasing the receiver's sensitiveness to the world about him, and giving him greater power to act with forethought and judgment.

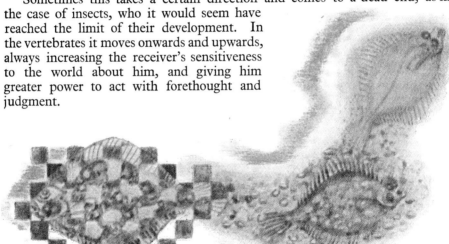

Some creatures can change their colour according to their background. Flatfish, who spend most of their lives on the sea floor, adapt their colouring to sand or gravel in a few seconds. The square pattern takes longer.

Form and Colour

WHEN in danger, some animals feign death even when touched. Others just keep quite still, either crouching or taking up some position which suits their particular shape and colouring. Others again behave in an aggressive way, and try to frighten their enemies by adopting terrifying attitudes. In every kind of defensive behaviour, the animal is helped by its colour and form.

The most usual kind of animal colouring is "protective." The creatures which are protectively coloured harmonise with their surroundings, and it is difficult to see them if they keep quite still. Those who live in snow-covered regions are white: the desert dwellers are buff, sandy or pale "PROTECTIVE" grey. In forests the tree dwellers are often green, and those COLOURING who wander beneath the branches are flecked with light spots, as of sunlight falling between leaf-shadows. The plains dwellers are a neutral brown, touched with dark spots which help their bodies to blend with the stone-covered ground. Animals which live in grassy jungles have a pattern of light and dark stripes, so that they are hidden in the tall grass.

The simplest form of concealing pattern is that of counter-shading. It is found in nearly all the vertebrates, whether plainly coloured, striped, spotted or otherwise patterned, but it is less marked in the invertebrates. In counter-shading the back is darker than the under part of the animal. If the body were all of the same tone, the light falling from the sky on the back COUNTER- would make it appear lighter, and there would be a dark shadow SHADING on the under side. When the body is counter-shaded, the effects of light and shadow are cancelled. The animal does not stand out solidly in relief against its background; it appears flat, and seems to fade into the surroundings. In fishes and birds, counter-shading serves its purpose in a slightly different way. When seen from above by their enemies, the dark backs of these animals blend with the darkness of the water or the ground, while their light bellies make them less visible to those looking up from below into the light.

The "dazzle" pattern is another kind of colouring which makes an animal's body look less solid. In this pattern the form is broken up into irregular patches of sharply contrasting colours. Such colours seem conspicuous when they are seen at close quarters, but at a distance they may become blurred into a neutral tint, and in any case the outline of the figure is lost.

It is difficult to see the reason for certain colourings, but a solution is usually found when the full facts of the animal's natural surroundings are known. The Malayan tapir is strangely coloured: the head, front and hind SPECIAL legs and forepart of its body are jet black and the rest of it is COLOURINGS pure white. In captivity the animal is startling enough, but in its native haunts it spends much of its time lying in dried-up river courses which are strewn with boulders. Here the great black and white masses of its body blend with the highlights and shadows cast by the sunlit stones. In the same way, the Giant Panda's black and white pattern helps

O   193

In the brilliant surroundings of the tropical seas
fish can escape the notice
of their enemies by being
brightly coloured, & striped
as with sunlight & shadow.
Many of them have several
colour-patterns which they
can change at will. Some

fish have large spots on
their bodies. These may look
like the eyes of a larger
creature when the fish is
half-hidden. Many of these
fish are very small but their
deep bodies & spiny fins
make them difficult for
a larger fish to swallow.

him to disappear among the snow and dark rocks of the Tibetan mountains.

Once they are full grown, most mammals and birds remain the same colour for the rest of their lives. But some of them, particularly the birds, in the breeding season put on special courting dresses, which they display before the females with whom they wish to mate. Others, who live in countries where winters are long and cold, change the warm browns of their summer dress to pale, frosty colours, or to snow white. (*See illustrations page* 198.)

Among the lower animals there are creatures who can change quickly from one colour to another, either from fear, rage, or hunger, or in order to suit their surroundings. Although the Chameleon is the best known of these changeable animals, his abilities are far exceeded by other lizards, by frogs and COLOUR CHANGES prawns, and especially by fishes. The flat-fishes, such as turbots and flounders, who spend most of their lives on the sea floor, can change their colour and pattern in a few seconds. A fine-grained, sandlike skin becomes covered with dark and light spots, as the fish swims from a sandy to a pebbly ground. A turbot which was placed on a chess-board pattern took half an hour to change its colouring. Although it could not fit its markings exactly to such an unnatural ground, its skin became covered with fairly regular light and dark patches. (*See illustration page* 192.)

Many tropical fishes can flash from one brilliant colour to another, and from a uniform tint to vivid stripes, spots and blotches. These colours blend with their surroundings as truly as the sand-like and gravel-like skins of the flat-fishes, for these lively-coloured creatures swim in a world of corals, sea-anemones, brightly tinted sponges, seaweeds and shells. Dull colours would be conspicuous except among the shadows, and so they are thrown off and put on again as the occasion demands. These quick changes of colour and pattern are caused by the contraction and expansion of the various colour-cells in the skin. As the cells of one colour spread out, they extinguish the colour which a moment before was dominant. The movement is controlled by the nervous system, and the stimulus to colour-change is usually received through the eyes. Every change of light due to change of colour in the surroundings, brings a fresh range of colours to the surface of the skin.

Other sea dwellers besides fishes have this power. The cuttlefish can both change its colour and send out a cloud of "ink" to serve as a screen between it and its pursuers. The Aesop-prawns, which are quite common on the English coast, are marked and coloured according to the seaweed to which each one clings during the day. At night, when they leave their seaweed and wander in search of food, they all become a pale, moonlight blue. Numbers of small land creatures can change their colour too, though as a rule they take longer to do this than water animals. Crab-spiders which lurk in flowers so as to catch the insects which come for honey, can change their colours in a few days to match the petals of the flower in which they hide. Many tree-frogs become green when among leaves, and brownish grey when on a branch; some lizards, also, take on the colours of their background.

These colour-changes are not always protective, for temperature, dampness and darkness can affect the colour cells as well as light. Hunger, or excitement of any kind, often causes a change of colour in the changeable animals. The Fighting-fish, though not usually dull in colour, when the males see each other become angry and shine with metallic colours of dazzling brightness. Then they fight fiercely until one is beaten. The vanquished fish then sinks to the ground, and two well-marked black stripes appear along its sides.

A great many animals are protected not only by their colour but also by the shapes of their bodies. These are formed or decorated in such a way as to look like part of their surroundings, so that when the animal is still it cannot be seen as a separate object. The lichen-like Gecko spends its days clinging close-pressed against the bark of a tree. This lizard is not only blotched in grey and black and brown, but its sides and tail are fringed with irregular lobes of skin. The Sea-dragon, a kind of sea-horse, has similar outgrowths which look like streamers of seaweed.

FORM AND COLOUR

The insects specialize in protective shapes. Most butterflies are brightly coloured : but the undersides of their wings are often dull-coloured so as to match their surroundings when at rest. The wings are sometimes leaf-shaped and scalloped at the edges, so that when the insect settles on a twig, with its wings folded together, it looks like a dead leaf. In the Leaf-butterflies, the closed wings are shaped and coloured exactly like withered leaves, with veins and a stalk, mould-like patches, and small clear spots which look like holes.

Moths often have dull-coloured fore-wings, which they fold over their brightly coloured hind-wings when at rest. The young of these insects are caterpillars and chrysalises, and they, too, are often well disguised, chiefly by colour and pattern, but sometimes by shape. A number of them look just like twigs. They have long, straight brown bodies, and few legs, and are marked with patches as a twig is marked by leaf scars. As they hold their bodies out stiffly from the branch on which they rest, they cannot be distinguished from other parts of the tree. The stick-insects are relatives of the grasshoppers and are very big, some of them being twelve inches long. Many of them have large and beautiful wings, but when the insect takes up a resting position the wings are folded tightly to the long, thin body like a fan. The insect then looks like a thin reed or stick, and the limbs are held in such strange positions that they seem to be twigs branching from it.

The leaf-insects belong to the same family as the stick-insects. Their wings are leaf-shaped, and so coloured, veined and marked, that they look exactly like leaves. Their legs have small, leaf-like outgrowths on them. The insects turn from green to brown in the autumn, and lay eggs which look just like the seeds of plants. Other insects of this family have bodies and limbs which are covered with sharp prickles, like the thorns and spines of plants; but the most perfect imitators are the tree-hoppers. These insects live in North and South America, and the front parts of their forebodies are strangely developed into the shapes of thorns, burrs, galls, and even ants ! They are so large that they cover the rest of the body, and the creature is completely disguised. Many other insects

pretend to be parts of plants also. There are beetles which look as if their bodies and limbs are covered with small pieces of lichen : there are insects which look like rolled-up dead leaves, and caterpillars which are flat and oval in shape, and look exactly like the galls of the beech-trees

CAMOUFLAGE on which they
IN ATTACK live.

The small and defenceless are not the only animals which make use of protective colouring, for it is found among the hunters as well as the hunted. Animals so coloured can steal upon their prey unawares. Lions in the desert, leopards in the forest, and polar bears, arctic foxes and ermines in the snow, are all flesh-eaters who can come upon their prey without being seen.

Other animals, disguised as something harmless or offering a lure, wait for their food to come to them. The crocodile looks like a log of wood, half sunk beneath the water, and seizes the unsuspecting animal which comes to drink. A certain tropical spider lies on its back with its legs crossed over and

The Mountain Hare, Willow grouse & Stoat are among those animals who change their colour according to the season. In summer they are brown, in winter they are white. The Stoat is then called an Ermine. Some animals merely become paler in winter.

198

pressed against its body, looking exactly like a bird's dropping. The unfortunate butterflies which settle by it are quickly caught and eaten. Near relatives of the stick-insects the mantises, lure their victims to death by their likeness to flowers holding nectar for the hungry. In America there are certain turtles which spend much of their time at the bottom of rivers. They look like sunken logs or pieces of bark, while on their heads there are long flaps of skin, which are so much like water weeds that small fishes are tempted to eat them. Suddenly an ample mouth opens, and the fishes are swept into it with the rush of water. Another loglike

Poisonous creatures are strikingly coloured so that other animals quickly learn to avoid them. Birds will not eat boldly-marked insects, & all animals flee from the skunk because he can eject a bad-smelling fluid. South American natives make use of the Poison-frog in preparing their poisoned arrows.

turtle has inside its mouth two white thread-like growths. These are thrust out, and as they move to and fro in the water, they look like small worms. Fishes which come to feed on the "worms" are caught and swallowed. The flat, mud-coloured Angler-fish not only has seaweed-like flaps of skin on its head, but part of its dorsal fin is developed into a long rod. At the end of the rod a piece of skin floats in the water like a small fish. Unsuspecting fishes which are tempted by such easy prey are swept into the Angler's huge mouth.

Deep-sea Anglers have luminous bulbs at the tips of their rods, so that other fishes may be attracted by this light in the complete darkness of the great depths. This fish is black and is studded with

A small fish known as the Sea dragon has long flowing ribbons of skin. These look like fronds of the seaweed in which it lives. A fish related to the sharks lays eggs which resemble small pieces of seaweed. Opposite: i. A prawn pouring out luminous fluid to baffle its pursuers. ii A gleaming sea lily. iii Coral animals giving out light.

luminous points, which can be dimmed or made to glow. There are many other deep-sea creatures, both black and red, which are provided with lights. The lights are of different colours, and are perhaps used to attract prey, or to keep members of the same tribe together. Some of the lights are fitted with a lens and reflector, and act as searchlights, throwing a beam for some way through the water. A few land animals have lights on their bodies, among them the glow-worms, fireflies and some centi-

LIGHT-
ORGANS

Dwellers in the deep sea are usually black, brown or red. These colours are inconspicuous in the darkness of the sea depths. Most of the animals have light-producing organs: the lights are of different colours & patterns. Perhaps the patterns help the animals to recognise their friends & foes. Some of the lights may be used to attract prey.

Some animals appear to have
alarm signals by which they
warn their fellows of danger.
The Spring-bok when disturbed
jumps 8 to 10 feet into the air,
showing long white hairs
which are usually hidden in
a fold of skin along its back.

202

pedes. Their use is not always known, but in some cases the males and females are attracted to one another in this way.

The bright colours of animals are often "warning" colours. Their purpose is not to hide the wearer, but to make him conspicuous with some bold pattern or colour. The wearers of these threatening colours can defend themselves by "WARNING" COLOURS means of bad-smelling fluids, poisonous bites, stings or loathsome taste; but they save themselves from what might be a fatal attack by displaying danger signals. Any animal which has once had dealings with one of such a kind is unlikely to do so again. The striking colour reminds it of some unpleasant experience, and it avoids for the rest of its life all animals of this or similar colour. Thus any animal which boldly displays bright colours, generally contrasted with black, is fairly safe from attack. The wasp, with its bands of black and yellow and its sharp sting, is the best-known of the warningly coloured creatures. The black-and-yellow salamanders, though they are harmless to man, can give off a liquid which is painful to small animals which take them in their mouths. The fire-bellied toad is similarly coloured for the same reason. Coral-snakes and Gila-monsters have poisonous fangs, and the porcupine's banded quills give warning of their sharpness. Bad-tasting butterflies are large and brightly coloured with black markings. They generally fly slowly, making little effort to escape.

Another kind of "warning" colour serves a quite different purpose. It is used as an alarm signal between members of a tribe. In mammals it is often a patch of ALARM COLOURS light or dark fur, which shows up clearly when the animal is frightened and running for safety. The rabbit warns his fellows of danger by stamping and then running for home, his white scut showing the others the quickest way to the burrows. Many antelopes and deer when alarmed raise their tails to show a patch of white; these signals help to keep the herd together in times of danger.

Some small, defenceless animals ward off attacks by bluff. The Frilled-lizard turns on his enemies, spreads his brightly coloured ruff, and opens his red TERRIFYING ATTITUDES mouth. He looks very frightening in this attitude, but in fact he could not hurt any animal which might be brave enough to attack him. The Puss-moth caterpillar defends itself with its ugly mask and tail-whips. The Lobster-moth caterpillar takes up a terrifying pose, rearing the forepart of its

The white tail of the rabbit flashes out a warning as the animal runs to the burrow & shows the path to safety.

Some small defenceless animals bluff their enemies by taking up a frightening attitude or by showing spots which look like the eyes of a larger creature. The Eyed Hawk-moth exposes its 'eyes': some caterpillars draw in the head and swell out the spots behind it: another rears its head and tail & waves its long legs. A certain Lantern-fly has a mask-like growth which looks like the head of an alligator.

body, making its four long legs quiver, and turning up the hindpart with its forked tail. Other caterpillars have dark spots on the segments just behind their heads. By drawing their heads back into their bodies, they can make these spots grow bigger and bulge out, until they look like the eyes of some strange snake-like creature. Many moths have eye-like markings on their wings, and some fishes have similar spots on their fins. In both cases these may look like the eyes of a larger creature when the animal is half hidden. The tropical lantern-flies have great hollow growths like masks, which stand out from the front of their heads. In one case the mask is shaped and marked like an alligator's head. It must look like some frightening reptile to any small bird which comes upon it while searching among the leaves for an insect meal.

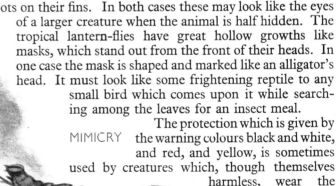

The protection which is given by MIMICRY the warning colours black and white, and red, and yellow, is sometimes used by creatures which, though themselves harmless, wear the livery of poisonous or unpleasant animals. Some butterflies which

204

birds like to eat, take on the colouring of inedible butterflies who live in the same district. The mimics do not always imitate creatures of the same kind. There are butterflies which mimic dragonflies, moths which mimic hornets and humble-bees, spiders which look like ants, or beetles, or even snails.

The functions of mimicry are varied. Most often the mimic seeks the protection which is given by likeness to a warningly coloured creature: or it may imitate some animal which is feared by others. There are a great many spiders which imitate ants, holding up their extra pair of legs (spiders have eight legs and ants only six) to look like antennæ. They even imitate the walking movements and behaviour of ants. In one of the tree-hoppers, the insects which grow such large and curiously shaped front parts, the outgrowth is green, and the little creature looks exactly like a leaf-cutting ant with its piece of leaf.

It is sometimes an advantage for one kind of animal to look like another. A defenceless plant bug [i] has a hood like the leaf of the Sauba ant [ii], & many spiders [iii] are protected by their resemblance to ants [iv]. Tasty butterflies [v] mimic those which have a nasty taste [vi]. Cuckoos' eggs [vii] often look like the eggs of the bird in whose nest they are laid [viii]. A harmless snake [ix] mimics the deadly Coral snake

It is not always the harmless which imitate the harmful. Sometimes the hunter puts on an innocent disguise. There are birds of prey which are dressed to look like insect-eating birds. They sit quite still on a bough, until smaller birds, thinking them to be harmless, perch beside them and are quickly seized. These fierce birds are coloured quite differently in regions where there are no insect-eaters to imitate. Cuckoos' eggs are often coloured to deceive the bird in whose nest they are laid. Hedge-sparrows are easy-going, and do not notice a strange egg in their nests, so the cuckoos which choose these birds as foster parents for their young, have eggs which are not disguised. Redstarts and Sedge-warblers are more particular, and turn suspicious objects out of their nests. Cuckoos' eggs which are hatched by these birds tend to match their own eggs in colour and markings.

Even plants may be mimics, though it is not always easy to see, as in the Bee-orchis, the reason for the mimicry. Some flowers are coloured blood-red and give off a smell of meat. In this way they attract flies, who visit one flower after another and cross-pollinate them. In other plants the seeds are taken by birds, and are sown far and wide, because they look like insects or their larvæ. A seed eaten by a grain-eating bird, and passed through the grinding mill of its gizzard, would have small chance of survival. Insect-eaters do not have such hard gizzards, so a seed can pass through their digestive tracts and be dropped unharmed some distance away from the parent plant. Some plants produce seedpods which look like centipedes: another kind has seeds which imitate beetles with long antennæ. The seeds of the castor oil plant mimic swollen ticks, and there are seeds which are exactly like the upper side of a beetle.

The harmless imitate the harmful, the fierce pretend to be innocent. A third kind of mimicry is that in which a common "trademark" is shared by many different animals. In these cases the members of several groups of harmful creatures all look alike. There are tropical butter-

DIFFERENT GROUPS: COMMON TRADEMARK

flies which are not related to each other, but which are all distasteful to birds. They all have wings similarly patterned and coloured in orange and black. In this way the same warning colours are spread over many different groups, and so the losses in each are fewer.

The mimics come into the world already dressed for their parts: other creatures put their disguises on themselves. The Spider-crab dresses itself in pieces of seaweed; the Sponge-crab holds a sponge on to its back; the Carrier-whelk covers its shell with other shells and small stones. The grubs of the

DISGUISES

Caddis-fly fasten together bits of wood, or small shells or stones, to form long tubes in which they live. When they want to move or feed, they thrust out the forepart of their bodies. When at rest, they are almost invisible even to the hungriest fish. Caterpillars of the Psyche-moths make similar tubes. Some are of silk, to which are fixed pieces of grass and leaves: others look like fallen catkins or the scales of leaf buds. Some of these caterpillars spin cases of silk which imitate exactly the shells of small snails. The

The males of many animals are more brightly coloured than the females, & some of them have a special dress during the mating season.

Each one displays his decoration to its fullest advantage. The Amherst pheasant presents his side view and spreads out his great ruff.

caterpillar of the Clothes-moth snips out pieces of silk or woollen garments, and makes a shelter for itself which harmonizes with its surroundings. The caterpillars of the Essex emerald-moths fasten leaf fragments of their food plant to the hooked spines on their bodies.

Bright colours hide tropical fish from their enemies, and flower-spiders and mantises from their victims. They give warning of poisonous properties and disguise the harmless mimic. Vivid colour serves other purposes at mating time, either in attracting mates or warning off rivals. In nearly all cases it is the male which is conspicuously dressed. He may wear this dress all the year round, or he may put it on only in the breeding season.

MATING DRESS

Male butterflies are often larger and more gaudy than the females, and the same difference is found among the birds. The scarlet-combed, long-tailed cock struts among the quiet hens. The peacock spreads his magnificent fan before the sombre peahen. The male lion looks bigger in his massive mane, and some male monkeys have imposing long moustaches or bushy beards. Certain animals develop special attractions at courting time. Birds grow strange wattles, throat pouches, and bill ornaments. The newt becomes handsome in orange and black, with a saw-toothed crest running from neck to tail tip. The salmon grows a kind of hook on his lower jaw at this season, and many other fishes become brilliantly coloured. All these colours and adornments help the male to keep off rivals or to attract the female to mate with him and rear a family.

Form and colour play very important parts in the lives of all animals living under natural conditions, and help them to hide, entice, deceive, give warning, terrify or attract. In almost every case, appearance alone is not enough: it must be allied with suitable behaviour. The Bittern stretches upwards and looks like a clump of reeds. Nightjars crouch motionless on their branch, or stretch bolt upright, in both cases looking exactly like a stump of wood. Sometimes these birds move very slowly round, following the movements of their enemy so that they always face him. Butterflies fold their bright-scaled wings together, and pose as withered leaves. Moths cover their patterned hind wings, and look like pieces of moss or lichen. The twig-caterpillars stand out stiffly at an angle to the supporting twig, and many stick-insects remain perfectly still and stick-like even when handled. The spiders which have changed their shape so much as to look like snails, cling to the undersides of leaves just as a snail would. There they stay, even when the plant is roughly shaken; and when torn from their hold, they still keep their snail-like shape with legs drawn up closely to the body.

Mimics not only imitate the shape and colour of their models, but usually copy their behaviour. Animals in courting dress do not wait idly to catch the eyes of the females; they pointedly display their particular charms to their best advantage, dancing and posturing in a variety of ways. In these and in hundreds of similar cases, the animal behaves so as to fit in with its appearance. Form and colouring are always bound up with and dependent on behaviour. If mind in some form did not govern the actions of animals, the effects of the most cunning disguise, the most exact mimicry, the most frightening pattern, the gayest and most charming courting dress, would be largely wasted.

HOMES
AND
FAMILIES

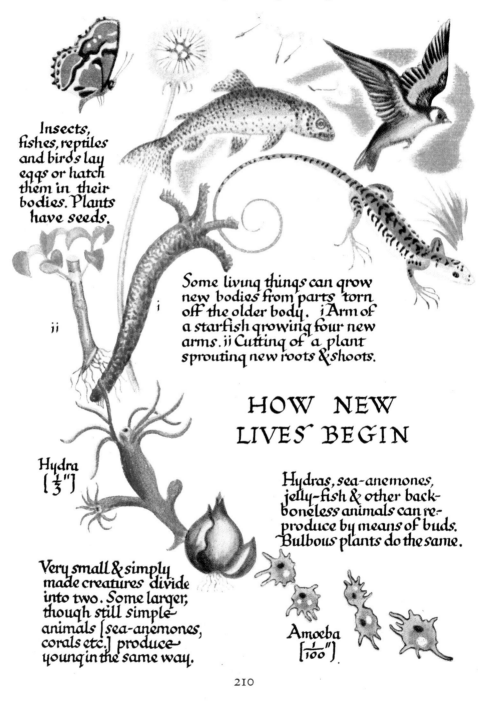

Insects, fishes, reptiles and birds lay eggs or hatch them in their bodies. Plants have seeds.

ii

i

Some living things can grow new bodies from parts torn off the older body. i Arm of a starfish growing four new arms. ii Cutting of a plant sprouting new roots & shoots.

HOW NEW LIVES BEGIN

Hydra [⅓"]

Hydras, sea-anemones, jelly-fish & other back-boneless animals can re-produce by means of buds. Bulbous plants do the same.

Very small & simply made creatures divide into two. Some larger, though still simple animals [sea-anemones, corals etc.] produce young in the same way.

Amoeba [1/100"].

210

The young of most pouched mammals are born in a very un-developed state [the new-born kangaroo is just over 1" long] They continue to grow in their mother's pouch, nourished on her milk. The young of the placental mammals grow inside the parent's body until they are almost completely formed.

Section 8 — Homes and Families

Living things differ from inanimate things in that they possess the power to take in substances from their surroundings and change them into the materials from which they build their bodies. These substances are the plant's or animal's food. As lowly creatures and the young of higher animals absorb food, their bodies become larger. This is called growing. All living things have a tendency to produce copies of themselves so that their race may go on. This making of copies is known as reproduction, and it always entails growth and separation.

FEEDING AND GROWING

When a simple living thing, such as a one-celled animal or plant, grows too large for its own convenience, it splits in half and becomes two beings. Bacteria and the cells which build up the bodies of the many-celled creatures reproduce themselves in this way. Certain of the simpler, many-celled animals, such as sea-anemones and some of the worms, also multiply by dividing themselves into

211

Most animals reproduce themselves by means of
female cells called 'eggs' & male cells called 'sperms.'
In flowers the process is much the same: the ovules
contain the egg-cells and the pollen grains contain the
male cells. Some simple plants like seaweed, which do
not have flowers, make eggs & sperms like animals.

SEAWEED

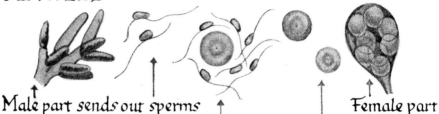

Male part sends out sperms   Female part

sends out eggs.

Sperms swim round the egg

SEA URCHIN'S
EGG & SPERMS

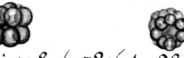

A sperm enters an egg and the two melt into one another
to form a single cell. This cell divides again and again
until it becomes a cluster of cells, which grows in size
until a new being is formed.

A fertilized egg divides into 2 cells, these divide & become 4

Then these divide into 8, 16, 32, 64, 128 and so on. At
first all the cells are alike, but later they grow differently and become nerve cells, bone cells, muscle
cells etc.. Thus a living creature is built up,

two or more parts. As living things become larger, and their cells more highly specialized, division becomes more difficult. Those simple creatures which do not split apart often reproduce by budding. They grow small copies of themselves on some part of the body. The bud stays on its parent until it is ready to look after itself, then breaks off and swims away. Jelly-fishes and other lowly water animals sometimes reproduce in this way. It is also common among plants. Bulbs grow little bulbils round them which eventually grow into full-sized bulbs; and other plants, such as the strawberry, send out long stems or runners from which spring small plants. Sometimes the buds stay fixed to the parent body and produce buds in their turn. In this way colonies of animals such as corals are made. Budding is a better way of reproduction than dividing.

REPRODUCTION :
DIVIDING

BUDDING

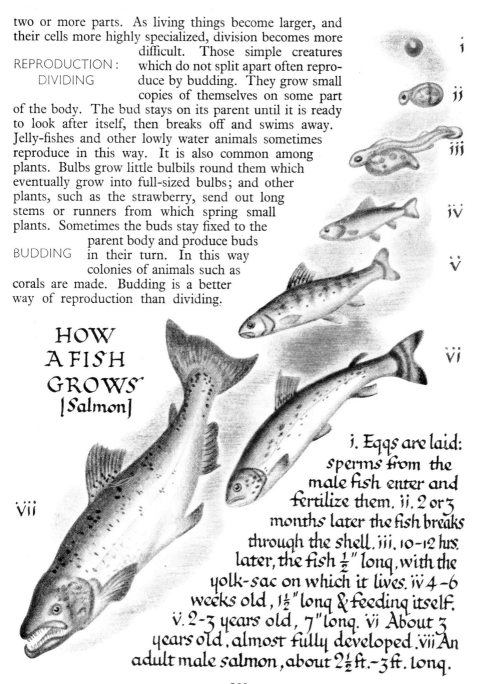

**HOW
A FISH
GROWS
[Salmon]**

i. Eggs are laid: sperms from the male fish enter and fertilize them. ii. 2 or 3 months later the fish breaks through the shell. iii. 10–12 hrs. later, the fish $\frac{1}{2}$" long, with the yolk-sac on which it lives. iv 4–6 weeks old, $1\frac{1}{2}$" long & feeding itself. v. 2–3 years old, 7" long. vi About 3 years old, almost fully developed. vii An adult male salmon, about $2\frac{1}{2}$ ft.–3 ft. long.

213

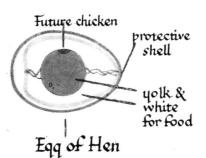

Future chicken
protective shell
yolk & white for food

Egg of Hen

future plant
protective outer cover
starch for food

Fruit of Maize

Eggs laid in water [1 & 2 in fresh water, 3 – 6 in salt]

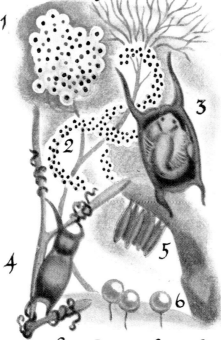

Eggs of :— 1. Common frog. 2. Common toad. 3. Skate : egg case is thrust into sand [here opened to show fish inside]. 4. Dog fish. 5. Goby : attached to rock or shell. 6. Sea worm : anchored to sand.

for the parent is not destroyed, but both methods can only be used by those living things whose cells are not very different from each other.

As animals evolve, the cells of which they are made become set apart for various duties in the body, and cannot do any other kind of work. Growth is no longer a matter merely of adding more cells of much the same kind as the rest of the body. There is a delicate balance between the different sorts of cells, which has to be carefully kept. It would be impossible for half an insect or half a lizard to add on the remaining half of its complex body. Even if it could do so, it would not be able to move about while re-growing, and would fall an easy prey to its enemies. For the same reasons, it would not be practical for complicated and swift-moving creatures to grow buds on their bodies. So the higher plants and animals are confined to another way of multiplying, that of making seeds or eggs. In this method two cells unite and become one cell, which is called a fertilized egg. The two cells which take part in this process are the germ cells of two living things of the same or similar kind. The cells are specially set apart for the one purpose of making new lives, and do not

214

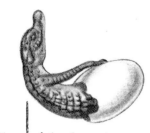 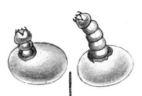

shoot growing upwards

Crocodile hatching   Caterpillar hatching

Maize sprouting

—root growing downwards.

SEEDS AND EGGS

do anything else in the body to which they belong. One of them is a male cell, the other a female cell. The male cells of animals and of the lower plants are called sperms; they are small and very active with long, lashing tails. The female cells are called egg-cells; they do not move by themselves like sperms, but are large with food stored for the use of the future plant or animal.

When a sperm enters into an egg-cell, the cell is said to be fertilized. It then behaves almost like a one-celled animal: it divides into two, but the two parts stay together instead oɪ becoming separate beings. They divide again and become four, then again into eight, until the egg-cell is split up into a great many sections. Then it begins to grow and develop, and at last becomes a being like its two parents. In this it has an advantage over the creature which is a half, or a bud, of one living thing only. Instead of being in every way exactly like the body which produces it, it is an entirely new being, combining qualities from its two parents. In this way new varieties of plants and animals have been and are still being made. The production of fresh forms of life, often better

Bird's egg

Turtle's egg

egg of Digger Wasp

7

eggs of Lacewing fly

8

eggs of a fly, 2 butterflies & a moth.—   9

7 Some insects provide food for their grubs by laying the eggs in the bodies of other animals. 8. Cockroaches lay 16 eggs in a horny case. 9 These eggs are of varied & beautiful shapes.

215

The Potter wasp makes her nests on heather plants. The nest is like a little vase with a short neck, & is made of clay & a sticky fluid from the wasp's mouth. Before closing the neck, she stocks the nest with small caterpillars and suspends a single egg from the roof.

surface of the sea where they find plenty to eat, lay fewer eggs, between thirty and forty thousand; and those fish which make nests for, and look after their young, lay only a few hundred eggs.

Among insects the flies lay from one egg to four thousand eggs at a time, according to their kind, and the queen termite may lay thirty thousand eggs every twenty-four hours. Reptiles lay from five to two hundred eggs in a clutch: birds' eggs vary from one to a dozen, and are usually four or five in number. A pair of rats can produce in a year six litters of eight or more rats, and mice increase at much the same rate. The farmyard sow has been bred so as to give a dozen piglets twice a year, but pigs in their wild state rarely have more than four young at a time. Two, three or four are the usual numbers of young among the mammals, but many of them give birth to only one at a time.

Young creatures leave their eggs or their mothers' bodies at very different stages of development. When a great number of eggs is laid, little food can be provided in them for each new life. Such animals, including YOUNG insects, fishes and frogs, hatch early, and do most of their growing ANIMALS outside the egg. At first they are quite unlike their parents, and it is some time, even several years, before they leave the larval stage. Most of these creatures begin to eat as soon as they hatch out of the egg, though tadpoles and young fishes are nourished for a time by the remains of the egg-food, which still clings to their bodies. In fishes, this hangs down underneath the body like a bag, and is called the yolk-sac. When animals lay fewer and larger eggs, they can provide them with plenty of food, so that the growing life need not hatch out until an advanced stage of development is reached.

Young reptiles, and many young birds, particularly the offspring of ground nesters, come out of the egg small but active and much like their parents. The chicks are warmly clothed in down, and can run about and feed themselves as soon as they are hatched. The nestlings of birds who build their nests high up or well-hidden are not so developed. They can lie safely in the nest for weeks instead of having to run the dangers of life in the open. Their parents are

218

usually smaller than the ground-nesting birds, and the hen cannot be burdened with heavy eggs while flying. Birds of the air rather than of the ground tend to lay small eggs, and the young are hatched in a helpless and unfeathered state. They have to be fed and kept warm by the mother and often the father too.

In the same way, the offspring of mammals such as cats and rabbits, who shelter their families in caves or burrows, are born blind, feeble, and often without fur. Those whose parents live in the open, trekking for miles in search of grazing grounds, and fleeing for their lives from beasts of prey, are born long-legged and can run with the herd in a few hours. The stilt-like legs of foals and lambs seem much too long for their small bodies, but must have saved the lives of their ancestors when they were still in a wild state.

The production of young ones always entails an effort on the part of the mother. They are small parts of her body, whether they are buds or developing eggs. The plant stores up food in its seeds, on which its offspring can feed until they are developed enough to look after themselves. It takes care that the little plants shall have the chance to grow big and strong. If the parent plant simply dropped its seeds round its own body, they would fall on ground which had already been used by the older plant. They would, besides, be so thickly sown that they would not have enough space for their roots, nor enough light for their leaves. So most seeds are provided with some means of getting away from their parent. They may be made in such a form as to be

PARENTAL CARE OF PLANTS

Most insects show no more care for their young than to lay the eggs where there will be a plentiful supply of food for the future grubs. Earwigs [and a certain birch tree bug] are exceptional, for they guard their eggs and brood their offspring as a hen does her chicks.

some fishes have evolved a better way. They lay fewer eggs and look after them until the young have hatched or until they can look after themselves. It is often the fathers who nurse these young fish. The male Stickleback builds a nest about the size of a golf ball, of water weeds and grasses. He persuades several female sticklebacks to go into the nest, one after another, and lay their eggs. Then the father mounts guard over the nest, and keeps the water fresh round the eggs by fanning it with his fins and tail. When the eggs hatch, he defends the young fish from their enemies, and if they stray too far from the nest, he seizes them in his mouth and brings them back to safety. In this way he devotes himself to his young family for three or four weeks.

Wrasses work together to make large, ball-shaped nests of weed and broken shell. Salmon and trout clear spaces in the stream bed with their tails; they lay their eggs in these hollows and cover them with sand or gravel. Bowfins make a clearing in a reed bed, biting through the stems of plants that cannot be broken or pressed aside. Then they make a shallow pool at the bottom of the clearing. The little Sea-horses and Pipe-fishes carry their eggs in pouches under their bodies near the tail, and for some time after they are hatched the young fishes rush back

The Sea Horse lays her eggs in the pouch of the male where they remain until hatched. After hatching, the fry stay with their father until they are large enough to fend for themselves.

222

to their father's pouch at a hint of danger. The male Butter-fish coils his body round his mate's mass of eggs, and the male Lumpsucker, after guarding his eggs until they are hatched, swims about with the young ones clinging to his body. A few fishes brood their eggs in their mouths, and shelter their young there while they are small.

Frogs and toads have many strange ways of rearing their families. British frogs and toads take no care of their offspring, but desert their eggs after shedding them in water, which is sometimes so shallow that it dries up before the young are hatched. Others take much trouble to ensure that their broods shall survive. Some build nurseries of mud, shaped like shallow basins, by the water's edge. Others again enclose their eggs in leaves overhanging a pool, so that when the tadpoles are ready, they can drop into the water beneath.

FROGS AND TOADS

There are toads and frogs who use their own bodies as nurseries. The Midwife-toad lays her eggs on land, and the father immediately twines them round his back legs. He carries them in this way for three weeks, staying hidden in the daytime, and coming out at night to feed and to bathe the eggs in dew. At the end of that time, he goes to a pond, where the fifty or sixty tadpoles bite their way through the egg-string and swim off on their own. The Chilian-frog carries the female's eggs in a great pouch, which runs underneath the whole length of his body. Here the tadpoles stay until they come out as perfect little frogs. In several kinds of frogs, the eggs are carried by the female on her back, sometimes enclosed, sometimes half-enclosed, in a fold of skin. In the Surinam-toad the eggs are hatched in small pits in the mothers' back. Each egg lies in a separate pocket, covered with a lid of skin. The young ones do not leave their cells until they are perfectly developed small toads.

Reptiles are not good mothers and do little for their offspring beyond burying the eggs in some spot where they are likely to keep warm. A few snakes take a slight

Using a hole or shell as a nest, the Butter fish lays a mass of eggs round which one of the parents, usually the father, coils his body. The female python incubates her eggs in the same way.

223

The Midwife toad lays her eggs in a string, which the male then winds round his hind legs. He carries them thus for about three weeks, spending his days in a hole in the ground & coming out at night to feed himself & to bathe the eggs in dew or water.

interest in their young ones after they are hatched, for some have been **REPTILES** found coiled up with twenty or more little snakes within their folds. The only snakes who are known to hatch their eggs themselves are the pythons, who for two months jealously guard their clutch of fifteen to a hundred eggs by coiling their bodies round them. Crocodiles and alligators make rough nests for their eggs, and stay near them until the young are hatched.

Birds are far superior to reptiles in the care of their young. Some of them are content to lay their eggs on the ground, or in the disused burrows of other animals; but most birds take pains to prepare nurseries for their young. The nests are made of many different materials, grass, twigs, mud, stones, cotton and wool, saliva, or large leaves sewn together. Both parents share in this work as a rule. The site is chosen with care, according to each kind of bird. Thrushes and finches choose trees, bushes and hedges : woodpeckers excavate holes in walls and trees : starlings, swallows and house-martins prefer houses and barns : and some birds, such as sky-**BIRDS** larks, curlews and partridges, build their nests on the ground. Some of the nests are carelessly made, particularly those of the ground-nesting birds. Others are elaborately woven with the bird's bill and feet, from twigs, grass, moss and wool. They are often beautifully lined inside with tiny feathers, wool, cotton, or down plucked by the mother from her breast. This lining makes a soft resting place for the fragile eggs, and helps to keep them warm. When the eggs are hatched, it forms a warm bed for the naked nestlings.

The mother bird usually sits on the eggs, while the father brings her food and sings to keep rivals away. Among the ostriches, emus and rheas, the cock birds do all the brooding, spreading their soft wings over the twenty great eggs laid by their several wives. The young ostriches, like the young of the other ground-nesters, come out of the egg clothed in down, and able to run about and feed themselves. The helpless offspring of the tree-nesters have to be looked after for some time after they are hatched. The parents protect them from cold and heat and bring them food. They usually keep the nest clean and healthy by taking out the droppings of the young. Later they encourage their children to fly, and birds of prey teach their young ones to hunt.

Mammals are on the whole more devoted to their offspring than any other living things. The mammal mother generally has fewer young to care for, so she can give her attention to each one separately. MAMMALS The children are dependent for their food on her body, before birth and for some time afterwards, for when they are born she feeds them

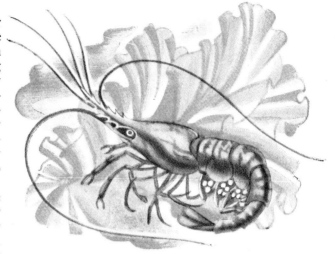

Lobsters, prawns, shrimps & crayfish carry their eggs stuck to their swimmerets until they are hatched. The young are usually quite unlike their parents & pass through many stages before becoming full-grown.

with milk, the liquid which only mammals have the power to make. She often carries her babies about with her after birth.

In the pouch-bearers the young are born at a very early stage, and are kept in the mother's pouch until they are fully formed. The kangaroo carries her young one in her pouch for some time after it can run and jump by itself. Other pouch-bearers have only a fold of skin instead of a deep pocket. The Australian Pouched-mouse has litters of ten, but instead of being carried about in the safety of a pouch, the young ones have to cling on to the fur underneath their mother. The Koala has lost her pouch altogether, and her baby rides pick-a-back. The American Woolly-opossum has to carry a litter of six on her tiny back. She has a very long tail round which the young ones twist their own long tails while they cling to her fur with their paws. The mother hippopotamus also carries her calf on her back. It sits astride her short neck while she moves about in the water.

Bats take their young about with them for some time after they are born. The babe hangs on to the fur on the front of its mother's body until it is old enough to fly. Young apes and monkeys cling to their parents in the same ways, holding on tightly as the older animals leap from tree to tree. If a monkey mother is shot, she quickly passes her child to another monkey before she falls

Q

to the ground. Human babies do not cling to their mothers like the young of other primates, though they can hang by their arms just like young monkeys. In civilized society they are usually pushed about in perambulators. Among more primitive folk they are carried in the arms, on the shoulders, or in some kind of sling.

Few mammals are such wonderful nest builders as birds, but their homes are used for sleeping and hiding in, as well as for nurseries. Sometimes they serve as storehouses for food. The Chipmunk, a Canadian relative of the squirrels, fills its nest with corn, nuts and acorns, which it MAMMALS' brings home in its large cheek-HOMES pouches. The burrow is the most usual kind of home among the mammals. Rabbits riddle whole hillsides with entrances to the underground passages in which they live. Molehills are common on lawns and in fields, and are made of the earth thrown up by moles when digging their tunnels.

The Kingfisher lays her eggs in a burrow near a stream, on a nest made of tiny fishbones. At first the young are fed on insects, or half-digested food disgorged by the parents. Later they have fish.

226

Parent birds may work as many as 17 hours a day while feeding their young ones. Most nestlings have brightly coloured mouths, perhaps so that the parents may see them easily if the nest is in a shady place.

Badgers can dig down through sixteen feet of solid chalk, though they are generally content with a shorter burrow. In this "set" or "earth" the female badger makes her nest and rears her three or four young. The nest is made of dry grass and bracken, and there is sometimes a larder as well as a nursery. Prairie-marmots line their sleeping quarters with freshly cut hay. They are particular about its being clean and dry, and on fine days they bring it out to air. If it is dirty, they renew it altogether.

Rodents are more like birds in their house-building than any other mammals. Some of them, such as the water-vole and porcupine, have only simple burrows, but the beavers build the most elaborate homes. Beavers are water animals, and in order to have enough water to live in and to float their logs in all the year round, they form artificial lakes by building dams across streams.

BEAVERS
The dams are built of tree branches, mud and stones, and when they have been repaired and enlarged by several generations of beavers, they are sometimes three hundred feet wide, and six to eight feet high. Beavers seem to take into account the pressure of water behind a dam. Where there is not much pressure they build the dam straight across, but where the current runs strongly, they curve the dam against it.

The beavers build their homes, or lodges, near the shores of the artificial pond. They live in them in winter and rear their families in them. The lodge is a circular, dome-shaped building, with walls four or five feet thick. It is made of branches plastered over with mud, and is about seven feet across inside. The lodge is built half in, half out of the water, and has two entrances, about seven to ten feet long, which open under water. One of these, which is usually curved, is used as the ordinary exit and entrance for the beaver family. The other, which is straight, is used for carrying pieces of wood into the lodge. The beavers' chief food is the green bark of tree branches, and they store many of these under water for use during the winter. With their strong cutting teeth

227

Among the flightless birds such as ostriches, emus, cassowaries & kiwis, the cocks either incubate the eggs themselves or share this duty with the hens.

The American woolly opossum, although one of the 'pouched animals,' has only a fold of skin in place of a pouch. So her young ones cling to her back & coil their tails round hers. This opossum is only the size of a large mouse or small rat.

they fell numerous maple and willow trees. These they drag and float to their larder, which is on the floor of the pond, close to their lodge.

After a time, trees of the right size and kind become scarce round the beaver pond, and the animals have to go further afield for their wood. They find it heavy to drag over the ground and as they will never go by land if they can swim, they make little canals along which the wood can be floated. Beavers breed only once a year, and have three, four or five young at a time. The children may live with their parents for years, most beaver colonies being formed by three or four families breeding one with another. Sometimes the babies ride on the wide, flat tails of their parents; but the tail is used chiefly as a rudder, or to help the animal to come quickly to the surface of the water to breathe or to work. Like most rodents, the beaver uses its front paws as hands.

Other rodent homes are much simpler than the beaver's; some of them are like the nests of birds. The dormouse makes a small nest of grass, leaves, or bits of paper, in which it sleeps through the winter and has its young

NESTS   in summer. The nest of the harvest-mouse is about the size of a cricket ball, and is made of thin, dry grasses woven loosely together. It is built upon a scaffolding of grass stems like the reed-warbler's nest, but it is not open at the top. Squirrels are near relations of the dormouse, and they make beautiful ball-shaped nests of woven grass, moss and twigs. The nests are lined with moss or leaves, and are built in hollow trees or in forked

SQUIRRELS   branches. Each squirrel makes several nests or "dreys," and uses them as sleeping places, and as nurseries for the three or four young. The mother tends her offspring with the greatest care, and if she thinks that they are in danger, she takes them to another drey. Like most mammals, she carries her child in her mouth by its head or neck.

FOXES   Foxes and many other animals take their young from one home to another if they are afraid for their safety. The vixen is a devoted parent, and may keep her cubs in two or three different earths. The slightest interference with them will make her shift her cubs to another burrow. The fox never starts an earth on her own, but chooses the disused burrow of a badger or a rabbit and enlarges it. Sometimes she shares a home with a badger, which must be unpleasant for the badger as it is a very clean and tidy animal, and the fox is dirty and untidy.

Monkey and apes, man's nearest relatives among the beasts, are wanderers who do not make fixed homes. Gorillas and orang-utans build platforms high up in the trees, which they use as sleeping places. They are made of small boughs plaited together and strewn with leaves, but each raftlike nest is used only for one night, or even for a short afternoon sleep.

MONKEYS AND APES

Some of the most beautiful homes of all are made by small and lowly creatures. There are one-celled plants and animals who surround themselves with finely sculptured shelters of flinty and chalky material, or clothe themselves with sand grains and the shells of other minute animals. Corals build homes of lime to protect their jelly-like bodies, and molluscs make their variously shaped and coloured shells of the same stuff. Many sea-worms live in tubes, which they build of sand, gravel, mud and shells. Sometimes they live in these tubes all their lives, or they may leave them and build others; but the tubes are almost always used as nurseries for the eggs. In one case the male and female worm live together in the same tube, and the

WATER HOMES

The little Harvest mouse builds its nest about 10" from the ground, on the stems of wheat & other plants. The nest is loosely woven of dry grass, & about eight young ones are reared.

230

eggs are laid in it also. The father arranges them with his proboscis, and then begins to wave his body to and fro. In this way he keeps a constant stream of water passing over the eggs, and for ten days he does not stop, even to feed. When the young ones hatch, he tends them until they are large enough to leave the tube and start life on their own. In most of these animals — radiolarians, corals, molluscs and worms, the house is used as a permanent hard coat or outside skeleton as well as a home. Caddis-worms, the soft-bodied larvæ of caddis-flies, cover themselves with tubes made of shells, sand, dead leaves and twigs in much the same way as sea creatures.

SPIDERS   The silken webs of most spiders are snares rather than dwelling places, though the young of some of them live for a short time in the parent's web. Two kinds of spiders make perfect little homes. The Trapdoor-spider lives in a burrow which it lines with silk from its spinnerets, while the entrance is closed with a circular hinged door, made of layers of silk and earth. The door is coated outside with moss, or whatever grows in the neighbourhood, so that it is well hidden. On the inside of the door there are often two small holes, into which the spider fixes its feet, so as to hold the door tightly closed against intruders.

The squirrel builds a ball-like nest of twigs & dry grass, & lines it with moss & leaves. She is a careful mother, and carries her children to another nest if she thinks that they are in danger.

231

In most living things the males and
females are much alike, but there are
cases where the two sexes look quite
different. [Some plants, such as the
cone-&catkin-bearing trees, carry
male &female flowers which are
unlike each other & may even grow
on separate trees but the trees themselves still look alike] Among butterflies, male and female often differ
in size, pattern & colour. In certain
deep-sea fishes the male is only one-
tenth of the female's size: after gripping some part of her body with his
jaws, he remains grafted to her for life.

1 and 1a. Flowers of Sallow willow
2 and 2a. Orange Tip butterfly
3 & 3a. m.& f. of one of the 'blues'
4 Two deep-sea Angler fishes
  m. ≈ male   f. ≈ female

232

In birds the difference between the sexes is often well marked, the male as a rule being more splendid than the female. In the breeding season the cock-birds usually court the hens by 'displaying' in various ways. The Argus pheasant bows before his future mate, spreading his beautiful wings. He woos her in a clearing in the forest, which he rids of all dead leaves & weeds & keeps very tidy.

The red tree-ant of India makes its nest of leaves joined together with silk. This silk comes from the ants' grubs which the— workers hold in their jaws & pass back-wards & for-wards between the leaf-edges, pressing out the liquid silk, which immediately sets. Meanwhile other workers hold the leaves together with their mandibles & hind-legs

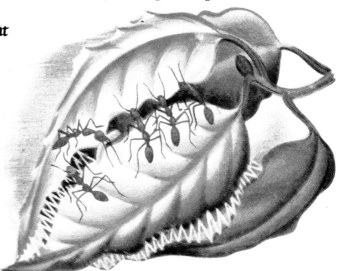

Some of the burrows have a second trapdoor which can be used as an emergency exit.

The Water-spider makes a hollow, bell-shaped home of silk, which she anchors to plants under the water. Then she brings down bubbles of air from the surface of the pond, entangled in the fine hairs which cover her body. Inside the silken bell she combs out the bubbles, and returns to the surface for more air. She does this many times, until the bell is filled with air. She lives in this home most of her life, and lays her eggs in a separate nursery within the bell.

COURTSHIP   Whether they build homes or not, many animals go through a form of courtship before they begin to rear a family. Animal wooing may range from the writhing of certain male seaworms among the coils of the females, and the brandishing of his large, coloured claw by the Fiddler-crab, to the beautiful and often elaborate courtship of birds. Most insects seem to do little courting beyond letting each other know where they are to be found. Moths and other insects give out strong scents from their bodies to attract their mates; the female glow-worm shines her green light; and grass-hoppers and crickets make music by rubbing their legs or wing-cases together. There are certain flies, however, who have a true courtship, for the males bring presents to the females. The gift may be a small insect wrapped in silk which they have spun themselves; or it may be a little silk balloon, empty or containing an insect, or a flower-petal, or a blade of grass.

The males of some fishes become brilliantly coloured in the mating season. The stickleback changes his usual olive colouring for a dress of shining green and gold and scarlet. Among amphibians, frogs and toads merely croak to give notice where they may be found, but the male newt has a magnificent marriage dress in which, with arched back, he dances before the female. Reptiles seem to have no kind of courtship, though some of the males fight one another at breeding time. Mammals rarely woo their mates, but they often fight for them, especially the beasts, such as deer and sea-lions, who live in herds.

The courtship of birds is the most elaborate of all, for the males not only wear richly coloured and highly ornamental dresses, but woo the females by displaying their charms in various ways. The peacock raises his glittering train; the pigeon blows out his crop, or dips his tail to the ground and droops his wings, and runs before the often indifferent female. Bower-birds make variously shaped runs, arched over with twigs and grasses, and ornamented with gaily coloured flowers, shells, feathers, or the wing-cases of beetles. The birds use the bowers as playgrounds, where they dance and curtsey in front of the females. In the Crested-grebes, the male and female go through a set dance, in which they dive under the water, leap up breast to breast, and present each other with pieces of water weed.

All these simple and intricate games lead up to mating and the bringing of a family into the world. If the young arrive fairly well developed, yet with a period of childhood before them, they often spend much of their time in play. Besides being good exercise, play is a form of schooling in which the

The Water-spider spins a bell-like nest under water & then fills it with air which she brings from the surface in the form of large bubbles held by her hind-legs. In this silken diving-bell she lives and rears her family.

235

Few animals play except the higher mammals, who have a longer childhood & more to learn than the lower animals. Play not only exercises their bodies but trains them to use their limbs and eyes so that they may grow up into skilled hunters and fighters.

young animal can learn to hunt and fight and run, as he will have to when he is grown up. Mistakes can be made and corrected without any serious results, and the learner can practise again and again, until he is fully trained. Play belongs chiefly to the higher animals, because they have a longer childhood than those who are lower in the scale. They have larger brains and a greater capacity for learning. They are not born with ready-made instincts, which will cover all the situations likely to be met in their lives; but have to learn to do many of the actions needed for the future. The kitten springing on a whirling leaf is learning to use its eyes and paws for catching prey later on. The gambolling lamb is learning to run and jump, as it had to in the days when its wild ancestors fled from wolves. Puppies have mock hunts, and young goats butt one another, preparing for the time when they will fight for their mates.

PLAYING AND LEARNING

The parents often help their children by giving them lessons. Flesh-eating mammals and birds bring them dead or half-dead prey, on which to practise springing and killing. Lion cubs are taken to hunt with their parents until some time after they are full grown. Badgers and monkeys school their offspring strictly, and punish them when they are slow or inattentive. The otter teaches her young to dive without splashing, and to lie hidden under the river bank. She shows them how to catch and skin frogs, and how to eat eels from the tail and trout from the head. She teaches them to find their way home without returning on their outgoing tracks.

Courtship and affection between mated animals; the building of homes and the bonds of family life; the devotion of parents, and the play and schooling of the young; all have been helped by the fact that the land-egg is different from the water-egg. In the sea or pool, eggs can be laid carelessly in the soft cradle of the water. On land they must be protected from drying up by a hard shell, or by the mother's body. A shell-less water-egg can be fertilized after it has left the mother, but the protected land-egg must be fertilized inside the body of the female. This has led to the wooing of the females by the males, and to the various courting dresses which the latter wear. It has also led to the bright colours and sweet scents of the insect-pollinated flowers, whose egg-cells are fertilized in the ovary by pollen from other plants. Land-eggs, if laid outside the mother, must be kept warm and hidden from the beasts who would eat them. So nests and homes are made. Animals who care for their young in this way, need not lay so many eggs or bear so many young, and parental care and family life have become possible.

WATER-EGGS AND LAND-EGGS

A long period of childhood gives a young animal time to develop its brain and body to a higher stage than those of animals who grow up more quickly. It increases the time during which the young one is dependent on its mother, so that a bond of tender feeling grows between parent and child. The care of children brings with it trouble and self-sacrifice, and the mother may give her life for the sake of the young. The longer the child stays with the parent, the stronger becomes the bond between them; but in the beasts this tie lasts only as long as the little one needs the protection of the older animal. As soon as it can look after itself the parent loses interest in it, and may even become unfriendly. In man the young are born helpless, and many years must pass before the brain is fully developed, and the young human can find its own living. The time of childhood and play and learning is longer. The bond between parent and child is stronger than in the other animals, and usually lasts throughout life. An instinct which urges the lower animals to guard their young so that they might carry on the race, has become in man the foundation on which are built his society and civilization.

CHILDHOOD

The parents of flesh-eating animals teach their young to catch food by bringing them captured prey to play with.

SOCIETIES
AND
PARTNERSHIPS

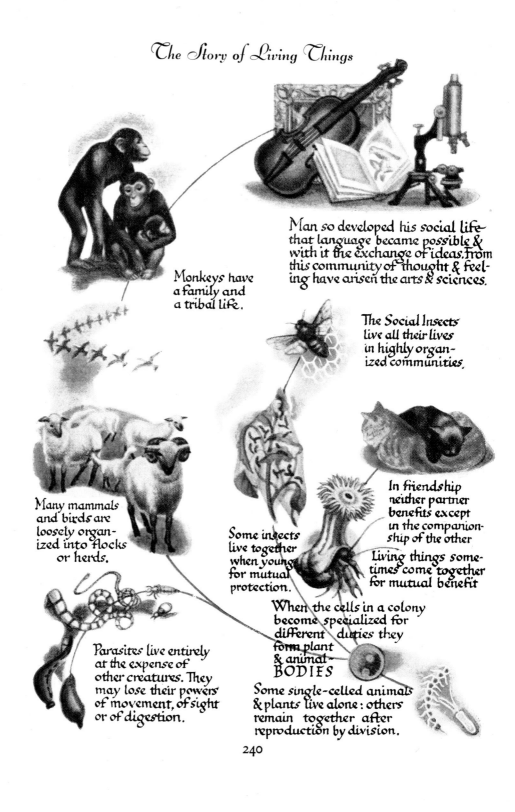

The Story of Living Things

Man so developed his social life that language became possible & with it the exchange of ideas. From this community of thought & feeling have arisen the arts & sciences.

Monkeys have a family and a tribal life.

The Social Insects live all their lives in highly organized communities.

Many mammals and birds are loosely organized into flocks or herds.

Some insects live together when young for mutual protection.

In friendship neither partner benefits except in the companionship of the other

Living things sometimes come together for mutual benefit

When the cells in a colony become specialized for different duties they form plant & animal BODIES

Parasites live entirely at the expense of other creatures. They may lose their powers of movement, of sight or of digestion.

Some single-celled animals & plants live alone: others remain together after reproduction by division.

Every plant-body & animal-body is a society of cells of different kinds, each group doing some particular work in the body to which it belongs. Some living things however consist of one cell only. Many of them live solitary lives: others may unite with similar cells for a time, but they form merely a GROUP OF CELLS and not a BODY.

Chlamydomonas is a single-celled plant-animal. Sometimes it swims about by itself: sometimes it forms a temporary colony with others of its kind and lives with them in a jelly-like mass.

— Section 9 —

Societies and Partnerships

When one-celled living things reproduce themselves by dividing, the new beings usually swim off in different directions and lead separate lives. Sometimes however, the division is not complete : the cells do not break away, but stay together and divide again and again. In this way they form clusters of various shapes which are known as colonies. The minute colonists may be either plants or animals, and they may live together all their lives or for a short time only. Each single being in such a colony lives its own independent life, although it may be linked with thousands of its fellows. There is a living-together but not a working-together.

CELL COLONIES
As plants and animals evolve, some of the cells in a colony take over special duties. Such a colony is seen in Volvox, which is a pale green, water-living globe about one fiftieth of an inch across. It is made up of thousands of cells, most of them having long tails and an eye-spot. These cells row the colony through the water, steer it and feed it, but they cannot reproduce. New Volvox colonies can only be started by the large, non-swimming cells of the colony, which have no tails nor eye-spots, and do no other work besides that of reproduction. Volvox shows in the simplest form the division of labour which is found in the higher, many-celled creatures. When cells take on different duties, they come under one of two headings. They may be concerned with the general *management* of the body, its living, feeding, growing,

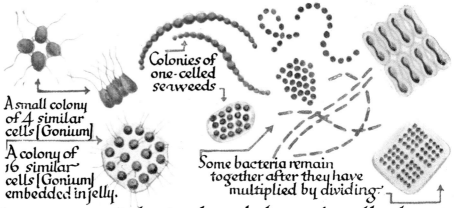

A small colony
of 4 similar
cells [Gonium]

A colony of
16 similar
cells [Gonium]
embedded in jelly.

Colonies of
one-celled
seaweeds

Some bacteria remain
together after they have
multiplied by dividing.

In some one-celled animals and plants, the cells do not
separate after they have divided: they remain together
in clusters, or colonies. Each cell leads its own life
independently of
the others, & every
cell in such a col-
ony is similar to
the one next to it.
There is no divis-
-ion of labour.

senses and movement : or they may concern themselves with the single duty of *reproduction*. In the
first case they busy themselves with the *individual;*
in the second case they look after the *race*.

A BODY is a cell-colony which consists of a
great number of cells working together in different
ways for the good of the whole. The management
of the many-celled body needs various kinds of cells,
and the more highly evolved and more complex the
plant or animal body, the more specialised must be its cells. The sponge is one
of the simplest of the many-celled animals. It has cells which by their lashing
movements keep a constant stream of water flowing through its body. The
water brings oxygen and food to the sponge, and carries waste matters
away. The sponge also has muscle-like cells which expand and con-
tract, flat cells which form its outer surface, and other cells which make
the skeleton. All these cells combine to build the body and to keep it working
or *living;* while its egg and sperm cells unite with each other to form new sponges.

BODIES

The cells in a sponge, like all cells which make up BODIES, cannot live
when separated from the colony for any length of time. They have lost their
independence and have become organized parts of a larger whole.

In animals such as the corals and Portuguese-man-of-war, the cells have
united to form small individuals, which in turn combine to make a larger body.
The coral colonies are formed by the continual budding of one polyp on another.
At the same time they build a skeleton of carbonate of lime, to protect and
support their soft bodies; so that the coral-animal eventually consists of thousands of polyps sharing a common covering. There is no division of labour

242

among the polyps. Each is a complete individual; but they are all connected with each other in such a way that it is impossible to say where one ends and another begins, and the food of each is shared by the others. The Portuguese-man-of-war and its relatives are not fixed like the corals, but swim freely about the sea. They, too, are made up of many polyps, but the various members of the colony are differently built according to their different work. There are small creatures which form swimming-bells, while others catch prey and carry it to those animals which digest the food. Others are very long and are armed with stings. They act as defenders of the colony; and individuals like clusters of dark blue grapes see to the reproduction of the animal. All these different beings are parts of one larger whole, and are able to act together by means of a primitive nervous system. They are not, however, like the limbs and organs of the higher creatures which are intimately bound up with the body to which they belong, and which take their orders from a single source of control. Such a colony has no government, there are as many "heads" as there are members.

The sea anemone is a near relative of these colony-forming polyps. It makes a single body instead of a colony, but its parts can still act as separate beings to a certain extent. If one of its tentacles is cut off, it will still catch food, and will pass it as if to the mouth of the creature. In an experiment in which the tentacles are taught to tell the difference between food and blotting paper, it is only the taught tentacles which remember the lesson. They do not pass on this acquired skill to the other tentacles. As animals evolve, an increasingly complex system of nerve cells connects their cells with the brain and with each other. The body becomes a cell-state, the cells work-

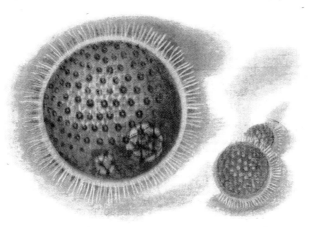

The collection of cells in Volvox begins to suggest a many-celled BODY. Thousands of cells live permanently together, embedded in a globe of jelly, each cell being connected with its neighbours. In this colony is found the simplest form of division of labour. Most of the cells have whiplike tails: these row the body through the water, steer it & feed it. The reproduction of the colony is carried on by larger cells which have no tails.

The cells which form a sponge have lost their independence: each one is a part of an organized body. The cells are of different kinds according to their various duties. Some of them draw in & force out a constant stream of water which brings oxygen & food to the sponge & takes away waste matter. There are also muscle-like cells and egg & sperm cells. Although it has no nerves, the sponge's cells seem to be able to communicate with each other & to work together.

A. Young sponge cut through centre.
B. Cavity [O] lined with cells with whiplike tails. By lashing these, the cells keep up a current of water.

C. One of the tailed cells.

ing together for the good of the community. The central government is taken over by the brain, which directs all the conscious activities of the body.

Although their bodies are communities of specialized cells, the lower animals are not so individual, or undividable, as the higher. Their cells are not so much held to one place and limited to one task. It is as if the cells have specialized half-heartedly, reserving the possibility of a certain amount of independence. In the earth worm, for instance, some of the cells creep out of the body and wander about over

GROWING NEW PARTS

the skin, eating up refuse and keeping it clean. These less individual animals, with their more adaptable cells, can replace larger parts of their bodies than the higher animals, who can only do minor repairs such as the healing of a wound. Starfishes, which are not highly organised, can grow four new rays on a limb which has been cut off

Just as cells may be united to form a BODY in which each has a special duty: so animals may themselves belong to a yet larger body. There are various water-living creatures whose bodies are formed of many animals joined together. Physophora is made up of swimming-bell animals [S] and animals who feed & reproduce the colony, [F & R]. There are also stinging 'defenders' & sensitive 'feelers' [D and T]

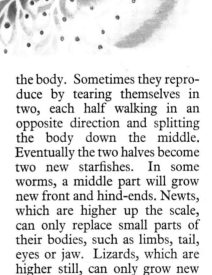

the body. Sometimes they reproduce by tearing themselves in two, each half walking in an opposite direction and splitting the body down the middle. Eventually the two halves become two new starfishes. In some worms, a middle part will grow new front and hind-ends. Newts, which are higher up the scale, can only replace small parts of their bodies, such as limbs, tail, eyes or jaw. Lizards, which are higher still, can only grow new tails. The warm-blooded vertebrates, birds and mammals, cannot renew themselves in this way. They come into the world small and undeveloped, but with the body which they must use all their lives. The cells increase in number while the animal is growing, and as they wear out they are replaced by new ones. But the cell-state is a complete whole, the unity of which cannot be seriously broken except at the cost of permanent disablement or death.

When cells have united to form individuals, these in their turn often com-

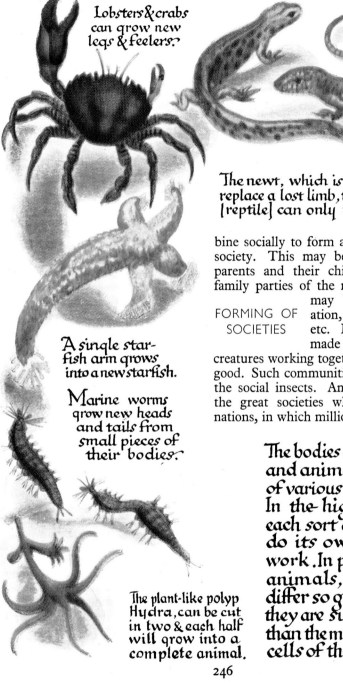

Lobsters & crabs can grow new legs & feelers.

The newt, which is an amphibian, can replace a lost limb, tail or eye. A lizard [reptile] can only replace a lost tail.

A single starfish arm grows into a new starfish.

Marine worms grow new heads and tails from small pieces of their bodies.

The plant-like polyp Hydra, can be cut in two & each half will grow into a complete animal.

bine socially to form a still greater unit, a society. This may be a small group of parents and their children, such as the family parties of the man-like apes; or it may be a larger associ-
FORMING OF ation, a tribe, flock, shoal,
SOCIETIES etc. It may be a society made up of thousands of creatures working together for the common good. Such communities are found among the social insects. Among men there are the great societies which are known as nations, in which millions of human beings

The bodies of most plants and animals are made up of various kinds of cells. In the higher animals each sort of cell can only do its own particular work. In plants & lower animals, the cells do not differ so greatly. When lost they are simpler to replace than the more specialized cells of the higher animals.

246

Butterflies, beetles, dragonflies & other insects, and various birds & mammals, sometimes migrate in vast swarms. The travellers usually come together for a short time only & there is little organization in these gatherings. They form a CROWD rather than a SOCIETY.

are linked with one another by ties of relationship, language, religion and social custom.

Animals come together for various reasons. They may be found in vast numbers when over-production of their kind has led to overcrowding of the available living space. They may also gather where food is plentiful, or living conditions are good. Bees hum by the thousand on a tree of sweet-scented blossom. Bats sleep and also hibernate together, hanging closely side by side in some dark and quiet place. Animals often hold mass meetings during their breeding season. Mayflies have only a few hours of winged life in which to mate and lay their eggs, and they come together in great swarms to perform their aerial dance of TEMPORARY ASSOCIATIONS a fluttering upward movement and graceful, slow descent. In spring the males of the black grouse meet at dawn in parties of fifteen or twenty birds. They sing their song of love and war, and fight each other, and dance before

The Sociable Weaver birds live in colonies. They build a large umbrella-shaped mass of sticks & grass and make their nests in the under surface. The community nest is sometimes twenty five feet across & may contain three hundred nests.

the hens when they arrive. Land-crabs of tropical countries go every year to the sea to breed, travelling over the land in millions. They are headed by the males, and their processions are often fifty feet wide and several miles long. They take no notice of obstacles, and walk through any house which may stand in their path.

Many creatures travel together when they are migrating. Some birds migrate regularly in the autumn and spring, but in other animals mass-migration may only take place when vast numbers of them are faced with famine. Occasionally the spring-bok trek across the South African veldt, when a long drought has withered their plant food. One such procession has been described as being fifteen miles wide and one hundred and forty miles long. Lions which try to snatch a spring-bok out of the herd, are sometimes caught up in the onrush and are carried with it, unable to escape. Even a flock of sheep may become entangled and carried off in the huge mass of moving animals. The small, rat-like lemmings of Norway, when pressed by famine, over-run the country in millions, and finally plunge to their death in the sea. Many insects seek fresh feeding grounds in great swarms. In hot countries the locusts are the best known and most dreaded of such insects. England is sometimes invaded by clouds of Large Garden-White butterflies, which fly over from the Continent and do much damage to the cabbage crops. In the tropics, swarms of butterflies sometimes gather in damp places to drink, or cover whole trees with their bodies when they are resting for the night or for the winter.

In all these cases, except the accidental one of overcrowding, animals have

JACKDAW

ROOK

come together
for some special
purpose such as
breeding, sleeping or searching for food. The
association is made for a certain time only, after
which the animals go their separate ways. There
are many creatures, on the other hand, who
spend all their lives in company
with their fellows. Some of them
do this because it gives greater
protection from their enemies,
and more chance of finding feeding grounds.
Some fish swim together in large shoals, and sea-
birds nest in thousands on the shore. Although
the birds do not form highly organized communi-

PERMANENT
SOCIETIES

Rooks live together in communities called rookeries. They seem to have certain rules of behaviour & to punish birds who break the rules. Jackdaws often build their nests in rookeries & feed with the rooks.

ties with various duties for different groups, there are always a few in each
flock who keep watch while the others sleep. Several kinds of land birds live
together in colonies. The large untidy nests of rooks are always seen in numbers
at the tops of tall trees. These birds seem to play games together. One game
consists of flying to a great height, then folding the wings and letting the body
fall to within fifty feet from the ground. Then the wings are suddenly spread,
and the birds skid about like a fast-moving car whose brakes have been put on
too quickly. The birds seem to enjoy the sense of danger, and caw and walk
about excitedly before climbing into the air again to repeat the performance.
Rooks appear to have their own laws, and members of the colony who break
these laws are punished. If a pair of young rooks decide to build their nest

249

An ant taking home the caterpillar of a Blue butterfly. This gives off a honey-like liquid & in return is fed on the ants' own larvae.

An ant whose body is used as a store for honey dew is giving some of the liquid to a worker.

An ant cultivating mushrooms under ground

Ants working together: carrying a small twig which is to be used as building material.

some way off from the rook village, the rest of the colony angrily pull the nest to pieces, and force the young couple to be more sociable.

Partridges, who live in small companies or "coveys," sleep in a circle, tails together and heads outwards, so that an enemy can be seen approaching from any direction. Sandmartins build their nests in tunnels which they dig in sandy banks. They form colonies whose members hunt and migrate together, returning each year to the same bank. If some new nesting place is chosen, the whole group goes together and leaves no stragglers behind.

Animals often band together when hunting. Pelicans go fishing in groups, and when they have found a suitable bay, they form a half-circle facing the shore. Then they narrow it by paddling towards the beach, catching all the fish which are trapped between them and the sand. Wolves live in cold parts of the world, where animal life is less plentiful

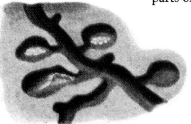

The underground nests of ants are usually built on this plan. Long galleries lead into rooms which are used as nurseries, granaries, mushroom vaults, etc.

All ants are social animals & their communities are highly organized. Each ant has one special duty to perform & no other. In ant communities there are queens who lay eggs, & males who fertilize them. The workers of some kinds of ants vary in size according to their duties. Ants who are soldiers have large heads and powerful jaws.

A Silverfish insect snatches food as it is passed from one ant to another.

A beetle is fed while standing on the back of a small ant. It pays for its food by giving out a sweet juice from its body.

Workers of the Slave-making ants raid the nests of other ants & carry off cocoons from which they rear slaves.

than in the tropics. They dare not risk losing their scarce prey, and band themselves together in packs under a leader. With such numbers they can surround the hunted animals and head them off. When the pack is sleeping, sentinel wolves keep guard.

The hunted animals on their side form herds to withstand the attacks of the hunters. They are usually animals which graze in open country, such as horses, sheep, oxen and deer. Although the herd is made up of little more than a number of animals under the leadership of an older one, there is a rough division of labour, especially in times of danger. When a flock of wild sheep is threatened, the lambs and ewes go to the rear, and the rams line up in front, the older ones to the fore. Then the whole flock slowly advances, and the rams stamp together with their fore feet. When there is no

Mites riding on an ant, which they gently stroke when they want it to give them food.

The nests of social insects usually include other creatures, who may be either helpful or harmful to the community. Ants cultivate various insects for the sake of their sweet juices. Some guests come uninvited & steal the food and eat the offspring of their hosts. They are called parasites: they live at the expense of the workers & give nothing in return.

Bees & wasps have many insect guests. Some are welcome scavengers & keep the nests clean: others, such as the Bee-hive beetle, feed on their hosts' grubs.

251

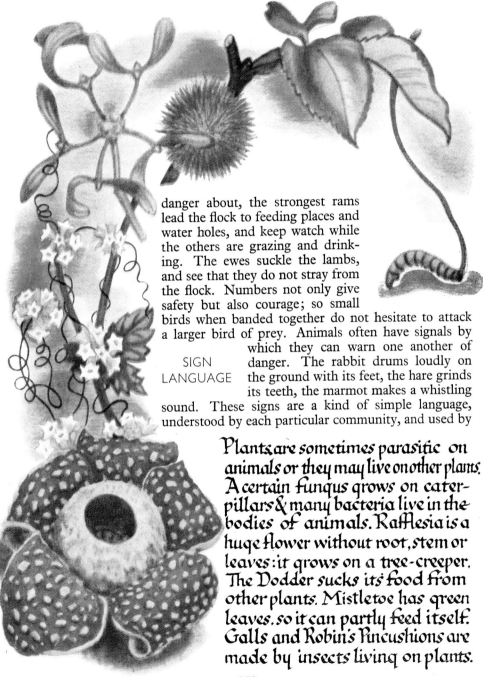

danger about, the strongest rams lead the flock to feeding places and water holes, and keep watch while the others are grazing and drinking. The ewes suckle the lambs, and see that they do not stray from the flock. Numbers not only give safety but also courage; so small birds when banded together do not hesitate to attack a larger bird of prey. Animals often have signals by which they can warn one another of danger. The rabbit drums loudly on the ground with its feet, the hare grinds its teeth, the marmot makes a whistling sound. These signs are a kind of simple language, understood by each particular community, and used by

SIGN LANGUAGE

Plants are sometimes parasitic on animals or they may live on other plants. A certain fungus grows on caterpillars & many bacteria live in the bodies of animals. Rafflesia is a huge flower without root, stem or leaves: it grows on a tree-creeper. The Dodder sucks its food from other plants. Mistletoe has green leaves, so it can partly feed itself. Galls and Robin's Pincushions are made by insects living on plants.

252

the animal for the safety of its fellows.

The fishes which make up vast shoals of millions of individuals, know neither father nor mother nor offspring. Even the fishes and amphibians which look after their eggs scarcely wait to see the hatched young set off on their new lives. The great groups of the higher animals, on the other hand, are often made up of families which keep together for a season at least, until the children are grown up and can look after themselves. Each family in the larger group may consist of one male, several females and their many offspring; or it may be like a human family, a father and mother and a few children. Among birds and mammals there are both kinds of families, and in a few cases parents and children keep together for several years. The groups which are formed by families of men are called tribes.

FAMILIES

A tribe is often one large family of grandparents, mothers and fathers, and numerous grandchildren. When they settle in one place, instead of wandering in search of food like herds and packs of animals, their cluster of homes becomes a village. Villages grow and become towns and cities. Villages, towns and cities, with the people

TRIBES

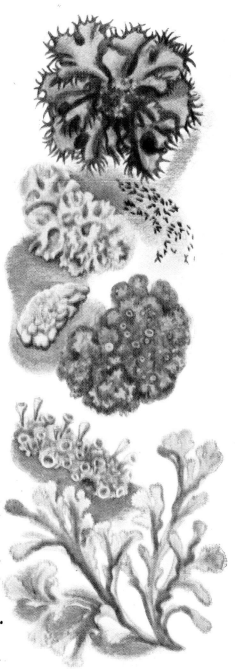

An organism may live in or on the body of another without being a parasite. Lichens are made of two plants, a fungus and an alga living in close partnership. The fungus feeds on some of the food which the green alga can make by means of its chlorophyll. In return the alga receives shelter, support, moisture & mineral salts.

253

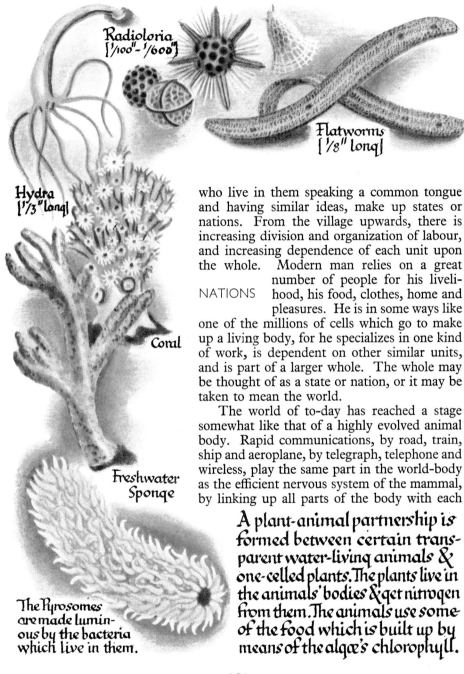

Radioloria
[¹/₁₀₀" - ¹/₆₀₀"]

Flatworms
[¹/₈" long]

Hydra
[¹/₃" long]

Coral

Freshwater
Sponge

The Pyrosomes
are made lumin-
ous by the bacteria
which live in them.

who live in them speaking a common tongue and having similar ideas, make up states or nations. From the village upwards, there is increasing division and organization of labour, and increasing dependence of each unit upon the whole. Modern man relies on a great number of people for his liveli-

NATIONS hood, his food, clothes, home and pleasures. He is in some ways like one of the millions of cells which go to make up a living body, for he specializes in one kind of work, is dependent on other similar units, and is part of a larger whole. The whole may be thought of as a state or nation, or it may be taken to mean the world.

The world of to-day has reached a stage somewhat like that of a highly evolved animal body. Rapid communications, by road, train, ship and aeroplane, by telegraph, telephone and wireless, play the same part in the world-body as the efficient nervous system of the mammal, by linking up all parts of the body with each

A plant-animal partnership is formed between certain transparent water-living animals & one-celled plants. The plants live in the animals' bodies & get nitrogen from them. The animals use some of the food which is built up by means of the algæ's chlorophyll.

Orchids have many strange ways of getting insects to pollinate them. One orchid has a honey-spur 11" long & is pollinated by a moth with a very long trunk.

other. No large part of the highly organized animal body can be hurt or diseased without bringing suffering to the rest. In the same way, the various parts of the world and the people who make up those parts, are so closely interlocked that war, famine or poverty in one place must in time affect the whole.

THE WORLD STATE

Man has reached the highest degree of social development among the vertebrates. Among the invertebrates the social insects have reached a similar position. Most insects live alone, but some share a common dwelling for the sake of protection, especially when they are in the caterpillar stage and particularly tempting to birds. They spin silk tents, or make a communal cocoon; or live in crowds on the undersides of leaves, tails in, heads out, and bodies curved to

The lines on the petals of many flowers point towards the place where the insect may find honey.

Many plants depend on insects to pollinate their seeds. In this partnership the insect may feed on pollen & nectar in return for carrying the fertilizing pollen from one flower to another. Some flowers are made so that only one kind of insect can visit them. Others trap insects so that they cannot crawl out without touching the stigma & stamens.

The cultivated fig depends on a small wasp for the pollination of its internal flowers.

255

Animals as well as plants may depend on the help of other creatures for their reproduction. The young of the freshwater mussel attach themselves by their sticky threads to small fish like minnows or bitterling. Then they grip the fish with their hooked shells & live in its skin for three months.

fit tightly together. There is no community life beyond a simple coming together like the shoaling of fishes, except in the common construction of the tent or cocoon. When the caterpillars become butterflies, each one goes its own way.

Some insects, however, live together all their lives and share the work of the community between them. These are the social insects, the bees, wasps, ants and termites, whose societies have reached a high level of organization. Though sometimes compared to the societies of man, actually they are built on quite a different plan. Social insects have no leaders: their queen round whom the life of the community centres is the source of its being. She is the mother of every member of the society, and devotes all her energies to the laying of thousands of eggs. There is no family life; the eggs are taken from the queen by the workers and are brought up in specially built nurseries. There are few males or females, for most of the insects are undeveloped females called neuters. One or two true, egg-laying females are reared as future queens, and the males are kept to fertilize their eggs. The workers have their different duties, and these vary according to the society to which the insect belongs.

SOCIAL INSECTS

There are between three and four thousand kinds of ants, and about twenty thousand sorts of bees, though less than a thousand kinds of bees are social. There are various sorts of wasps, some large, others small, some social but most of them solitary. The many kinds of termites, or "white ants," all live in highly organized societies.

The social insects run their communities in ways which are sometimes alike and sometimes widely different. The workers of the honey bees are all of one kind though they have various duties to do at different times. Soon after the worker bee comes out of the chrysalis, it becomes a nursery maid, and for three days it does nothing but clean out the used cells and get them ready for a fresh batch of eggs. During this time the worker rests a good deal. For the next seven days it is a nurse, and feeds the grubs on honey and HONEY BEES bees' bread. When it is ten days old, the worker comes down near the door of the hive and acts as porter: its duty now is to take the honey from the bees that come in, and to carry it to the combs to be stored. During this time the bee is also wax-maker and cell-builder. At the age of eighteen days it passes three days as sentinel, and while on guard duty the young worker begins to take short flights from the hive. Gradually it learns to know the country near by, so that when its time comes to make journeys from the hive, it does not get lost. The time for setting out comes when the bee is about three weeks old, and it is then promoted to duty of the highest grade, that of collecting nectar and pollen.

The few kinds of wasps which are social, run their communities in many ways like those of the bees; but the societies of ants are rather different. They still consist of an egg-laying queen, a few males, ANTS and a main body of sexless workers; but in the ants the three castes differ from each other much more than the queens, drones and workers of bees and wasps. The workers of some kinds of ants are of various shapes and sizes according to their particular work. The soldiers are distinguished by their specially large heads and great, sharp mandibles. The jaws of others are adapted for cutting leaves, and of others for

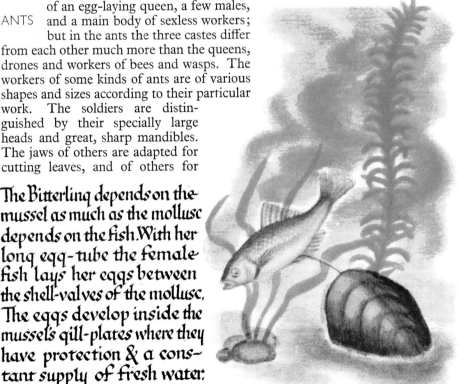

The Bitterling depends on the mussel as much as the mollusc depends on the fish. With her long egg-tube the female fish lays her eggs between the shell-valves of the mollusc. The eggs develop inside the mussel's gill-plates where they have protection & a constant supply of fresh water.

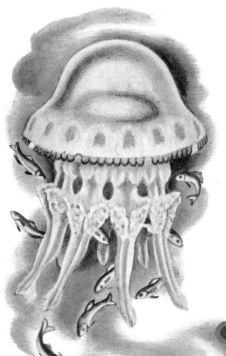

chewing up grain to make the ant-cakes on which the community feeds. Animal workers have to grow their tools on their bodies since they cannot make or handle them. The duties among the different kinds of ants are more varied than among the bees and wasps. Ants have a more varied diet than bees, which feed on and store honey, or than wasps that feed chiefly on flies and caterpillars. The driver ants do not make nests, but wander from place to place, occasionally pitching camp in a hollow tree or under a fallen log. From their shelter they go out in search of prey, in broad columns several hundred yards long. In these raids they clear their path of every insect, besides attacking small reptiles

Some small fishes seek protection in the bodies of other animals. Young Horse mackerel shelter beneath the bell & among the tentacles of jelly fishes. A little coral fish takes refuge when alarmed in the body cavity of a sea anemone. Other small fishes live among the stinging tentacles of the Portuguese man-o'-war. The Fierasfer fish makes its home in the body of a sea cucumber.

258

and small mammals. They will even destroy such large animals as birds, pigs and monkeys.

The more highly specialized groups of ants are plant-feeders only. They may owe their greater degree of social organization to the fact that plant food is more abundant and is obtained more easily than animal food. Ants which are content to live on seeds or tiny mushrooms, or on the sweet juices of flowers, can gather their food at leisure and can store it for a considerable time. They are freed from the continual strain of hunting and killing. At the same time, the growing and storing of the various crops calls for a high degree of organization within the community. Just as man began to develop his society when he ceased to wander and settled and grew crops, so for the same reason, perhaps, the plant-feeding ants have evolved their wonderful communities.

The harvester ants gather seeds from plants and from the ground, remove the husks and store the grain in special granaries. Some harvesters usually

grow their own "ant-rice" in carefully weeded ground around the nest. The Sauba ants collect quantities of fresh leaves which they cut up with their jaws, and pack into underground rooms. In time, the leaves decay and form hotbeds on which are grown crops of small mushrooms which the ants use as food for the larvæ and adults. In this way the community is sure of having food all the year round, whatever the weather outside the nest. Some ants take other insects home to their nests, and tend them for the sake of the sweet juices which they get from their bodies. Greenfly, scale-insects, and the caterpillars of some blue butterflies are all used for "milking" purposes.

Termites are often called "white ants," but they are in no way related to the true ants. In spite of this, they are very ant-like in many of their ways. There are about a thousand different kinds of termites, and they all live in small or large communities, which may consist of more than half TERMITES a million insects. They have five different castes : three capable of reproduction, and two take on the duties of workers and soldiers. The workers feed the queens, forage for food, take care of the eggs and young, and build the big, strong nests which sometimes tower twenty-five feet from the ground. These palaces are made of earth and wood, cemented together with saliva. Inside there is a maze of tunnels, galleries and rooms, all surrounding the cell in which live the king and queen. Food is stored in many of the chambers, but some termites, like the Sauba ants, grow their own mushrooms.

Both man and beast, bird and insect, have found that living and working together in a larger whole make for the good of each separate part. Man and, in a far lesser degree, the sociable monkeys and apes have greater mental powers than the other mammals. Parrots and rooks live in

The claws of the Melia crab are too small and feeble for it to catch prey or ward off attacks. So the crab arms itself with two sea anemones and uses them as weapons, and as a means of collecting food.

societies and are very intelligent birds. The social insects are, in their peculiar instinctive way, the most highly evolved of the invertebrates. They have, however, lost their individuality, and have no existence outside that of the larger body to which they belong. Man has not entirely merged himself in the greater whole, but can think and act for himself and to a certain

INSECT SOCIETIES AND MAN SOCIETIES

extent plan his own life. Sometimes he takes a line of thought which is different from and perhaps better than that of his fellows. Human society is continually being re-formed in this way, sometimes in great sweeping movements, but more often in small ways, almost unnoticed yet not unimportant. If men should become merely the passive parts of a large State machine, as the social insects have done, they would lose that individual initiative through which is slowly but surely evolved a better state of society.

All animals are more or less dependent on each other in some way, either for food or for protection. Some live in communities, others form temporary or life-long partnerships with creatures of the same or of quite another kind.

PARTNERSHIPS

Sometimes these partnerships are good for both sides, or at least cause no annoyance to either. Sometimes the advantage is all on one side, and the partner which benefits brings trouble and even death to the other. When one creature lives entirely at the expense of another it is called a parasite. The parasites, which live on the skin or inside the bodies of other animals, pay for their laziness by the loss of many advances in evolution made by their ancestors. Their sense organs and digestive organs become less efficient, and some of them lose to a great extent their powers of

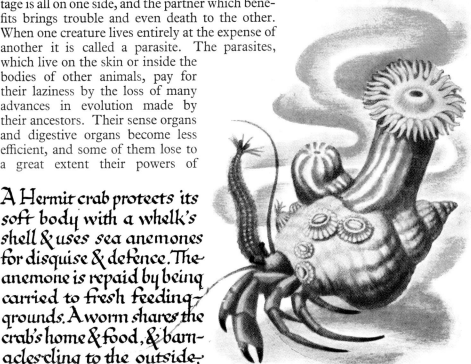

A Hermit crab protects its soft body with a whelk's shell & uses sea anemones for disguise & defence. The anemone is repaid by being carried to fresh feeding-grounds. A worm shares the crab's home & food, & barnacles cling to the outside.

The Cuckoo is a parasite when it is young: it kills the offspring of its foster parents & is given the food which should have gone to the true fledglings. When it is full grown it finds its own food but it makes use of the nests of other birds for the laying of its eggs.

moving from one place to another. Plants which live wholly on other plants lose their leaves, stems or roots, and often their green colouring matter, chlorophyll, which gives the green plant the power to build up its food in its own body.

PARASITES   The parasitic plants which give up their green-ness thus become completely dependent on their host for their very being. By giving up the struggle for life, and by letting other creatures provide them with food and shelter without making any return, the parasites have gone backwards instead of forwards in evolution.

Some parasitic animals do not live on the bodies of others but find their way into their homes. There they steal the hosts' food and often eat their offspring. The social insects are the animals most troubled by these unwanted guests : bees, wasps and ants are all victimized by other insects and by mites, spiders and crustaceans. Sometimes the ants themselves introduce the robbers into their nests, for they have a craving for sweetness which many kinds of beetles, and some plant-lice and caterpillars, can satisfy. These insects give off a sweet,

"GUESTS"   syrupy liquid, and in return the ants allow them to live in their homes, rifle their store cupboards and cat their children. The silverfish-insect seems to give no payment for its board and lodging but waits until one ant is passing food to another, then snatches the drop of liquid and makes off at high speed. Some beetles stroke the ants until they go into a kind of doze, then take their fill from the ants' food store.

Bees and wasps are also troubled in this way, though some of their guests pay well for their lodging by eating up the refuse of the nest and cleaning out the cells. These paying-guests are drone-flies, and they are treated with respect by their wasp and bee landlords. Other flies and beetles, like the cuckoo among birds, have their offspring brought up at the expense of their unwilling hosts. The foster children either eat up the grubs of the bee or wasp, or are fed by the workers on the food of the rightful children.

Among the vertebrates such uninvited lodgers are rare. The best known example is that of the prairie-marmot, the rattlesnake and the owl. The marmot is a little animal somewhat like a guinea-pig; it lives in burrows which it digs with much labour in the hard, sun-baked soil. Sooner or later a rattlesnake and a burrowing-owl save themselves the drudgery of digging their own homes by coming to live in the marmot's burrow. Unfortunately for the little animal, they expect free board as well as free lodging, and eat up her young ones as well as those of each

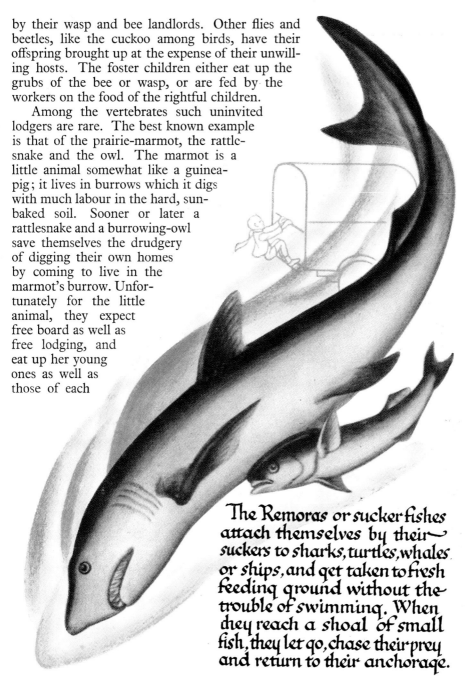

The Remoras or sucker-fishes attach themselves by their suckers to sharks, turtles, whales or ships, and get taken to fresh feeding ground without the trouble of swimming. When they reach a shoal of small fish, they let go, chase their prey and return to their anchorage.

263

Many animals have attendants who feed on the débris & parasites which collect on their bodies. An Egyptian plover eats the leeches which infest the skin and gums of the crocodile. The bird also warns the reptile of approaching danger by flying off with loud cries of alarm.

other. At last the marmot leaves, and digs a new home somewhere else, but quite often she is not allowed to enjoy it by herself for long. An owl or a rattlesnake, or both these creatures, notice the new burrow and come to live in it, and the marmot's troubles begin again. Petrels and other seabirds often share the burrow of the Tuatera, a lizard-like reptile, which does not seem to mind its lodgers and their offspring. Shell-ducks and puffins share the burrows of rabbits when they are bringing up their chicks. The shell-duck is well behaved, but the puffin sometimes kills the young of the rabbit to make room for its own.

In the sea there are many cases where a defenceless creature seeks a temporary shelter within the body of a larger animal. Young horse-mackerel swim in shoals beneath the umbrella of the jellyfish. This hides them from the hungry eyes of gulls above, while the stinging tentacles shield them from enemies in the

Cattle-egrets ride on large animals such as the hippopotamus & dig out ticks & warble-flies from their thick hides.

water. The fishes pay for their shelter by eating the small crustaceans which otherwise take food out of the jellyfish's mouth.

LIVING SHELTERS

Other fishes hide among the stinging-bodies of the Portuguese-man-of-war, which occasionally takes payment for this privilege by eating one of the little fish. Certain coral-fishes seek shelter within the body-cavity of a large sea-anemone. They share this refuge with another guest, a prawn. The brightly coloured little fishes attract the attention of carnivorous fish which follow them to the sea-anemone, and are themselves caught by the hungry tentacles. Guests and host then share the captured prey.

Sea-cucumbers, starfish and giant-whelks are all used as shelters by various fishes. Animals such as sponges, sea-anemones and hydroids, which cannot swim of their own accord, attach themselves to some animal which can move from one place to another. Here the benefit is on both sides; the non-swimming animal is carried to fresh feeding grounds, and in return it gives protection to its carrier by disguising it from its enemies. There are hydroids which grow on the spines of a tropical fish and save it from being eaten by larger fish : other hydroids grow on the shell inhabited by a hermit-crab. The shells are usually those of the whelk or periwinkle, and are used by the hermit-crab to protect its soft, shell-less hind-body. As the crab grows, it has to change its adopted shell several times for a larger one : but sometimes a sponge settles on the small shell-house of a young crab, and crab and sponge grow together at the same rate. In this way the sponge eventually takes the place of a shell, and the crab lives in the sponge's body.

Hermit-crabs often plant sea-anemones on their borrowed shells, pulling the animal off its native rock, and holding it on to the shell until it has taken a firm hold. When the crabs change to larger shells, they transplant the anemones

Mixed partnerships are rare among the higher vertebrates, who usually live only with their own kind. The Tuatera however often shares its burrow with seabirds. The fox sometimes brings up her family in a badger's earth. Badgers are very clean and orderly animals, & foxes are dirty and untidy, so this partnership is rather one sided.

also. In this case the anemones profit by the scraps which float up to them while the crabs are tearing their food to pieces. In return they hide the crabs' shells, while their stinging tentacles discourage the enemies of the crabs from coming too near. Sometimes a bristle-worm shares the inside of the shell with the crab and

LIVING WEAPONS

feeds on the floating food scraps. One of the tropical crabs has small and feeble claws which are of no use as weapons; so it picks two sea-anemones off the rocks, and walks about with one in each claw. The anemone, although it benefits by being taken to fresh feeding grounds, has to work hard, to collect food for the crab and to protect it against cuttlefish.

On land, animals of similar size do not grow upon one another as they do in the sea, but many small parasites, such as mites, ticks, worms, leeches and flies live in or on the bodies of larger creatures. Bison, hippopotamuses, rhinoceroses and other large, plant-eating animals, are much troubled by the various parasites which live on their skins. They gladly entertain the birds which settle on their heads and backs, and feed on these nuisances. The crocodile's bird friend is a plover, which not

SCAVENGERS only pecks about on the reptile's head, but scuttles in and out of its great mouth as it searches for leeches, and scraps of past meals which may lodge in the teeth. Even insects seem to harbour such scavengers. The female of the carpenter-bee is very hairy, and spends much of her time burrowing in wood and earth. She always has a number of mites on her body, but as she has a little pocket in her back for these small creatures, it seems probable that they are friends rather than enemies. It is likely that they keep her clean by feeding on the debris which clings to her long hairs. The male carpenter-bee does no work, but spends his time in the air and sunshine. He does not get dirty, and he has no mites and no mite pocket. Many kinds of burrowing beetles have mites on their undersides, which probably keep the insect clean in those parts which it cannot reach with its own legs.

Sometimes the lives of two creatures are so bound together that one at least of the partners would die without the other. The lichen is made up of two plants, a fungus and an alga. The fungus has no chlorophyll, so it cannot make food from the air with the help of sunlight as the green plant can. The alga is green and can make its own food, but it has no firm parts to hold it up into the air or to help it to climb. So the green

PARTNERS alga makes food which partly feeds the fungus, and the fungus gives support and mineral salts to the alga. Many animals rely on algæ, tiny one-celled water-plants, for at least part of their

A temporary partnership is often formed between the Honey-guide bird & a small badger. The bird feeds on the grubs of bees & wasps but is not strong enough to attack a nest of several thousand insects. The badger is fond of honey but his legs are too short for making long treks in search of it. When the bird finds a hive it guides the badger to it. He breaks it open & eats the honey while the bird feasts on the grubs. Sometimes a man notices the bird-animal procession and joins it and takes his share of the honey.

food. The algæ live in their transparent bodies and give them a green colour. In this kind of partnership the animal absorbs the sugars which the green plant makes, and sometimes feeds on the plants themselves; while the plant uses the nitrogen compounds in the animal's body for making its own food.

Some animals digest their food with the help of the still smaller, plantlike bacteria or of minute fungi. All the creatures which suck plant-juices, such as greenfly, have such internal partners; so do the bloodsuckers—ticks, mosquitoes, fleas, leeches and the rest. Bacteria and fungi help the processes of digestion in nearly all the wood-eating and many of the plant-eating animals, such as some of the beetles, wood-wasps, rodents, hooved mammals and certain birds. Termites depend on a one-celled plant-animal to digest the wood on which they feed. All leguminous plants, the peas, beans, lupins and clovers, have swellings on their roots in which live millions of bacteria. The bacteria have the power of taking nitrogen from the air, which they make into a food-stuff which the plant needs. By means of its chlorophyll the plant in its turn can make food on which the bacteria feed. Insect-pollinated flowers and flower-visiting insects, although they do not live together in close partnership, are as dependent on each other as the fungus and alga which make up a lichen.

It is only among the higher vertebrates that partnerships are found in which neither partner benefits except in the companionship of the other. There is no friendship among the invertebrate animals, though they work together conscientiously and even, it would seem, unselfishly. Most vertebrates appear to need the company of their fellows. A fish in an aquarium thrives if it has a fish or two of the same kind to share its tank, though it shows no joy in their company. The warm-blooded vertebrates show quite clearly that they take pleasure in the fellowship of other animals. Parent birds are usually devoted to each other and to their children, and they not only work together, but play together with much enjoyment. The friendship between mammals is even more marked, and a mammal which is denied the comradeship of one of its own kind will make friends with some other sort of animal. Such strange companions as a goose and a cat, a dog and a badger, a horse and a reindeer, or a lion-cub and rabbits, are only found in domestic or captive animals; since in the wild state there is always an opportunity for animals to meet their own kind.

FRIENDSHIP

There is a tendency in all living things to draw together. This is seen in its simplest form in the loose clusters of single-celled plants and animals, and in its most complex form in the great nations of men. The purposes may be varied and the societies formed may be temporary or permanent. Temporary associations are usually made for reasons of self-interest only; food may be plentiful in some spot and animals meet there to feed in numbers, each one for itself. Other conditions, of temperature, of wetness or dryness, darkness or sunshine, may bring animals together in a similar way. Crowds of them may be driven by the same urge, resulting in hunger-marches, breeding-swarms, and migration. In these temporary

269

gatherings the animals meet for their own convenience and part when their need is satisfied. But in permanent societies they combine to create a social unit.

Such a drawing-together always brings with it not only benefit, but a certain degree of self-sacrifice, or at least of help to one another. Society, whether of two or of large numbers of individuals, implies a mutual CIVILIZATION tolerance and a working together for the common good. Those creatures which take all and give nothing, the parasitic plants and animals, are sliding backwards in the course of evolution, while the rest of life goes forward. The phrase "survival of the fittest" may have several meanings, for living things have evolved many kinds of fitness : but in some ways those animals are fittest which support and are dependent on one another. Mammals have won their high place, not by constant warfare with each other, but by care of their offspring and the consequent establishment of family and social units.

It is on the social unit that man and his civilization have been built. His body is a society of millions of cells, each playing its part in the complex whole, as he himself plays his part in the greater society to which he belongs. Without the close association of other human beings, and the mutual aid and interchange of ideas which such fellowship brings, man would scarcely have evolved beyond the other mammals. It is through contact with his fellows, which enriches while demanding sacrifice, that man has developed language, giving him the power to speak and write his own thoughts, and to hear and read the thoughts of others.

A cat & a jackdaw go hunting together. True friendship is only found among man & the higher animals. If animals live in surroundings where they cannot meet with their own species, they often make friends with animals of a different kind.

270

THE HEAD
OF
THE FAMILY

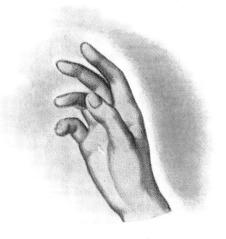

Man's hand has given him power
over other living things. It
may be used to
destroy or protect
them.

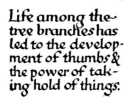

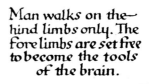

Man walks on the
hind limbs only. The
fore limbs are set free
to become the tools
of the brain.

Life among the
tree branches has
led to the develop-
ment of thumbs &
the power of tak-
ing hold of things.

In the bear, as in
most mammals,
the body is rais-
ed on strong
legs.

HOW HANDS & ARMS EVOLVED FROM FINS

Man's hands & arms, together with
his larger brain, have made him
master of the other living things.
They have evolved through stages
similar to those seen in these
animals who, except ape man,
are all living at the present time.
Five bones in each paired-fin of
the fish became fingers & toes in
the land creatures. Some animals including man kept to the
early, five-fingered form of hand
instead of developing specialized
hoofs, claws, wings or flippers.

Lizards carry their
bodies clear of the
ground on short legs

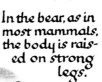

Newts drag their bodies
along the ground using
their limbs as oars
rather than as supports.

The mudfish uses its
fins to push itself
along on the bottom. The mud-
hopper comes on land & scrambles
about on its fins.

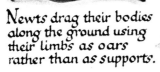

Fishes have 2 paired-fins
which correspond to the
4 limbs of land animals.

From being a hunter and a wanderer, man changed his way of living when he learnt to till the soil. While his crops were growing he had to settle in one place: this led to building of homes & development of human society. The first harvest may have been gathered 10,000 or 15,000 years ago. In Egypt and Irak the land was certainly tilled 6,000 years B.C.

The Head of the Family

There has been life on the planet Earth for about one thousand million years. Reptiles, the first true land vertebrates, have been in existence for about two hundred and seventy million years, and mammals for over one hundred million years. The mammal which carries and nourishes its young in its body until they are well developed, has been on earth for perhaps seventy million years. Man-ape appeared less than ten million years ago, but humans who were no longer apes did not emerge until about one million years ago. Man in his present form is only about twenty thousand years old; his era has scarcely begun. Yet in his short time on earth he has learnt to control, to a certain extent, his own surroundings and the lives of other living things.

THE NEWCOMER

In many ways man is inferior to the other animals. He has not the beauty of glossy fur nor of glowing feathers. He does not possess the strength of the bull, nor the grace and swiftness of the gazelle. He can neither swim under water like the fish, nor soar in the air like the bird. Yet he has gone farther along

T

273

the path of evolution than all the other living things. Where they have specialized each group in its own peculiar direction, man has remained adaptable. Animals' bodies are more rigidly set for one particular environment, their minds only ready to deal with one special set of circumstances. In the long process of evolution, they have had to adapt and re-adapt themselves many times; but their changes have been slow, each change taking perhaps hundreds of generations to bring to completion. Man, by means of his brain and his hands, can adapt himself quickly to changing conditions; not by altering slowly the shape and size of his body, but by making use of the things which surround him.

Man sprang from the same stock as the higher apes. He has a great deal in common with them, particularly in his earliest history and in the early stages of his present-day body. He owes much to the fact that his far-off ancestors lived in

Wheat may have been the first cultivated plant. The grain was crushed between a flat stone of hard rock & a long grinding stone flattened on one side. This wooden statuette is probably six thousand years old.

trees. In these remote forbears of man and ape, the five-fingered limbs of the primitive mammal had not changed into rigid hoofs, or clawed talons, or webbed flippers. They had remained plastic, and had developed the power of grasping the branches, with four fingers curved one way and the fifth, the thumb, curved round to meet them. With these useful limbs, the animals swung themselves from branch to branch, and tails were gradually discarded. Since their lives depended on the accurate judgment of distance from bough to bough, sight grew keen and quick, and the sense of touch became more important than the sense of smell. A life of this kind drew the body from a four-footed to an upright position; and when, perhaps because the climate changed and their forests disappeared, these tree-dwellers came to live on the ground, they still held their bodies upright. Their forelimbs, now freed from being a means of transport, were used for grasping sticks, and later on for using weapons and tools. The muzzle was no longer needed as a tool for catching or gathering food, or as a weapon of defence. As the hand learned to feed the body and defend it, the teeth and the muscles for biting were reduced. The muzzle grew smaller and smaller, until at last it flattened itself into a face.

MAN'S PEDIGREE

At the same time the brain and brain-case grew larger as these animals, once safely hidden in trees, led their fuller and richer but more dangerous life on the ground. During their long ages of tree life, these creatures had not developed the usual animal defences of teeth, claws or speed. When they came defenceless to the ground, they had to rely on their wits to save them from their enemies. The increased danger of their lives brought about the need for hunting, living and working together. This encouraged the development of speech and the growth of language. Language gave man the ability to share the thoughts and feelings of his fellows, and helped to bring about his society and civilization.

Man, like other animals, has always been dependent on plants for some of the oxygen which he breathes, and for all of the food which he eats. He took a great

MAN, THE TILLER OF THE SOIL

step forward when instead of relying entirely on wild plants for food, he began to grow them for himself. When he had sown seeds, he had to wait for them to sprout and mature. This took nearly a year, and during that time man had to settle near his crops instead of wandering from place to place. Homes were built, and the civilized arts, such as spinning and weaving, pottery and metal-beating, were developed.

The word "cultivate" comes from a Latin word meaning to plough or till. The first ploughs were probably hooked pieces of wood, which merely roughened the surface of the soil. Later, the ploughs were armed with metal, and beasts were trained to pull while man guided them. By choosing seeds from the best plants to sow the following year, and by watering the crops when rainfall was scanty, man gradually pro-

CULTIVATION duced "culti-vated" varieties.

Later he found that he could pollinate and cross-pollinate his plants, and produce new and better

The date palm bears male and female flowers on separate trees. The ancient Babylonians used to cut branches of male flowers & shake them over the female flowers. This method of cross-pollination ensured the fruiting of the date.

Present-day apples have been developed from the small crab apple. The plum may have descended from crosses between the sloe & cherry-plum.

Oranges have less rind than formerly.

The wild cabbage has given rise to the garden cabbage, savoy, curly kale, brussels sprouts, broccoli, cauliflower & kohl rabi.

kinds. Cross-pollination is still used to-day in order to combine the good qualities of two or more plants in one. The stigma of one plant is brushed with the pollen of another, and in this way the seeds are fertilized. The resulting offspring will inherit the qualities of both parents, the bad as well as the good. The bad qualities, such as liability to disease or late flowering may, in turn, be cancelled out by crossing the new plant with another plant which has no such weaknesses. Another way is to join or graft one kind of plant on to another of similar kind ; so that, for instance, the strength of one is combined with the sweetness of the fruit of the other. In these ways man has produced flowers, fruits and vegetables which are very different from the original plants.

The most important plant food comes from grasses. When these are cultivated and their seeds are used for food, they are known as cereals. The word "cereal" comes from the Latin *Ceres*, the name of the Roman goddess of growing plants. In the East, rice is the main cereal, and in other parts of the world maize, barley and rye are the staple GRASS foods. Wheat was probably the first grass to be cultivated, between ten thousand and fifteen thousand years ago. Western civilization depends on this grain more than on any other cereal, and during the

276

The wild heart's-ease is the ancestor of the garden pansies.

The cultivation of the wild straw-berry probably began in the 15th. century.

past fifty years especially, man has worked to produce new and better strains. Not only does he want full-eared wheats with large grains, but the grain should be "beardless," "hard," of good milling and bread-making quality, and resistant to disease. By breeding early-ripening wheats, man can grow this crop farther north where the summers are shorter. Between 1911 and 1916 the limit of wheat farming was pushed fifty miles northwards. Since then other wheats have been bred which ripen still more quickly, and another forty miles have been added to the northern limit. This gives the world a wider belt of this valuable grass.

All the cereals contain a good deal of starch. This important food is found in all plants. Potatoes are especially rich in it and they can be used to take the place of cereals. The potato

By seed-selection, cross-pollination & various methods of cultivation, plants have been evolved which are very different from their original ancestors. Cabbages, lettuces & onions have more leaves, cereal grasses bear fuller seed-heads; fleshy fruits have thinner skins & less seed, & garden flowers have larger & more numerous petals.

The many-shaped chrysanthemums were evolved from daisy-like flowers.

277

The domestication of animals, probably preceded the cultivation of plants. The Egyptians of five thousand years ago had their tame oxen, gazelles, cats & dogs.

was cultivated in South America for centuries before it was brought to Europe. The first tuber reached Vienna some time between 1580 and 1590, and was brought to England soon afterwards. Gerarde, the English herbalist, writing in Shakespeare's time, described the potato as having roots "as a ball, some oval or egg-fashion, some larger, some shorter, the which knobby roots are fastened into the stalks with an infinite number of thready strings. It groweth naturally in America where it was first discovered, as report says, by Columbus." The potato was not used much as a food until about two hundred years later. It grew well in Ireland, where the population increased from two millions in 1784 to over eight millions in 1845. In that year potato blight ruined the crop; many people died of starvation, and all who could do so emigrated to America. Just as plants made animal life possible on this planet, so they have helped to mould the history of mankind.

POTATOES

During recent years, man has made great advances in the art of cultivation. There are centres for experiment and research in plant-breeding and crop-rearing all over the civilized world. Man has realized that the substances taken out of the soil by growing plants must be replaced if the next crops are to flourish. Farmyard manure is becoming scarce since machines have taken the place of horses, so artificial manures are used instead.

MANURE

Electricity may play a part in the cultivation of the future. This, in various forms, has been found to have a quickening effect on crops. Sometimes the soil is electrically heated with low current electric cables laid beneath the forcing beds; sometimes overhead wires are used, and electricity is discharged directly into the soil. Experiments have been made in the electrification

ELECTRICITY

of seeds before they are sown, and seeds treated in this way have grown into plants which yielded fifty per cent. more food. Artificial lighting and soil-warming are used to grow plants during the long winter within the Arctic circle, and land which has been useless until now has produced good food. By means of artificial heat of various kinds, plants are forced for early markets or grown completely out of season.

Water plays as great a part in the growing of plants as soil and heat. In early days, man could choose the most fertile places in which to make his home, but as the numbers of human beings increased, less fertile areas had to be used. Strong peoples drove weaker tribes to the very edge of the deserts, where they had to find new ways of cultivation in order to coax grain and fruits IRRIGATION from the parched earth. It is not known when man first began to water his crops, but the remains of ancient canals, which must be thousands of years old, are found in widely scattered places in the world. The Egyptian shadoof, the Persian water-wheel and Archimedes' screw were all in use two thousand years ago and are still used to-day, though they have been largely replaced by more effective

The silkworm has been reared for several thousand years. Chinese legend says that the empress Lei-tsu who lived some time about 2600 B.C. was the first to raise silkworms & to unwind and weave the threads from their cocoons.

The cocoons are heated before the silk is unwound.

water-carriers. Pumps worked by steam, or by an internal combustion engine, or by electricity, can pour water out upon the thirsty land. In this way desert places in the Soudan, in India, and in the western United States have been made fertile. Great dams and reservoirs are built, and water is stored to be used when it is needed; and more and more waste land is producing food for man and his beasts.

One of man's earliest relationships with the other animals was that of the hunter. At first he probably ate wild fruits and grasses and roots. Then a period of cold, perhaps the same that killed his forests and forced him from the trees to the ground, may have deprived him of his plant food, and have driven him to kill other animals, and to eat their flesh and wear their skins for warmth. Animals then became of great importance to man, for he depended on them for his food and clothing. When he was hunting them, he had to follow and to watch them for nearly all his time. He grew to know their various habits and natures. He learnt to fear some and admire others. In many of them he saw the symbol of some admirable quality, such as strength or patience or wisdom, and these animals became sacred to him. Others were deified because of man's dread of them. Animals are used as religious emblems in every nation to this day.

MAN, THE HUNTER

The dog was probably the first animal to become friendly to man. Perhaps he used to slink round the camp in the hope of picking up odd pieces of meat and accompany the hunter, in order to feed on the carcase when man had taken home the best joints. By attaching himself to a particular tribe, the dog felt that they belonged to him, and snarled and barked at intruders, whether men or animals. In this way he was useful to the tribe, and they probably encouraged him by food and kind treatment to keep with them. The hunter found the dog's keen nose helpful to him in his search for other animals, and so man and dog became friends.

MAN, THE TAMER OF BEASTS

It is not known how man first domesticated other wild animals, for their flesh and skins, their milk and wool. Perhaps tribes following herds of wild sheep or deer or oxen, began after a time to look upon the animals as their

Animals became sacred to man either because he feared them or saw in them some quality which he admired. Sometimes they were used as symbols of natural facts or religious ideas. In Egypt the scarab beetle was sacred and was used to represent the Sun-god.

280

own. They might protect them from wolves, or from other hunters, and might pen them into glades and valleys. As young ones were born to these animals, they would become more used to closed-in spaces and the presence of man. They would rely on him for food and protection, and would become less wild.

From such beginnings the mighty herds and flocks of civilized man may have sprung. As he selected and cross-bred plants, so he culled and bred from the finest of his animals. To-day there are birds and beasts almost as different from their ancestors as the highly cultivated flowers and vegetables are different from wild plants. The merino sheep is a mass of curling wool, which hangs in heavy folds round the neck and shoulders. The bull is no longer a gaunt, fast-moving beast, but a square-set bulk of solid muscle on short legs. The pig has lost its savage leanness, and has become a long, low mountain of flesh whose chief joy is the food trough. These animals have been made monstrous for man's needs; others have become more comely under his hand. The noble, heavy shire-horses, and the high-stepping racers, with their sleek coats and flowing manes and tails, are handsomer than the wild horse of Mongolia. This horse is a small, dun-coloured beast, with thick legs, a heavy head and a short, bristly mane. It is called Przhevalski's horse, and is thought to be somewhat like the original wild horses from whom the many breeds have sprung. The modern dog is sometimes more beautiful to look at than its wolf ancestors. The cocks of some breeds of poultry are the most resplendent creatures under the sun.

Except when breeding animals as pets, man usually puts other qualities before beauty. Horses are bred for swiftness or strength, sheep for the quantity and fineness of their wool. The hen may lay from two hundred to three hundred eggs a year, instead of the fifteen to thirty of her wild forbears. The modern cow produces her first calf when she is from two to three years old, and gives about a thousand gallons of milk after it and each succeeding calf is born. Wild cattle do not breed until they are six years old, and yield up to three hundred gallons of milk after their calves are born.

BEASTS OF BURDEN Man moulds the shapes, speeds the growth, and forces the reproductive abilities of animals for his own ends. He may also use them without changing them a great deal. In spite of the spread of mechanized transport, two-thirds of the world's people still depend on animals to carry their burdens. In India the elephant is called "the beast that hath between his eyes a serpent for a hand"; and because he is strong and intelligent, he is used for lifting and hauling timber. He can be trained to lift logs with his trunk and arrange them tidily; and he is always found in State processions, magnificently dressed and jewelled.

The yak of Northern India is like a humped and shaggy bull. It is very useful to the dwellers in these mountainous districts; it carries packs, and provides milk and clothing and even fuel. The camel and llama do much the same work as the yak, the camel serving dwellers in the deserts of the Old World, and the llama helping those in the southern mountains of the New World. The reindeer is invaluable to the people who live in the cold countries of the north, for besides giving milk and meat, it carries men and goods on its back or draws them in a sledge. Cloth can be made from its dark brown hair, its fat is used to make oil for lamps, and its skin is turned into leather.

BIRDS   Birds are not so easily tamed as mammals nor are they so intelligent but they can be used to help man in several ways, besides providing him with eggs and meat. Falconry, or the taking of game by means of trained falcons, was known in China four thousand years ago. Although it was no longer fashionable in England after the early seventeenth century, it is practised to-day in North Africa and in most Asiatic countries. In Central Asia wild horses used to be captured with the aid of a falcon. The bird was trained to settle on the horse's head, and to flutter its wings about his face. This blinded him and made him stop until the hunter came. The Chinese fishermen train cormorants to catch fish with their strong hooked beaks and bring them back to the boats. A collar round the bird's neck prevents it from swallowing the fish. Carrier pigeons are used in peace-time for sport, but in time of war they carry messages which may save the lives of many men.

FISHES   Fishes are scarcely teachable animals, but the Remora or sucker-fish, is used by West Indian fishermen to catch other sea creatures, especially turtles. The Remora has a large sucker on its head. The fishermen tether the fish to a long line and launch it at a turtle. As soon as the Remora touches the turtle, its sucker becomes firmly fixed to the reptile's shell, and the two animals are hauled aboard.

Animals have been used for man's amusement for many centuries, though the sports are gradually becoming less cruel. Bull-fights are still held in several parts of the world. The last bull was baited in England in 1835, but the "blood-sports" of fox hunting, deer stalking and the yearly slaughter of specially bred game birds are still carried on. Cock-fighting was common among the ancient Greeks and Romans, and there are few countries where it has not been practised at some time. It has been made illegal in America and in most European countries, but it is still carried on secretly. It is a favourite pastime among the Siamese, who also hold fish-fights between the beautiful, fierce, little Betta-fishes.

In the breeding of plants and animals, man has sometimes stepped beyond the bounds of beauty and fitness. Flowers have been grown which are merely shapeless masses of colour, with neither the graceful lines nor the sweet scents of earlier flowers. In animals the case is worse, for many of the fancy breeds are doomed to a life of misery. The goldfish has been bred from the grey-green carp into endless forms and colours. One variety, the veil-tail, has long streaming fins and a trailing, double tail-fin, instead of the short crisp swimming organ of its ancestor, the carp. The tumbler fish suffers from a curved spine and turns continual somersaults. The telescope fish is a grotesque creature, with a very short, thick body, a large double tail-fin, and eyes which are set at the ends of stumpy stalks. The unfortunate, half-blind star-gazer must spend its days looking upwards at the water-surface above it. The lion-head cannot breathe properly, and has to be kept in running water

Pigeons have suffered
from freak-breeding almost
as badly as the goldfish. The
fantail's head is thrown backward
almost to the tail, and it cannot walk
properly; the tumbler cannot fly straight.
The pouter with its great, distended crop,
and the jacobin buried in its hood, stagger and
totter their way through life. In the dragoons and
trumpeters, the bill bears a mass of flesh which sometimes weighs more than the head of the bird. Other
breeds have such heavily feathered legs that they
must live in specially built cages. Domestic fowls
have been misshapen in various ways, though their
usefulness to man has saved them from being bred
into extreme forms. One of the strangest products of
the poultry fancier is the Yokohama fowl, whose tail-
covert feathers may be twenty feet long. The birds
are kept on high perches in cages, with their long
feathers curled up and wrapped in soft paper.

Dogs seem to be the most easily changed of the
mammals. The horse and cat have altered little

The ibis also was sacred, perhaps because
it used to return to Egypt from its
yearly migration at the same time as the
Nile flooded the land with fertile soil.

In India the cheetah is trained to hunt other animals, as the hunting cat was used in Egypt five thousand years ago.

through the centuries which they have spent with man; but in many of the fancy breeds of dogs it is difficult to see their wolfish ancestry. The Skye terrier is a short-legged mass of long, flowing hair, and the animal can scarcely see through the tresses which fall down over its eyes. The bulldog and the Pekingese breathe with difficulty through their distorted noses, and the almost hairless toy terrier shivers and trembles in its nakedness.

Artificially bred plants and animals, once freed from man's interference, tend to go back in a few generations to their original form. The richly-coloured polyanthus, which was probably bred from a cross between a RETURN primrose and a cowslip, goes back in a few years to the pale TO NATURE yellow of its original parents. Goldfishes carefully re-bred slip back into the grey-green livery of the ancestral carp.

Living things provide a rich storehouse for man to draw upon. They provide him with most of the necessities and many of the luxuries of his elaborate civilized life. From the sea he gets not only fish for food, but whale-oil and whalebone, sponges, amber, coral and pearls. The sheep and silk-MAN'S USE worm give warm, soft clothing, and so do the musk-ox, alpaca and OF LIVING camel. The fibres of flax, and cotton seed-hairs provide fine THINGS threads for cool, light clothes. The grasses give cereals, on which most of humanity depends for its chief food. They give esparto-grass, which makes some of the best kinds of paper, besides baskets and hats. In the warmer climates, grasses take the form of sugar-cane and the mighty bamboo.

Sugar-cane not only gives a sweet food, but the fibre is used after the sugar has been crushed out of it. This fibre is called "bagasse" and it used to be thrown away or dried GRASSES and used as fuel. Now it is made into a board-like material which is used in a great many ways, in the building of houses, factories and ships. In Japan most of the poorer houses are built entirely of bamboo both inside and out. Bamboo is used in the building of bridges, in ladders, in fences; the masts of boats are made from it, and farm tools, and numberless small articles. The outer skin when cut into strips provides material for making baskets and furniture, and the inner parts of the stem are pulped to make a fine, smooth paper. The succulent shoots form a delicate food, PALMS and the seeds can be used instead of rice. The palms are as valuable to man as the bamboo: the Tamils of Southern India have a poem in which they sing of the eight hundred different uses of the Palmyra palm.

In China cormorants help men to catch fish. When unleashed the bird dives into the water, seizes its prey & returns to its owner. A ring is put round the bird's neck to prevent its swallowing the fish.

285

Small plants provide food in the form of leaves, shoots, seeds and roots. Many of these can be seen in every kitchen garden, and are known as vegetables. Man eats the leaves of lettuces and cabbages, the tender shoots of the asparagus, the seeds of peas and beans, and the roots of carrots, parsnips and beetroots. One of the most valuable vegetables

The Indian jungle fowl is thought to be the parent bird of all the modern breeds of domestic fowls. Most of them are reared for use but some are bred as fancy birds.

is the potato, which is a swollen underground stem. Bushes and trees give juicy fruits and the hard-shelled seeds known as nuts. The dried and partly fermented seeds of the cacao tree are ground to make cocoa and chocolate. Coffee is made from the roasted and ground seeds of the cherrylike fruit of a **FRUIT** tropical, evergreen shrub. Tea comes from the dried and fermented leaves of a small tree which grows in hot countries.

Trees provide the greatest riches of all the plants save cereals. Their strong stems give wood from which man builds his houses and makes his furniture. Wood pulp has made possible the manufacture of cheap paper, and this has brought with it the spread of books and newspapers. From the bark of the cinchona tree comes the drug quinine. The milky juice of **TREES** another tree, when mixed with sulphur, hardens and becomes rubber.

One of the most important products of trees was made between two hundred and three hundred million years ago. This is coal, the valuable black rock on which nineteenth-century civilization was founded, and which has made the life of the twentieth century so different from life in the eighteenth. In the

The tail coverts of the Yokohama cock, which has been reared in Japan for 2500 years, are sometimes eighteen feet long. The Houdan and Cochin are useful birds in spite of their appearance.

second half of the last century, it was found that coal had uses besides that of being burnt in homes, in factories, in railway engines COAL and in steamships. Coal gas had been taken from it for some time, but the resultant sticky, black, strong-smelling coal-tar had been thrown away. While experimenting with coal-tar in 1856, a chemist discovered "mauveline," which was the first of the aniline dyes. New colours followed quickly, and the natural and more expensive sources of dye were no longer wanted. Red dyes had been made from the madder plant and the cochineal insect, indigo from an Indian plant related to the British woad. Tyrian purple came originally

287

from a sea-snail, Murex. The coaltar colours took the place of all these dyes and brought new colours into men's lives.

There are a great many other substances which are made from coaltar: ammonia, naphtha, creosote, carbolic acid, and other disinfectants: and drugs such as aspirin and veronal. Other coal-tar products are saccharin and petrol, and scents which smell like roses and orange flowers, besides a variety of flavourings. All these come from the unwanted liquid which was burned as useless less than one hundred years ago.

The word "synthetic" is often used nowadays; it means "put-together." The chemist analyzes some natural product SYNTHETIC and finds out what it PRODUCTS is made of. Then he tries to discover these ingredients in a cheaper and more plentiful form, and "puts-them-together" to make an *artificial*, or "made-by-art" substance. The silkworm feeds on mulberry leaves. It grinds them up and changes them in its body to a yellowish, gummy

The various kinds of tame pigeons have all been evolved from the wild Rock Dove. Homing pigeons are used to carry messages which are fixed to their legs. The fancy pigeons have been bred into many strange shapes which often prevent the birds from walking or flying properly.

288

liquid. When this is pressed through its spinnerets and comes out into the air, it hardens into a shining delicate thread. The first chemist to make artificial silk, or rayon, used mulberry leaves, grinding them up and treating them with an acid until they were a sticky liquid. Then he forced the mixture through very fine holes like the spinnerets of the silkworm, and in this way he made a kind of silk. This experiment took place at the end of the nineteenth century. To-day the making of rayon is a large industry, and the trunks of trees are used instead of mulberry leaves. The twentieth century has seen the invention of a great many synthetic materials, and in the years to come there may be few natural products without their synthetic counterparts.

It is well that man should learn to build things up out of simple substances, for in many ways he is using up the world's wealth more quickly than it can be made. For ages he has been a destroyer and a spendthrift, and MAN, THE he is only just beginning to realize that things which are used DESTROYER must be replaced. He cannot re-make plants and animals which he has utterly destroyed, but he can preserve those which are in danger of disappearing, so that they may reproduce their kind and carry on their race.

For centuries man has killed animals in sport and for pleasure, but at first he killed only for food and clothing. In order to cultivate his crops and build homesteads where he could live in safety, he had to destroy many wild things. They stood in his path, and as he was the most cunning among animals, they had to make way for him. Wolves, brown bears, lynxes and boars have all disappeared from Britain and from most parts of Europe. Man has unwittingly destroyed other animals, by clearing forests, draining marshes and cultivating wild places. The animals have lost their homes and means of livelihood, and have gone to other countries or died out from lack of food. Many harmless and interesting creatures have been destroyed in this way, though often the cause of their death has been the means of giving life and comfort to men and their families.

On the other hand many animals have disappeared for ever because they have been slaughtered for man's sport and greed. In the seventeenth century the dodo was destroyed in its only home, Mauritius, by the Dutch sailors and their pigs who landed there. The birds were so easily killed that the sailors used to slay them merely for the sake of the stones in their gizzards, which **EXTINCT** they found good for sharpening their clasp knives. The pigs used to **ANIMALS** catch the slow, clumsy birds, and ate their eggs and young. Steller's sea-cow, a large animal like the whales, though not related to them, was exterminated in the eighteenth century, twenty-seven years after its discovery. These huge animals were slow-moving and defenceless, and their bodies were rich in oil; so they were killed until there was not one left. The quagga, a half-striped kind of zebra, was ruthlessly hunted by collectors, and died out in the nineteenth century. The whale and the elephant-seal may be going the same way as Steller's sea-cow; zebras and antelopes are butchered for the making of hides, soap and bone-manure. The Koala has been massacred for gloves. Soft-

All the varieties of goldfish have been bred from the olive-green carp Some of them are beautiful: others are grotesque. The Lionheads cannot breathe properly & often have to swim upside down. The Skygazer is almost blind & swims with difficulty.

furred animals are slaughtered for the sake of their rich pelts. The birds of paradise, white herons and crested cranes are struck down at the time when they are most beautiful, for their mating plumes.

Sometimes the extinction of a plant or an animal may mean little more than the loss of beauty or interest to the world. More often it means the upsetting of the very delicately poised balance of nature. When man cuts down great forests for their timber, disaster follows unless he plants new FORESTS trees. In Syria and Asia Minor, AND DESERTS Palestine and the north of Africa, deserts have for this reason replaced the cities of the past. There are great tracts of treeless desert in China; and in the nineteenth century the forests of Canada and the United States were felled without a thought for the future. When land is stripped of its trees, it also loses its soil and moisture. The results are drought and dust storms, and the whirling away of freshly planted farmland. At the same time, the shifting soil silts up the waterways and causes widespread floods. While man was recklessly cutting down wood in the nineteenth century, he was also plundering the soil. By taking crop after crop out of the land, without putting back enough fertilizer, he has almost exhausted the once-rich earth of Western America. He is

doing the same to the grasslands of the world, by forcing them to feed huge flocks and herds of his domestic animals.

The thoughtless destruction of animals nearly always leads to an unwanted increase of their prey. Snakes are killed for various reasons, but mice and other vermin multiply alarmingly when the reptiles are no longer there to keep their numbers down. While alligators were steadily being killed in Louisiana, musk-rats increased and did much damage by burrowing in the banks of the Mississippi. Monkeys now slaughtered for their long fur did much to help keep down the numbers of locusts. Cormorants were massacred in Australia because they were thought to eat the fish of the rivers, but after they were killed, the fish became even scarcer. It was discovered, too late, that the birds fed mainly on the crabs and eels which devoured the spawn and fry of the fishes. In England, thousands of small useful animals, such as hedgehogs, stoats and owls, are wilfully killed every year. They are good friends to the farmer, for they rid him of insects and grubs, rabbits, and rats and mice, but they are supposed to be the enemies of poultry and game.

The bamboo is a large grass which has a great many uses. In China and Japan it is used to build houses & bridges, to make furniture, ladders and fences, farming tools, water-pipes, paper and many other things. The young & tender bamboo shoots are eaten like asparagus, the seeds are used in the same way as rice.

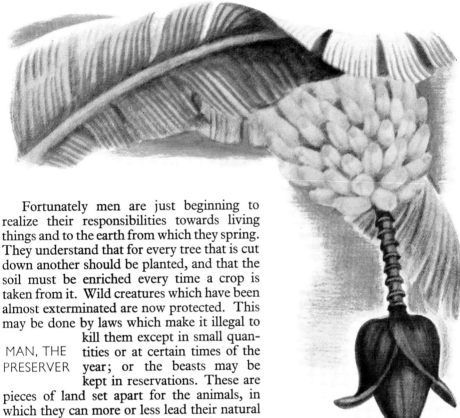

Fortunately men are just beginning to realize their responsibilities towards living things and to the earth from which they spring. They understand that for every tree that is cut down another should be planted, and that the soil must be enriched every time a crop is taken from it. Wild creatures which have been almost exterminated are now protected. This may be done by laws which make it illegal to kill them except in small quantities or at certain times of the year; or the beasts may be kept in reservations. These are pieces of land set apart for the animals, in which they can more or less lead their natural lives, and where they are free from the persecution of man. Canada and the United States have great National parks, thousands of square miles in area, where bears, moose, deer, bison and birds live protected lives. In the Belgian Congo and in the Transvaal, there are similar large sanctuaries, where firearms and fishing rods are forbidden. Formerly animals were protected in order that they might be hunted and killed. Now man is trying to save animal life for its own sake, and because it gives him pleasure to look at and study these graceful creatures.

MAN, THE PRESERVER

In hot countries the banana forms the chief food of many people. Each tree bears a great weight of fruit: 4000 pounds of bananas may be grown on as much ground as would yield only 99 pounds of potatoes or 33 pounds of wheat. The fruit may be eaten fresh or dried. It is also ground into flour & made into a drink. Houses are thatched with the leaves & clothes are woven from the fibres of the stalks.

293

There is little need in the world to-day to kill the larger animals in self-protection. Hungry wolves and man-eating

MAN'S ANIMAL ENEMIES

tigers still molest people in a few parts of the earth, but on the whole, most of man's enemies are small or minute. Rats and rabbits are serious scourges, for the rat ruins millions of pounds' worth of food and spreads disease. The rabbit destroys forest-land, by gnawing the bark and nibbling the seedlings of trees. It also burrows in fields and makes them difficult to plough, and forty rabbits will eat as much grass as one cow. These menaces are serious enough, but they are equalled or surpassed by the danger from much smaller creatures. Man is dependent for most of his food on crops of cereals, vegetables and fruit. All over the world his livelihood is threatened by hosts of insects. In warmer countries, clouds of locusts come down so that they "cover the face of the earth, that one cannot be able to see the earth." Everywhere there are grubs of other insects which live unseen beneath the soil, and gnaw at the life-giving roots. On the stems and leaves above the ground, insects such as greenfly and scale-insects suck out the vital juices of the plants on which they live.

Sometimes the cures for these pests do as much harm as the disease. The

The koalas of Australia were killed by the million until their slaughter was forbidden by the government.

deadly poisons which are sprayed on crops can kill the insect-eating birds as well as the insects. The European stork has become much rarer than it was in the days of Hans Andersen. The bird spends the winter in North Africa where it feeds eagerly on locusts; but the locusts are now sprayed with arsenic to kill them, and the stork, feeding on the poisoned insects, shares their fate. There are other ways of fighting insects besides poison. Some crops can be planted earlier, so that by the time the pest becomes active, the plants will be too far advanced to suffer from attack. This method has been used against the Frit-fly, which destroys whole fields of growing oats.

Perhaps the most satisfactory way of dealing with insect pests is to let loose upon them their natural enemies. In some countries special laboratories have been set up, where men search for the particular enemies of pests. When they have found them, they rear them in large numbers and send them to any part of the world which may need them. Ladybirds are among the most important of these insect helpers; others include ground-beetles and their grubs, and many different kinds of wasps. Parasitic flies are also useful, such as the ichneumon fly, which lays its eggs in the bodies of caterpillars. The ENEMIES OF MAN'S ENEMIES larger enemies of man's pests are not usually reared in this way, though some are protected and encouraged. The hedgehog eats insects and their grubs, besides slugs and small snails. The plover feeds on the troublesome wireworm, yet its eggs used to be sold and eaten in large numbers. Mosquitoes can be controlled not only by keeping watch on their wet and swampy breeding grounds but by rearing and protecting gnat-eating fish such as the stickleback and golden orfe. This is actually done in Italy. In some parts of America bats, which eat insects, are encouraged and protected.

Plants may sometimes prove almost as harmful to farm and garden as insects, and some of them may be controlled in the same way. In 1920 the prickly pear cactus, which had originally been introduced into Australia as a CACTUS AND COCHINEAL curiosity, had become so rampant that it was said "the vision arose of Eastern Australia becoming in about a hundred years' time a vast desert of prickly pear, with a few walled cities holding out against it." After much research, the cochineal insect and three other small creatures were bred in large numbers and turned out to feed upon the plants; with the result that great forests of the cactus were destroyed and its spread was checked.

There is one danger in this way of dealing with pests. The destroyers of the unwanted plant or animal may, when they have finished their allotted work, turn their attention to food which man is rearing for his own use. This often happens in the case of the backboned animals, which are more adaptable to new diets than the insects. The European sparrow was taken to the United States, partly to check the spread of the elm-tree caterpillars. It did this to a certain extent, but became in its turn a greater pest, by damaging the crops and driving away other insect-eating birds. Mongooses were introduced into the West Indies to cope with the plague of rats. When this food became scarce, they changed their diet to one of poultry and wild birds. Ferrets which were taken to Australia to reduce the number of rabbits were found to eat the sheep as well. Then foxes were tried, but they mated with the native dingoes, and produced a race of dog-like animals which also harried the sheep.

Pests, whether plant or animal, are nearly always aliens which have been let loose upon a new country without the check of their natural enemies. Many pests have started as apparently innocent reminders to homesick settlers of their native land. Daisies, plantains and dandelions are as common in North American lawns as in those of England, but all these plants came from Europe. Scottish colonists treasured their solitary thistles in California and New Zealand, and now the plant has infested great tracts of country. The brambles which were imported into New Zealand have become a serious

UNWISE
INTRODUCTIONS

nuisance, helped by the imported starlings which eat the fruit and, passing the seeds out undigested, spread the weed to new areas.

The rabbit was probably introduced into England at the time of the Norman Conquest. From being a protected animal in the Middle Ages, it has become a plague, especially since its enemies in nature, the stoats and weasels, are killed for the protection of the pheasant. It has become an even greater menace in Australia, where it was taken, without its enemies, in 1860. In Australia also the dogs and pigs, which were introduced as animals useful to man, are in many places destroying the native animals. A few years ago, the musk-rat was brought to England to be bred for the sake of its fur. It spread rapidly and became a serious pest. It tunnelled into and broke down river banks, and caused the collapse of bridges by riddling their foundations. Luckily it has now been exterminated in this country. At the end of the last century a few American grey squirrels were introduced into England. They were allowed to roam in the parks for the amusement of visitors, but many of them escaped, and now they have to some extent ousted the more attractive red squirrel from certain parts of England.

New creatures are often introduced accidentally, especially since trains and ships have carried goods to and from every part of the world. The rat and the cockroach, both aliens in England, have followed man's civilization all over the earth. Insects and the seeds of plants are taken in bales of goods from one country to another. In 1869 an American naturalist imported a few European Gipsy-moths for use in his experiments. By an accident some of the caterpillars escaped, and though the naturalist tried to recapture them all, some remained free. Along with another introduction, the Browntail-moth, the Gipsy-moth increased enormously, and does much damage to trees by eating all their leaves. Many pests are encouraged by the artificial yet unavoidable conditions of farming and cultivation. The herding together of animals and the planting of fields of crops, provide fertile breeding-grounds for the fungi, bacteria and insects which prey upon them. The colorado-beetle has even changed its diet from deadly-nightshade to the potato, and has prospered and multiplied with disastrous results.

The Head of the Family

Man's efforts as distributor of plants and animals are, however, often successful. Most of England's loveliest garden flowers and many vegetables have been brought from other countries. Some of the trees, such as the horse-chestnut and fir, which seem typical of the English countryside, have actually come from other lands. Wheat, which was perhaps the first cultivated plant in the Old World has become the most important crop in the New World, where it was taken by European settlers. Fruit trees have been taken from Europe to South Africa, and their fruit is now shipped back so that people of northern countries can eat summer food in winter. Turkeys were brought to Europe from the warmer parts of North America, and the cocks and hens of the poultry yard came originally from India. The camel from the deserts of Asia was taken to Australia in 1860, where it has been useful in exploration and other work. Sheep were taken from Scotland to New Zealand, and grass from the Welsh uplands is taken to make pasture for them. In these and other way; the plants and animals most useful to man have been spread all over the world. The successful introductions are nearly always domesticated animals and cultivated plants, over which man has some control.

SUCCESSFUL INTRODUCTIONS

MAN AND EVOLUTION

Evolution means an "unrolling" or "unfolding." The word is used to describe the development of plants and animals, through hundreds of millions of years, from single-celled creatures to the rich variety of past ages and the present time. The first minute specks of life must have contained all the possibilities of the millions of different plants and animals which have evolved from them. Nature does not make new things; she unfolds and develops something already existing, in such a way that

Great herds of bison once roamed over the prairies of North America. Then the white man came & killed vast numbers of these animals for sport & food. The bison nearly disappeared but it is now protected by 'bison societies' and its numbers are increasing again.

it serves a new purpose. Thus, the fin becomes a limb, the limb becomes a wing: the swim-bladder which adjusts the fish to the right depth becomes an air-bladder which helps it to breathe in stagnant water; as life gradually takes to the dry land, the air-bladder becomes a lung. This unfolding is a slow process; up to the present it has taken perhaps a thousand million years, and is still going on. The steps which living things have taken can be read from the fossils which are found in the various layers of rock. Each layer was at some time on the surface of the earth, and in time became buried by the following layer, together with the bodies of the plants and animals which lived on it.

Living plants and animals as well as fossils show in various ways the course of evolution which their ancestors have taken. Sometimes there are links, such as Peripatus and the lancelet, which seem to connect two such apparently different groups of animals as, in the first case, the worms and insects, and in the second case, the invertebrates and the vertebrates. These living links may represent steps taken long ago, stages at which a few animals have stayed still, neither going forward nor back nor altogether dying out. Such animals are generally small and humble creatures, which escape the notice of other animals by living under stones, or in mud, or in some well-hidden place. The others, which have travelled onwards and upwards, have had to struggle and endure, and to adapt themselves to changing conditions or die out altogether.

In many of these creatures, so different from each other, there can often be found traces of a common history. Nearly all bear signs of their far-off ancestry. The bird has reptilian scales on its feet; some large snakes and the whales have traces of hind limbs, which show that they are descended from four-footed beasts. Man bears in his body many reminders of his ancient pedigree. In its undeveloped, unborn or unhatched state, the story of an animal's racial development is still easier to read. The unborn cat and human baby are at one stage

The Barn owl is a valuable ratcatcher but it is not so common as it used to be. Its nesting places have been destroyed and it has been killed by eating poisoned rats. The Little owl which was introduced into England about fifty years ago has taken much of its food supply. Egrets & Crowned cranes had become very rare before steps were taken to preserve them. The 'aigrettes' which were used to trim hats & fans were taken from the egrets during their breeding season. Not only were the parent birds destroyed but the young ones were left to starve.

Many wild animals are useful to man. The plover is a good friend to the farmer. It is now illegal to take its eggs. The hedgehog feeds mainly on slugs, insects and grubs, but it is slaughtered by the gamekeeper.

almost the same as each other, and are also not unlike unhatched chicks and lizards and newly-hatched fish. All these little creatures bear gill-slits. In the land animals these become changed or disappear; in the fishes feathery gills are grown. The human baby at one time has a tail like the cat and the lizard and the other backboned animals; but while they keep theirs, the baby loses his before he is born. In the whale and in man, which are both furless animals, the unborn are at one stage covered with a hairy coat like other mammals. The frog spends its early days as a fish-like tadpole, a reminder of the time before its ancestors left the water for life on land.

In their development, young animals run through in a few weeks or months, stages which have taken millions of years in evolution. Since man has appeared on the world's scene, he has greatly quickened the slow pace of the unfolding drama. Environ-

Bats & freshwater fishes such as the stickleback & golden orfe eat a great many mosquitos. In some countries these animals are protected & encouraged in their useful work.

300

Some creatures are actually bred to be used to keep down pests. Scale insects were accidentally taken to California on some Australian orange trees. They did much damage among the orange and lemon groves, until certain ladybirds were sent from Australia to feed on them. The ladybirds have since been bred & sent all over the world to clear up these pests.

a. Some of the kinds of scale insects which live on orange trees.

b. A scale insect.

c. A ladybird which feeds on these insects.

ment has always played an important part in evolution, for it is by their power or inability to adapt themselves to new conditions that animals have advanced or died out. Man has altered, and is always altering these conditions, by clearing forests, draining swamps, building cities, reclaiming land from the sea, and taking plants and animals to new countries. Before man hastened their distribution, for his own ends or unwittingly by some accident, plants and animals had slowly to spread themselves over the world.

When the Continents changed their shape, and land bridges which connected them sank into the sea, creatures were marooned for millions of years in one particular land mass. That is the reason for the very different groups of animals which are found in the various continents. The land bridge which connected Australia, either with Asia or with Antarctica and Cape Horn, must have disappeared when the mammals had evolved as far as the pouch-bearing stage. The few mammals which were trapped there had plenty of space and food and few enemies, and so had no reason to continue their evolution, except as pouch-bearers. They remained primitive, while their brothers in the greater land-masses, who had to face more competition, evolved into higher and yet higher forms. In the last five hundred years, man has distributed plants and animals all over the world. The pouch-bearers are already losing the battle for existence which the other mammals fought millions of years ago. In other countries also, plants and animals which have been introduced by

301

Wild plants & animals introduced into other countries may find themselves with abundant food and no enemies. The Prickly Pear Cactus was taken from America to Australia and was cultivated as a garden plant. It escaped from the gardens & quickly spread over the land until it became a serious pest. Then the insects which feed on it were brought from America & the spread of the plant was checked.

f.

m.

The cochineal insect bores into the cactus & sucks up the sap. Red spiders & caterpillars also feed upon the plant.

man, are struggling and adapting themselves to new surroundings and enemies.

By cultivation man alters the size, shape and surroundings of plants. He also provides ready-made feeding and breeding grounds for insects which would otherwise have to search far and wide for their particular food. In this way, and by faulty distribution, he makes plagues and pests. He has changed the vegetation of the world; he has made deserts where once were forests, and seas of wheat where once was desert land. Under his selective hand, animals go through in a few generations stages which might take thousands of years without his interference. He moulds and hastens the process of evolution for his own purposes. Yet he can only hasten the pace of a movement which was rolling its slow way long ages before he was evolved, and which would continue to unfold without him. The spirit of adventure which prompts living things to make the best of an opportunity; their adaptability to new surroundings; the occasional production of "novelties" or "sports"

302

The Head of the Family

The thistle was introduced into California by a Scot who wished to be reminded of his native land. A Scotsman in New Zealand built a fence to protect the first thistle which grew on his farm. The plant has become a pest in both these countries.

which, if they have any advantage over their fellows, quickly swamp the more conservative types; all these are qualities in living things which nature has always used in the evolution of new forms, and on which man depends for his moulding of living matter. He may curb or hasten the processes of nature, but he cannot make new life; and he must obey natural laws if he wishes to succeed.

All living things are linked with one another in time and space. The plant or animal of this moment is the grandchild of tens of thousands of generations and the grandparent of millions to come. Its life is bound up with its fellow creatures of the present. It eats and is eaten. It grows from the earth and goes back to it. It cannot live to itself alone, but only as a small part of the great body of living things. It is closely connected with creatures which are in turn connected with yet others, until the pattern of life is like a finely woven net. This net is not still and fixed, but is constantly changing as the balance of life swings now this way, now that. Man can follow this movement and work with it, or he can roughly pull the net so that the balance is upset. This happens when he slaughters great numbers of animals, so that their usual prey increases into a plague; or when he introduces a new thing into a country without its natural enemies. Living things multiply so quickly, that any one kind without check would soon encumber the earth. It has been estimated that if there were no insect-eating birds, the world of men and beasts and plants would come to an end in about eight years. There would be nothing but a vast mass of flying and crawling insects, darkening the sky and filling the earth with their swarming bodies. It is dangerous to meddle unknowingly with such a delicately swaying balance; but great forces are given into man's hand if he learns to respect the mutual dependence of living things.

THE PATTERN OF LIFE

Since he has evolved further than his fellow creatures, man has the power to control them. He also has the power to learn of some of the properties of life

303

itself. With the help of his microscope, he has been able to discover a world of things which he had not seen before. The microscope has shown him that even minutely small creatures may be unbelievably complex. The radiolarians, which are one-celled animals invisible to the naked eye, surround themselves with shells which are pierced and spiked into intricate and regular designs. There

THE MICROSCOPE

is a certain beetle about one-hundredth of an inch long, whose anatomy is much the same as that of the four-inch Goliath-beetle. This minute animal has brain and nerves, muscles and food-canal, air-tubes and blood and germ cells.

The microscope reveals that the living body-material of all plants and animals consists of a semi-fluid substance, which is called protoplasm. This takes the form of a single cell in the simplest creatures, and of many cells, some-times countless

The Indian Mongoose is an expert snake- and rat-catcher. It was taken to the West Indies to rid the sugar plantations of rats, but when it had done this it took to eating birds & their eggs, poultry, fruit & sugar cane, and became in its turn a serious pest.

millions, in the larger plants and animals. The cells are of many shapes and sizes, but nearly all of them are too small for the human eye to see without a microscope; yet they have activities and structures which are peculiar to each kind of cell alone. The study of the structure of cells, and of the way in which they develop and behave, has helped man to understand how living things grow and reproduce themselves. The microscope has shown him the "bricks" of which the bodies of living things are built, and has taught him that he is of the same stuff as the rest of life.

The patient watching of the ways of living things has shown that there has been an evolution of mind as well as of body, and that the one has helped the other. It has shown that in the upward trend of evolution mutual help has been as important as the struggle of one creature against another.

Man's sense of kinship with the other living

It is usually safe to take cultivated plants & tame animals into other countries for they are more easily controlled than the wild things. Many flowers & vegetables have been taken from one land to another during the last few hundred years.
← All these plants were brought to England in the reign of Queen Elizabeth.

things becomes deeper as he learns more about them. The realization that they are not given into his hand as tools or playthings, but that they are part of the same scheme of life as he himself, has awakened his sense

EVOLUTION OF MIND

of responsibility towards them. He is learning to what extent they may be wisely used, preserved and controlled. In doing this, men of all nations share their knowledge and resources, and use them for the common benefit. A world-wide community of interest is in itself another step in the course of evolution. It is a step in the evolution of mankind which brings understanding between peoples, and a desire to work to a common end.

Plants use carbon dioxide which animals breathe out.
Plants give out oxygen: animals breathe it in.
Plants produce foods which animals can eat.
Plants use the energy of the sun to make their food.
From the soil-water plants take in nitrates which are supplied by waste products & dead bodies of animals.

Living things depend on each other & all depend upon the sun. Animals feed on plants, or on other animals who have fed upon plants. The green plant makes its food by using the energy of the sun, but it gets valuable ingredients for its body-building from the waste products of animals.

ENGRAVED AND PRINTED
IN GREAT BRITAIN
BY
THE SUN ENGRAVING CO., LTD.
LONDON AND WATFORD